BetaMathematics 2

Compiled by

T. R. Goddard & A. W. Grattidge

In association with

J. W. Adams & R. P. Beaumont

 Schofield & Sims Ltd Huddersfield

©1969 **Schofield & Sims Ltd**

First printed 1969

7217 2103 6

Designed and Printed in England by Chorley & Pickersgill Ltd Leeds
Bound in Scotland

Contents   Beta Mathematics   2

Number tens and units

number	number word
1	One
2	Two
3	Three
4	Four
5	Five
6	Six
7	Seven
8	Eight
9	Nine
10	Ten

1	2	3	4	5	6	7	8	9	10
11	12	13	14	15	16	17	18	19	20
21	22	23	24	25	26	27	28	29	30
31	32	33	34	35	36	37	38	39	40
41	42	43	44	45	46	47	48	49	50
51	52	53	54	55	56	57	58	59	60
61	62	63	64	65	66	67	68	69	70
71	72	73	74	75	76	77	78	79	80
81	82	83	84	85	86	87	88	89	90
91	92	93	94	95	96	97	98	99	100

number word
Ten
Twenty
Thirty
Forty
Fifty
Sixty
Seventy
Eighty
Ninety
Hundred

Spell the number words to your partner.

A
1 Write these numbers in words
   a 56   b 13   c 72   d 90   e 85   f 64   g 37   h 49.
2 Change these words to figures
   a Thirty-seven   b Eighteen   c Seventy
   d Eighty-three   e Forty-six   f Ninety-nine.
3 Write all the **odd** numbers between 20 and 42.
4 Write all the **even** numbers between 49 and 71.
5 Count on in **threes** from 24 to 48.
6 Count back in **fours** from 64 to 36.
7 Count on in **fives** from 15 to 60.

B
1 Count in tens from   a 37 to 77   b 93 to 13.
2 Add 10 to each of these numbers   21   7   59   73   90.
3 Take 10 from each of these numbers   17   34   10   66   100.
4 Multiply each of these numbers by 10   6   3   0   9   10.
5 Divide each of these numbers by 10   70   50   80   10   100.
6 Write the remainder when each of these numbers is divided by 10
   53   26   99   82   40.

C
Complete these number series
1 71   66   ☐   ☐   51   ☐.
2 13   16   ☐   ☐   ☐   28.
3 69   65   61   ☐   ☐   ☐   45.
4 29   35   41   ☐   ☐   ☐   65.
Look at these numbers   39   27   58   70   93   12   7.
5 Which is   a the 6th   b the third number in the row?
6 93 is the ☐th number in the row.
7 Put the numbers in order of size, largest first.

D
Write the answers only

	a	b	c	Fill in the missing numbers
1	34 + 20	67 + 30	79 + 10	5 57 = ☐ tens ☐ units.
2	7 + 50	28 + 60	13 + 70	6 3 tens 4 units = ☐.
3	86 − 10	68 − 50	92 − 90	7 73 = ☐ tens ☐ units.
4	75 − 20	53 − 40	49 − 30	8 100 = ☐ hundred ☐ tens ☐ units.

1

Counting money
Make sure you can recognise all the coins

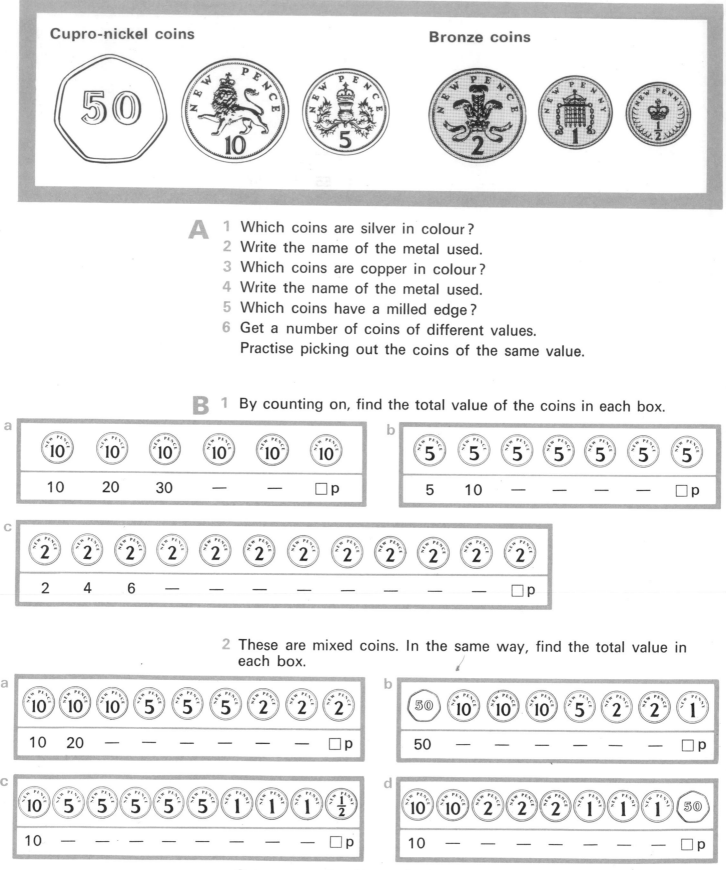

Cupro-nickel coins   Bronze coins

A 1 Which coins are silver in colour?
2 Write the name of the metal used.
3 Which coins are copper in colour?
4 Write the name of the metal used.
5 Which coins have a milled edge?
6 Get a number of coins of different values.
Practise picking out the coins of the same value.

B 1 By counting on, find the total value of the coins in each box.

a

| 10 | 20 | 30 | — | — | ☐ p |

b

| 5 | 10 | — | — | — | — | ☐ p |

c

| 2 | 4 | 6 | — | — | — | — | — | — | — | — | ☐ p |

2 These are mixed coins. In the same way, find the total value in each box.

a

| 10 | 20 | — | — | — | — | — | — | ☐ p |

b

| 50 | — | — | — | — | — | — | ☐ p |

c

| 10 | — | — | — | — | — | — | — | — | ☐ p |

d

| 10 | — | — | — | — | — | — | — | ☐ p |

Get some real coins, make up some boxes and practise counting the total value in each box.

3 Find the total value of
a 50p, 10p, 5p, 2p, 1p
b 10p, 10p, 2p, 2p, 1p, $\frac{1}{2}$p
c 5p, 2p, 2p, $\frac{1}{2}$p, $\frac{1}{2}$p
d 5p, 5p, 5p, 5p, $\frac{1}{2}$p, $\frac{1}{2}$p, $\frac{1}{2}$p
e 50p, 1p, 1p, 1p, $\frac{1}{2}$p
f 10p, 10p, 10p, 10p, 2p, 1p.

2

Counting money

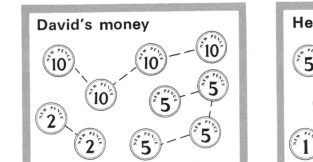

David's money

Helen's money

A 1 David and Helen emptied the coins out of their money boxes. The pictures show how the total value was counted in an easy way.
Find the value of   a David's money   b Helen's money.

2 Describe an easy way of counting the value of mixed coins.

3 Get a bag of mixed coins. Empty them on the table, then find their total value.

B   Which two different coins together make these amounts?
1 a 2½p   b 7p   c 15p
2 a 3p   b 11p   c 12p
3 a 52p   b 55p   c 60p

Which three different coins together make these totals?
4 a 3½p   b 8p   c 12½p
5 a 7½p   b 17p   c 53p
6 a 13p   b 57p   c 65p

C   Find the missing number of the given coins.
1 16p = ☐ TEN and ☐ TWOS.
2 35p = ☐ TENS and ☐ FIVE.
3 28p = ☐ TENS and ☐ TWOS.
4 65p = ☐ FIFTY and ☐ FIVES.
5 70p = ☐ FIFTY and ☐ TENS.
6 43p = ☐ FIVES and ☐ new pence.
7 14½p = ☐ TEN and ☐ new halfpence.
8 62p = ☐ FIFTY and ☐ TWOS.

100 new pence = £1 note									
50p					50p				
10p	10p	10p	10p	10p	10p	10p	10p	10p	10p
5p 5p	5p 5p	5p 5p	5p 5p	5p 5p	5p 5p	5p 5p	5p 5p	5p 5p	5p 5p
2p 2p 2p 2p 2p 2p 2p 2p 2p 2p 2p 2p 2p 2p 2p 2p 2p 2p 2p 2p 2p 2p 2p 2p 2p 2p 2p 2p 2p 2p 2p 2p 2p 2p 2p 2p 2p 2p 2p 2p 2p 2p 2p 2p 2p 2p 2p 2p 2p 2p									

D   Study the diagram, then write the following
1 Count in TENS   10p   20p   30p — — — — — — to 100p (£1).
2 Count in FIVES   5p   10p   15p ---------------- to 100p (£1).
   How many
3 a FIFTIES for £1?   b TENS for £1?   c TENS for 1 FIFTY?
4 a FIVES for 1 TEN?   b FIVES for 1 FIFTY? c FIVES for £1?
5 a TWOS for 1 TEN?   b TWOS for 1 FIFTY? c TWOS for £1?   3

Number addition facts

+	0	1	2	3	4	5	6	7	8	9
1	2	3	4	5	6	7	8	9	10	
2	3	4	5	6	7	8	9	10	11	
3	4	5	6	7	8	9	10	11	12	
4	5	6	7	8	9	10	11	12	13	
5	6	7	8	9	10	11	12	13	14	
6	7	8	9	10	11	12	13	14	15	
7	8	9	10	11	12	13	14	15	16	
8	9	10	11	12	13	14	15	16	17	
9	10	11	12	13	14	15	16	17	18	

Use this **ready reckoner** to help you to ADD.

Examples

6 + 7 Place your ruler along the **6** line.
Under **7** on the top row is the answer 13.
6 + 7 = 13.

8 + 4 Place your ruler along the **8** line.
Under **4** on the top row is the answer 12.
8 + 4 = 12.

Table race
Try to beat the clock

2 minutes for one column

10 minutes for the page

1 First practise these addition facts with a partner.
2 Then put a strip of paper alongside Test **A** and write the answers. Then go on to Tests **B**, **C** and **D** in the same way.
3 Work quickly without using the ready reckoner if you can.

	A	**B**	**C**	**D**
1	2 + 3	5 + 3	9 + 6	0 + 6
2	5 + 4	9 + 3	7 + 7	9 + 7
3	3 + 3	3 + 2	6 + 8	9 + 9
4	5 + 6	7 + 3	7 + 9	6 + 0
5	3 + 8	6 + 7	8 + 5	4 + 2
6	6 + 2	7 + 8	4 + 4	2 + 9
7	2 + 8	9 + 5	5 + 0	7 + 2
8	4 + 7	8 + 8	1 + 8	8 + 3
9	3 + 5	7 + 5	6 + 3	5 + 2
10	9 + 4	2 + 6	2 + 5	3 + 9
11	8 + 6	8 + 2	6 + 5	4 + 8
12	9 + 8	4 + 3	3 + 4	9 + 0
13	8 + 0	3 + 6	0 + 3	6 + 9
14	2 + 2	2 + 4	3 + 7	5 + 8
15	2 + 7	4 + 6	6 + 6	4 + 9
16	4 + 5	9 + 2	5 + 9	7 + 4
17	6 + 4	8 + 4	7 + 6	8 + 9
18	5 + 5	5 + 7	8 + 7	9 + 1

Number subtraction facts

Use the **ready reckoner** on the opposite page
to help you to SUBTRACT.

Examples

15 − 8   Place your ruler along the **8** line.
           In the top row above 15 is the answer **7**.
           15 − 8 = 7.

13 − 5   Place your ruler along the **5** line.
           In the top row above 13 is the answer **8**.
           13 − 5 = 8.

1 First practise these subtraction facts with a partner.

2 Then write the answers to Test **A** on a strip of
   paper. Go on to Tests **B**, **C** and **D**.

3 Work quickly without using the ready reckoner
   if you can.

Table race

Try to beat the clock

2 minutes for one column

10 minutes for the page

	A	B	C	D
1	4 − 2	9 − 4	13 − 4	14 − 8
2	10 − 8	10 − 7	12 − 8	17 − 9
3	8 − 7	10 − 3	14 − 6	8 − 0
4	7 − 4	12 − 4	13 − 7	8 − 8
5	10 − 6	11 − 6	17 − 8	7 − 2
6	8 − 2	12 − 7	15 − 7	9 − 6
7	11 − 5	14 − 9	9 − 1	7 − 5
8	10 − 2	12 − 6	8 − 4	8 − 3
9	14 − 5	16 − 8	11 − 9	6 − 2
10	15 − 6	14 − 7	9 − 5	11 − 2
11	11 − 7	7 − 7	7 − 3	12 − 3
12	13 − 8	9 − 8	9 − 2	10 − 4
13	16 − 9	8 − 5	11 − 3	13 − 5
14	10 − 9	5 − 3	5 − 2	12 − 9
15	8 − 6	9 − 9	12 − 5	9 − 0
16	6 − 4	9 − 3	13 − 6	15 − 8
17	11 − 8	11 − 4	16 − 7	18 − 9
18	6 − 3	7 − 0	13 − 9	15 − 9

E

Find the missing numbers in each of these statements

	a	b	c
1	8 + 7 = □ + 10	□ − 8 = 11 − 4	13 − 2 = 6 + □
2	6 + 5 = 8 + □	18 − 9 = 13 − □	6 + □ = 15 − 4
3	□ + 9 = 6 + 8	12 − □ = 17 − 9	18 − 2 = □ + 9
4	4 + □ = 7 + 6	13 − 6 = □ − 9	□ + 5 = 17 − 5

5

Number
addition and subtraction

A

See how quickly you can write the answers.
First add from left to right, then check by adding from right to left.

	a	b	c	d
1	3 + 7 + 5	7 + 8 + 2	9 + 3 + 6	3 + 9 + 7
2	2 + 8 + 7	9 + 3 + 7	2 + 9 + 8	1 + 8 + 4
3	5 + 5 + 9	2 + 6 + 4	5 + 8 + 3	0 + 3 + 9
4	6 + 4 + 3	6 + 5 + 5	8 + 7 + 4	4 + 9 + 6
5	1 + 9 + 6	7 + 6 + 5	6 + 6 + 7	9 + 8 + 3

B

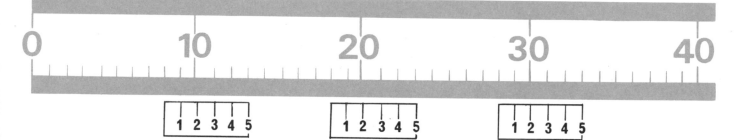

You know that 8 + 5 = 13.   Look at the number track.
You see that 18 + 5 = 23, and that 28 + 5 = 33.
Each time, you count on to the next ten.
Write the answers to the following. Use the number track.

B

1	2	3	4
9 + 3	7 + 4	6 + 7	8 + 6
19 + 3	17 + 4	16 + 7	8 + 16
29 + 3	27 + 4	26 + 7	8 + 26

You know that 13 − 5 = 8.   Look at the number track again.
You see that 23 − 5 = 18, and that 33 − 5 = 28.
Each time, you count back to the next ten.

Write the answers to the following. Use the number track.

5	6	7	8
12 − 3	11 − 6	14 − 7	16 − 8
22 − 3	21 − 6	24 − 7	26 − 8
32 − 3	31 − 6	34 − 7	36 − 8

See how quickly you can write the answers to the following

	a	b	c	d
9	9 + 12	16 + 9	18 + 6	7 + 16
10	7 + 13	4 + 19	14 + 7	5 + 18
11	22 + 9	8 + 23	26 + 6	4 + 27
12	23 − 4	26 − 8	25 − 9	22 − 6
13	21 − 8	27 − 9	24 − 5	28 − 9
14	32 − 7	35 − 8	36 − 9	34 − 5

Number
addition and subtraction

A

1 Find the total of 7, 16 and 5.
2 Which number is 8 more than 17?
3 Seventeen plus 9.
4 Increase nineteen by eight.
5 What must be added to 3 fours to make 20?
6 John plays darts and scores 7, 9 and double 4. Find his total score.
7 Joan spent 9p and had 7p left. How much had she at first?
8 David is 6 years older than his sister who is 17. How old is David?

B

1 23 minus 8.
2 From 17 take 9.
3 What is left if 3 is taken from 21?
4 How much greater than 6 is 25?
5 From 14 subtract 7.
6 Take 8 from   a 15   b 25.
7 What is the difference between   a 5 and 14   b 7 and 27?
8 How many less than 12 is 4?
9 Decrease 18 by 9.
10 What must be added to   a 5   b 15 to make 23?

C

1 Add 17 and 9. From the answer take 15.
2 What number is 8 less than the sum of 19 and 9?
3 Find
  a $(16 + 7) - 4$ b $(9 + 19) - 20$
  c $(25 - 10) + 6$ d $(18 - 9) + 17$.
4 Father gave Jill 8p each week for 3 weeks.
  a How much has she?
  b She bought a book and had 13p left.
    What did the book cost?
5 Charles is 5 years younger than Mary and
  3 years older than James who is 4.
  a How old is Charles?   b How old is Mary?

Letters for numbers

D

1 Each of these letters stands for the given numbers
  $m = 17$ $n = 8$ $p = 5$ $q = 0$.
  Find the value of
  a $m + n + p + q$ b $m + p - q$
  c $n - p - q$ d $(m + q) - (n + q)$
  e $(m - q) + (n - q)$ f $m - (n + p + q)$.

2 In each of these statements, the letter x stands for
  a number. Find the value of x.
  a $17 - x = 8$ b $x + 16 = 24$
  c $21 - 9 = x$ d $5 + 7 + x = 20$
  e $x - (3 + 7) = 5$ f $12 - 3 = 9 - x$
  g $12 - x = 6 - 2$ h $x - 7 = 10 - 3$.

7

Money addition

A Number   Write the answers only

1	2	3	4	5	6
13 20 +24	26 30 +42	36 12 +22	17 15 +25	28 36 +13	35 27 +24

Money

7	8	9	10	11	12
26p 12p +22p	41p 5p +23p	7p 31p +32p	14p 25p +13p	15p 50p +28p	47p 16p +35p

B 1 What sum of money is 13p more than 27p?

2 Increase 55p by 15p.

3 Find the total of 46p and 39p.

4 Mother went shopping.
She spent
   $14\frac{1}{2}$p on fruit and vegetables
   33p at the butcher's
   29p at the grocer's.
How much did she spend altogether?

5 a David had these coins in his money box. How much money had he saved?

50	10	5	2	1	$\frac{1}{2}$
1	2	2	3	5	2

b Find how much each of these children had saved.

	50	10	5	2	1	$\frac{1}{2}$
Peter	1		2	6	4	2
Joan		6	1	3	5	
Ann	1	1	4	4	2	3

6 Check the answers to **5a** and **5b.** Then write the totals of their savings in order putting the largest first.

C The stamp album costs   18p

It can be paid for in several ways by using different coins like this

50	10	5	2	1	$\frac{1}{2}$	Total
	1	1		3		
	1			8		
		3	1	1		

1 Check the value of the coins and see if the total value is 18p in each case.

2 There are other ways of paying for the album. Draw a table and fill in three more ways of paying 18p.

3 Find three ways of paying each of these sums of money   a 30p   b 28p   c 54p   d 70p.
Write your answers in the table.

4 Find out the prices of 6 articles which are less than £1.
Practise making up each price using different coins.

Money subtraction

A Number   Write the answers only

1	2	3	4	5	6
48 −26	75 −30	60 −47	53 − 8	82 −29	95 −16

Money

7	8	9	10	11	12
37p −15p	96p −40p	70p −18p	48p − 9p	87p −58p	64p −56p

B
1. From 46p take 10p.
2. What is left if 19p is taken from 60p?
3. Find the difference between 57p and 39p.
4. Decrease 75p by 35p.
5. What must be taken from 86p to leave 30p?
6. How much more than 68p is 95p?
7. What must be added to $28\frac{1}{2}$p to make 85p?
8. (50p) By how much is this coin greater in value than
   a $7\frac{1}{2}$p   b 23p   c $41\frac{1}{2}$p?
9. £1 note By how much is this note greater in value than
   a 19p   b 43p   c 91p   d $72\frac{1}{2}$p?
10. (10p) How much change from this coin after spending
    a 4p   b $6\frac{1}{2}$p   c $9\frac{1}{2}$p?
    d Find the change from 2 TENS after spending each of these amounts.
11. Find how much change from   a 30p after spending $14\frac{1}{2}$p
    b 15p after spending $8\frac{1}{2}$p   c 70p after spending 41p.

C

Shopping List	
Groceries	32p
Cakes	15p
Meat	25p
Fruit and vegetables	$17\frac{1}{2}$p

Mother went shopping
1. How much more did she spend on
   a groceries than on meat   b fruit and vegetables than on cakes?
2. How much did Mother spend altogether?
3. How much change from a £1 note did Mother have after shopping and spending 9p on bus fares?

The shopkeeper gives change by counting on from the cost of the article. Write the value of each coin given as change.

D

	Money given	Cost of article	Coins counted as change
1	10p	6p	6p ○ ○
2	10p	$3\frac{1}{2}$p	$3\frac{1}{2}$p ○ ○ ○
3	50p	34p	34p ○ ○ ○
4	50p	28p	28p ○ ○ ○
5	£1	38p	38p ○ ○ ○
6	£1	65p	65p ○ ○ ○ ○

9

Time
the clock

A

1 Write the times shown on these clocks in figures and in words for both morning and afternoon.

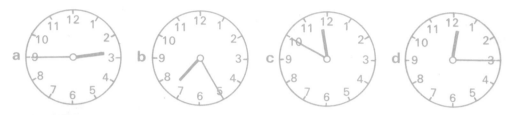

A clock should show the correct time.
Sometimes clocks are either fast or slow.

What is the correct time if

2 Clock **a** is 5 minutes slow?
3 Clock **b** is 10 minutes fast?
4 Clock **c** is a quarter of an hour fast?
5 Clock **d** is half an hour slow?
6 Find out all you can about
   a Greenwich Mean Time (G.M.T.)
   b British Standard Time.

B The figures on the clock faces above are called **Arabic** numerals.
Sometimes **Roman** numerals are used.

Arabic	Roman	Arabic	Roman
1	I	7	VII
2	II	8	VIII
3	III	9	IX
4	IV or IIII	10	X
5	V	11	XI
6	VI	12	XII

Write the times shown on these clocks

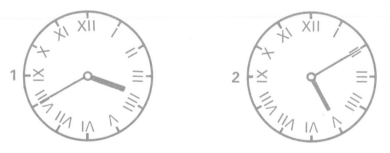

C Some clock faces have no numbers on them at all.
Write the times shown on these clock faces

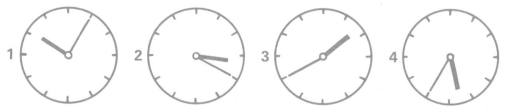

How many minutes are there between

D
1 9 a.m. and 9.40 a.m.?
2 3.15 p.m. and 4 p.m.?
3 12.10 p.m. and 12.35 p.m.?
4 6.25 p.m. and 6.40 p.m.?
5 9.5 a.m. and 9.55 a.m.?

6 7.45 p.m. and 7.50 p.m.?
7 8.30 p.m. and 8.35 p.m.?
8 4.35 a.m. and 5 a.m.?
9 7 p.m. and 8 p.m.?
10 11.15 a.m. and midday?

Time the calendar

A

	January	February	March
Sunday	(1) 8 15 22 29	5 12 19 26	5 12 19 26
Monday	2 9 16 23 30	6 13 20 27	6 13 20 27
Tuesday	3 10 17 24 31	7 14 21 28	7 14 21 28
Wednesday	4 11 18 25	1 8 15 22	1 8 15 22 29
Thursday	5 12 19 26	2 9 16 23	2 9 16 23 30
Friday	6 13 20 27	3 10 17 24	3 10 17 (24) 31
Saturday	7 14 21 28	4 11 18 25	4 11 18 25

	April	May	June
Sunday	2 9 16 23 30	7 14 21 28	4 11 18 25
Monday	3 10 17 24	1 8 15 22 (29)	5 12 19 26
Tuesday	4 11 18 25	2 9 16 23 30	6 13 20 27
Wednesday	5 12 19 26	3 10 17 24 31	7 14 (21) 28
Thursday	6 13 20 27	4 11 18 25	1 8 15 22 29
Friday	7 14 21 28	5 12 19 26	2 9 16 23 30
Saturday	1 8 15 22 29	6 13 20 27	3 10 17 24

	July	August	September
Sunday	2 9 16 23 30	6 13 20 27	3 10 17 24
Monday	3 10 17 24 31	7 14 21 (28)	4 11 18 25
Tuesday	4 11 18 25	1 8 15 22 29	5 12 19 26
Wednesday	5 12 19 26	2 9 16 23 30	6 13 20 27
Thursday	6 13 20 27	3 10 17 24 31	7 14 21 28
Friday	7 14 21 28	4 11 18 25	1 8 15 22 29
Saturday	1 8 15 22 29	5 12 19 26	2 9 16 23 30

	October	November	December
Sunday	1 8 15 22 29	(5) 12 19 26	3 10 17 24 31
Monday	2 9 16 23 30	6 13 20 27	4 11 18 (25)
Tuesday	3 10 17 24 31	7 14 21 28	5 12 19 26
Wednesday	4 11 18 25	1 8 15 22 29	6 13 20 27
Thursday	5 12 19 26	2 9 16 23 30	7 14 (21) 28
Friday	6 13 20 27	3 10 17 24	1 8 15 22 29
Saturday	7 14 21 28	4 11 18 25	2 9 16 23 30

This is a **calendar** for a certain year.

Look at it carefully.

1 Write the names of the months which have
   a 30 days   b 31 days.

2 Which month is not in either list?

3 How many days has this month on this calendar?

4 Reckon the number of days in the year.

5 This is not the calendar for 1972. How do you know?

6 How can you tell a Leap Year?

7 Which of these years is a Leap Year
   1960   1970   1982   1996?

8 How many days in a Leap Year?

9 Count the number of whole weeks in the year.

10 Say to your partner the rhyme of the months.

B

1 From the calendar, what is the date of
   a the first Sunday in May
   b the third Thursday in September
   c the last Saturday in March?

2 Write the name of
   a the 2nd month of the year
   b the 5th month of the year
   c the 8th month of the year
   d the 11th month of the year.

3 Here are some children's birthdays
   Anne 18.4.64   Tom 21.10.65
   Mary 7.7.65   Peter 16.2.64.
   a Which child is the oldest?
   b Which child is the youngest?
   c Using the calendar, on which day of the week does each child's birthday fall?

4 John is 12 days younger than Helen whose birthday is on 24th July. When is John's birthday?

5 Some of the days on the calendar above have been marked by a circle. Which of the marked days is
   a Good Friday   f Guy Fawkes Day
   b Christmas Day   g the longest day of
   c New Year's Day   the year
   d Spring Bank Holiday   h the shortest day of
   e Late Summer Bank Holiday   the year?

6 Write the date of   a Boxing Day   b Easter Sunday
   c the last day of the year.

7 Count the number of days from
   a 9th January to the end of the month
   b 3rd June to the end of the month
   c 15th February to 6th March
   d 20th November to Christmas Eve.
Do not count the first given day.

Number multiplication and division

1 Counting

Do these exercises many times.
Count on and count back
a in TWOS from 2 to 20
b in THREES from 3 to 30
c in FOURS from 4 to 40
d in FIVES from 5 to 50.

2 There are some wrong numbers in each of these
rows. Which are they?

a 2   4   6   11   20   17   16
b 3   6   9   21   28   27   19
c 4   8   23   28   32   18   40
d 5   15   20   45   30   14   39.

B

means
MULTIPLY BY
or TIMES

Example 6×4

Place your ruler along the
6 line.
Under **4** in the top row is
the answer 24
$6 \times 4 = 24$

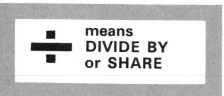

means
DIVIDE BY
or SHARE

Example $27 \div 3$

Place your ruler along the
3 line.
Above 27 in the top row is
the answer **9**
$27 \div 3 = 9$

**The ready reckoner will multiply and divide
numbers for you.**

1	2	3	4	5	6	7	8	9	10
2	4	6	8	10	12	14	16	18	20
3	6	9	12	15	18	21	24	27	30
4	8	12	16	20	24	28	32	36	40
5	10	15	20	25	30	35	40	45	50
6	12	18	24	30	36	42	48	54	60
7	14	21	28	35	42	49	56	63	70
8	16	24	32	40	48	56	64	72	80
9	18	27	36	45	54	63	72	81	90
10	20	30	40	50	60	70	80	90	100

The tables in the
shaded part
are those which
you have yet
to learn.

**Notice that in learning tables to 5 times
you have also learnt half of the tables 6 to 10 times,
e.g. 7×5 is the same as 5×7.**

Write the answers only.
Work quickly without the ready reckoner if you can.

	a	b	c	d	e
1	4×2	2×6	8×2	10×2	2×3
2	3×5	3×7	3×4	5×5	5×4
3	4×3	9×5	5×6	4×8	2×9
4	5×8	6×3	10×3	8×3	5×10
5	4×10	9×4	3×9	7×4	7×5
6	$6 \div 2$	$9 \div 3$	$10 \div 2$	$18 \div 2$	$14 \div 2$
7	$10 \div 5$	$50 \div 10$	$30 \div 10$	$27 \div 9$	$20 \div 5$
8	$24 \div 4$	$8 \div 4$	$21 \div 3$	$16 \div 4$	$32 \div 4$
9	$24 \div 8$	$28 \div 7$	$30 \div 5$	$40 \div 5$	$27 \div 3$
10	$15 \div 3$	$50 \div 5$	$40 \div 4$	$36 \div 4$	$45 \div 5$

multiplication and division

Multiplication with adding

When working multiplication later you will have to multiply two numbers together and then add on another number.

Examples $(5 \times 5) + 2 = 25 + 2 = 27$

             $(8 \times 4) + 3 = 32 + 3 = 35$

Work these examples. Mark the answers and correct any mistakes.

A

	a	b	c	d
1	$(5 \times 2) + 1$	$(1 \times 3) + 2$	$(6 \times 4) + 1$	$(4 \times 5) + 2$
2	$(9 \times 2) + 1$	$(0 \times 3) + 1$	$(3 \times 4) + 3$	$(7 \times 5) + 4$
3	$(0 \times 2) + 1$	$(7 \times 3) + 2$	$(1 \times 4) + 2$	$(0 \times 5) + 3$
4	$(7 \times 2) + 1$	$(4 \times 3) + 1$	$(8 \times 4) + 3$	$(9 \times 5) + 3$
5	$(4 \times 2) + 1$	$(8 \times 3) + 2$	$(0 \times 4) + 2$	$(6 \times 5) + 1$
6	$(8 \times 2) + 1$	$(9 \times 3) + 1$	$(7 \times 4) + 2$	$(8 \times 5) + 4$

Division — remainders

If 9 new pennies are shared among 4 children, they will each receive 2 new pennies and there will be 1 new penny left over.

$9p \div 4 = 2p$ rem. 1p   (rem. stands for **remainder**)

Here are two more examples

18 sweets shared among 5 boys is written $18 \div 5 = 3$ rem. 3

23 sweets shared among 3 boys is written $23 \div 3 = 7$ rem. 2

Here are more examples. Write the answers only

B

		a	b	c	d	e
1	Divide by 2	3	7	9	15	19
2	Divide by 3	10	14	19	23	25
3	Divide by 4	10	13	26	31	38
4	Divide by 5	16	24	28	32	48

C

1 Double seven and add 1.

2 What number is 4 more than 9 times 5?

3 Treble 9 and then add 2.

4 Add 9 to three times eight.

5 4 children each had 8 sweets and 3 sweets remained.
How many sweets were there at first?

6 Share 30p among 4 children.
How many each and how many left?

7 6 boys each eat 3 biscuits and there are 4 left.
How many were there at first?

8 Dart scores
John 3, 7 and double 6.
David 8, 6 and treble 4.
Who won and by how many?

13

Money multiplication

1	24	2	32	3	17	4	35	5	25	6	13
	× 2		× 3		× 5		× 2		× 4		× 5

Money

7	47p	8	24p	9	29p	10	19p	11	17p	12	20p
	× 2		× 4		× 3		× 5		× 4		× 3

13	$3\frac{1}{2}$p	14	$6\frac{1}{2}$p	15	$9\frac{1}{2}$p	16	$27\frac{1}{2}$p	17	$23\frac{1}{2}$p	18	$18\frac{1}{2}$p
	× 5		× 3		× 4		× 2		× 4		× 5

B

1 Write the following as examples in multiplication. Find the answers.
  a 23p + 23p + 23p
  b 18p + 18p + 18p + 18p
  c $5\frac{1}{2}$p + $5\frac{1}{2}$p + $5\frac{1}{2}$p + $5\frac{1}{2}$p + $5\frac{1}{2}$p.
  Check each answer by adding.

2 Father pays 13p per day for bus fares.
  How much does he pay in a 5 day week?

3 Bacon costs 28p per $\frac{1}{2}$ kilo.
  Find the cost of
  a 1 kg
  b $1\frac{1}{2}$ kg.

4 Susan saved 25p each week for one month to go
  to London.
  a How much has she saved?
  b The railway fare is 49p.
    How much has she left to spend?

5 Mother buys 16 metres of ribbon at $4\frac{1}{2}$p per metre.
  a How much does the ribbon cost?
  b She pays for it with a £1 note.
    How much change does she receive?

6 Find the total value of these coins
  a 4 TENS
  b 3 FIVES
  c 5 TWOS
  d 12 new pence and 8 new halfpence.

C

PRICE LIST	
Fruit and vegetables	
Apples per $\frac{1}{2}$ kg	$7\frac{1}{2}$p
Pears per $\frac{1}{2}$ kg	10p
Bananas per $\frac{1}{2}$ kg	6p
Tomatoes per $\frac{1}{2}$ kg	14p
Oranges each	$2\frac{1}{2}$p
Potatoes per bag	8p
Tinned fruits	
Pineapple per tin	9p
Apricots per tin	12p
Peaches per tin	10p

1 Find the cost of
  a $1\frac{1}{2}$ kg apples
  b 1 kg pears
  c 2 kg bananas
  d 5 oranges
  e 4 bags of potatoes.

2 Find the total cost of these orders and then give
  the change.
  a $\frac{1}{2}$ kg tomatoes, 3 tins pineapple.
    Change from £1 note.

  b 4 oranges, 2 bags potatoes, 2 tins peaches.
    Change from a FIFTY.

  c $\frac{1}{2}$ kg each of apples, pears, bananas and
    tomatoes.
    Change from 4 TENS.

Money division

A Number   Write the answers only

1 2)48   2 4)84   3 5)90   4 3)78   5 5)85

Money

6 2)56p   7 5)75p   8 4)68p   9 5)65p   10 3)72p

11 4)79p   12 2)71p   13 3)83p   14 5)71p   15 4)53p

B
1 Find the value of
   a one half ($\frac{1}{2}$) of 94p
   b one quarter ($\frac{1}{4}$) of 76p
   c three quarters ($\frac{3}{4}$) of 60p.

2 A bar of chocolate costs 5p.
   How many bars can be bought for
   a 30p   b 5 TENS and 2 FIVES?

3 Four times a sum of money is 96p.
   What is the sum of money?

4 A £1 prize is shared equally among 3 children.
   How many new pence will each child receive
   and how many will be left?

5 Find the price per $\frac{1}{2}$ kilo if
   a 2$\frac{1}{2}$ kg of fish costs 80p
   b a chicken weighing 2 kg costs 68p.

C
1 Joan saves 14 FIVES. She changes them for TENS.
   How many does she receive?

2 Change each of the following to TENS
   a 70 new pence   b 45 TWOS
   c 32 FIVES   d 80 new halfpence.

3 Change each of the following to FIVES
   a 65 new pence   b 35 TWOS
   c 90 new halfpence.

4 Change the following
   a 80 new pence to TENS
   b 95 new pence to FIVES
   c 35 TWOS to TENS
   d 20 FIVES to FIFTIES
   e 60 new halfpence to TWOS.

5 David saved 56p. He spent three-quarters on a game
   and the rest on a book.
   How much did he pay for each?

D

This is a **ready reckoner** which gives
the cost of tins of fruit up to 5 tins.

Number of tins	1	2	3	4	5
Pineapple	9p	18p			
Peaches	10p	20p			
Apricots	12p	24p			

1 Complete the ready reckoner.
   Mark each item.

2 From the ready reckoner find how many
   a tins of pineapple can be bought for 30p.
      Give the change.
   b tins of peaches can be bought for 45p.
      Give the change.
   c tins of apricots can be bought for 70p.
      Give the change.

15

Numbers from pictures
graphs

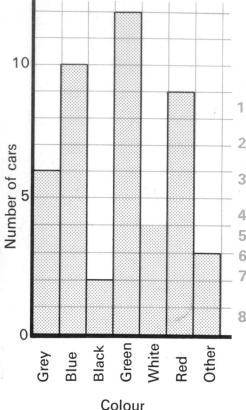

Number of cars (vertical axis)

Colour (horizontal axis, labelled: Grey, Blue, Black, Green, White, Red, Other)

A

Richard and his partner counted the number of cars of different colours which passed the school in 10 minutes. They then drew this column graph to show the result.

Answer these questions.

1 Which colour is
   a the most popular   b the least popular?

2 Write the colours in order putting the most popular first.

3 How many more cars were green than
   a blue   b grey   c white?

4 What does one square on the graph stand for?

5 How many cars of each colour did they see?

6 How many cars did they see altogether?

7 At the side of the graph is a vertical line.
   What is shown on this line?

8 At the bottom of the graph is a horizontal line.
   What is shown on this line?

These two lines have special names.

One is called the vertical AXIS, the other, the horizontal AXIS.

B

Jane and her partner then went out to count the colours of the cars.

They first made a record sheet like this.

As each car passed, a mark (/) was put against the colour.

5 cars were shown in this way 卌.

After 10 minutes the record sheet looked like this.

Colour	Number of cars	Total
Grey	卌 ////	
Blue	卌 卌 卌 ////	
Black	///	
Green	卌 卌 卌 卌 ///	
White	卌 卌 //	
Red	卌 /	
Other	////	

1 Find the total number of cars of each colour.

2 On squared paper draw a column graph to show the numbers.

3 From this graph, answer questions **A1, 2, 3, 6.**

Numbers from pictures

graphs

A

Now make your own graph of the cars of different colours which pass your school.

1 First draw a record sheet like Jane's.

2 Then go outside and make the count. Ask your teacher the best place to stand and for how long.

3 Find the totals of each colour and then draw a column graph on squared paper.

Remember to mark the vertical axis and the horizontal axis.

4 From your graph answer questions **A 1, 2, 5, 6** on page 16.

You can perhaps make up some other questions of your own.

B

David and his partner counted the number of pets kept by the children in the class. They then made a graph but this time it was drawn in rows, not columns, on squared paper.

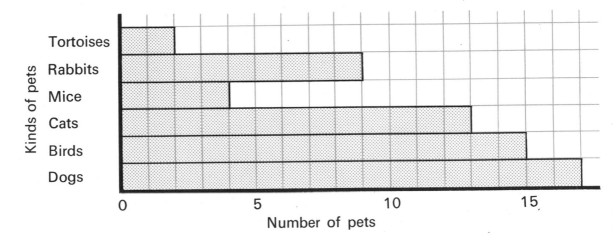

Answer these questions

1 What is marked
   a on the vertical axis   b on the horizontal axis?

2 What does one square on the graph stand for?

3 Make a list of the kinds of pets in order putting the most popular first.

4 Find the total number of pets kept by the children in the class.

C

Make a graph in rows of the kinds of pets which are kept by the children in your class.

First make a record sheet and then go quietly to every child in the class and mark the kinds of pets which are kept, then find the totals.

Answer the questions **B 1 to 4** from your graph.

D

Draw a graph in rows showing the car colours found in **Section A** above.

17

Hundreds tens and units

Make sure that the picture number is correct.
Count for yourself.

The number shown in the picture is

1 hundred   5 tens   7 units
or 157

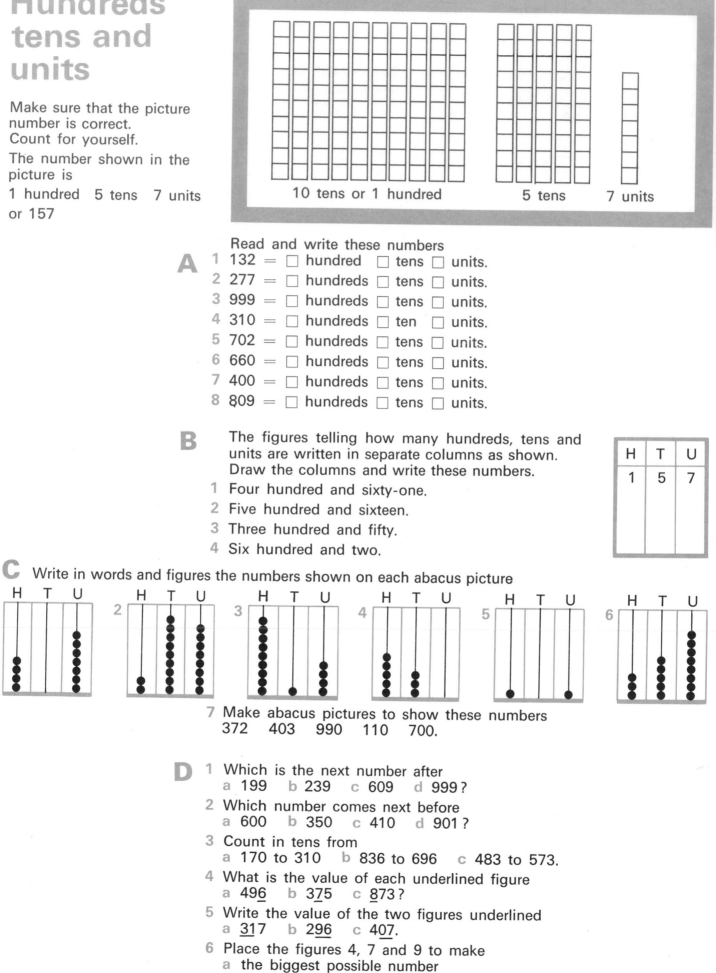

10 tens or 1 hundred   5 tens   7 units

Read and write these numbers

A
1 132 = ☐ hundred ☐ tens ☐ units.
2 277 = ☐ hundreds ☐ tens ☐ units.
3 999 = ☐ hundreds ☐ tens ☐ units.
4 310 = ☐ hundreds ☐ ten ☐ units.
5 702 = ☐ hundreds ☐ tens ☐ units.
6 660 = ☐ hundreds ☐ tens ☐ units.
7 400 = ☐ hundreds ☐ tens ☐ units.
8 809 = ☐ hundreds ☐ tens ☐ units.

B The figures telling how many hundreds, tens and units are written in separate columns as shown. Draw the columns and write these numbers.

1 Four hundred and sixty-one.
2 Five hundred and sixteen.
3 Three hundred and fifty.
4 Six hundred and two.

H	T	U
1	5	7

C Write in words and figures the numbers shown on each abacus picture

7 Make abacus pictures to show these numbers
   372   403   990   110   700.

D
1 Which is the next number after
   a 199   b 239   c 609   d 999?
2 Which number comes next before
   a 600   b 350   c 410   d 901?
3 Count in tens from
   a 170 to 310   b 836 to 696   c 483 to 573.
4 What is the value of each underlined figure
   a 49$\underline{6}$ b 3$\underline{7}$5   c $\underline{8}$73?
5 Write the value of the two figures underlined
   a $\underline{31}$7   b 2$\underline{96}$ c 4$\underline{07}$.
6 Place the figures 4, 7 and 9 to make
   a the biggest possible number
   b the smallest possible number.
7 Make these figures into the biggest and smallest
   possible numbers   a 7 0 5   b 0 5 1.

18

H	T	U
2	6	9
2	6	9
2	6	9

Hundreds tens and units

A

1 Study the diagram. Then complete and write these statements
   a 269 = ☐ hundreds ☐ tens ☐ units

   b 269 = ☐ hundreds ☐ units

   c 269 = ☐ tens ☐ units.

2 Write each of these numbers as in **a, b** and **c** above
   185   356   570   608.

3 Write as hundreds and units only
   a 296   b 409   c 750.

4 Write as tens and units only
   a 304   b 556   c 690.

5 Complete and write this statement

   One thousand = ☐ hundreds = ☐ tens = ☐ units.

H	T	U
		1
	1	0
1	0	0

B How many **times** is

a	b	c
1 10 bigger than 1	60 bigger than 6	170 bigger than 17 ?
2 1 smaller than 10	8 smaller than 80	29 smaller than 290 ?
3 100 bigger than 10	700 bigger than 70	450 bigger than 45 ?
4 10 smaller than 100	50 smaller than 500	63 smaller than 630 ?

C

> **To multiply by 10**
> Move the figures ONE place to the LEFT.
> Put a 0 in the units column.
>
> H T U　　　　H T U
> 　 1 8 × 10 = 1 8 0
> 　 5 9 × 10 = 5 9 0

Multiply each of these numbers by 10.
1 27   2 52   3 86   4 10   5 45   6 70

7 Multiply these numbers by 20. (Remember 20 = 10 × 2)
   a 14   b 39   c 48

8 a 24 × 30   b 19 × 40

D

> **To divide by 10**
> Move the figures ONE place to the RIGHT.
> The units figure becomes the REMAINDER.
>
> H T U　　　　H T U
> 2 9 0 ÷ 10 = 2 9
> 3 4 6 ÷ 10 = 3 4 rem. 6

Divide each of these numbers by 10.
1 170   2 250   3 500   4 720   5 680   6 1000
Divide these numbers by 10 and write the remainder.
7 96   8 131   9 403   10 317   11 609   12 982

19

Number addition practice

First work Group **A**.
Mark the answers and correct any mistakes.
Then work Group **B**.
Do the same with each group.
Write the answers only.

First add upwards, then check by adding downwards.

A
1	2	3	4	5
62	235	320	14	503
13	51	164	501	242
+ 20	+102	+ 5	+463	+130

B
1	2	3	4	5
52	207	132	275	411
17	440	19	106	157
+ 28	+ 29	+246	+318	+238

C
1	2	3	4	5
56	135	221	106	194
32	62	194	370	571
+ 81	+ 52	+ 73	+163	+163

D
1	2	3	4	5
57	43	36	82	98
65	76	86	70	87
+ 33	+ 35	+ 17	+ 49	+ 66

6	7	8	9	10
136	371	254	77	678
108	90	176	509	9
+195	+229	+345	+286	+174

E

1 Add from right to left, then check the answer by
adding from left to right.
Write answers only.
a 59 + 32 + 21
b 17 + 44 + 36
c 64 + 71 + 28 + 12.

2 Find the total of
89 173 205 7.

3 Increase the sum of 75 and 89 by 500.

4 There were 157 boys and 165 girls in a school.
How many children were there altogether?

5 Peter threw three darts.
He scored treble 12, double 18 and 9.
Find his total score.

6 Father dug four rows of potatoes from which he
gathered 39 kg, 28 kg, 43 kg and 35 kg.
Find the total weight of potatoes.

7 Jack paces each of the four sides of a field.
He then draws this plan.

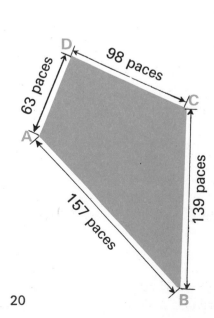

a What is the total length of the two shorter sides?
b What is the total length of the two longer sides?
c How far is it from D by A to B?
d What is the total distance all round the field?

20

Number subtraction practice

First work Group **A**.
Mark the answers and correct any mistakes.
Then work Group **B**.
Do the same with each group.
Write the answers only.

Check the answer by adding it to the line above.

A
| 1 88 − 27 | 2 545 −231 | 3 789 −326 | 4 672 − 51 | 5 987 − 73 |

B
| 1 56 − 26 | 2 437 −217 | 3 862 −562 | 4 745 − 45 | 5 974 −271 |

C
| 1 96 − 40 | 2 159 − 30 | 3 386 −230 | 4 566 −205 | 5 874 −301 |

D
| 1 80 − 29 | 2 90 − 72 | 3 240 − 37 | 4 560 − 29 | 5 406 −285 |
| 6 704 −652 | 7 800 −471 | 8 500 −235 | 9 610 −501 | 10 930 −901 |

E
| 1 82 − 65 | 2 67 − 9 | 3 73 − 68 | 4 332 −117 | 5 763 −256 |
| 6 616 −409 | 7 306 −256 | 8 826 −597 | 9 503 −427 | 10 703 −109 |

F
1 Find the difference between 265 and 303.
2 Decrease 500 by 147.
3 Two numbers when added together make 157.
One of these numbers is 88. Find the other.
4 After taking 127 from a number the answer is 56.
Find the number.
5 Father is 27 years older than Philip.
If Father is 43 how old is Philip?
6 A   C   B

From A to B is 150 metres.
From B to C is 96 metres.
How far is it from C to A?

G

Monday	103
Tuesday	210
Wednesday	181
Thursday	156
Friday	179

The numbers in the table tell you how many children went to the swimming bath on each of the days.

1 Write the numbers in order putting the smallest first.
2 Find the difference between the biggest and the smallest attendance.
3 How many more children were at the bath on
a Wednesday than Monday
b Tuesday than Friday?
4 Find the total number for the five days.
5 On Saturday there were 79 more children than on Thursday. How many attended on Saturday?

21

Money
£'s and new pence

£1 = 100 new pence

A
1. How many £1 notes have the same value as
   a 200p   b 300p   c 500p   d 700p   e 400p?
2. Jill saved these coins in her money box.
   a By counting find how many new pence she had saved altogether.

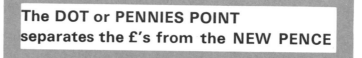

   b She changed two of the coins for a £1 note. Which were they?
   c How many new pence remained?

   Jill has now a £1 note and 30 new pence which is written £1·30.

**The DOT or PENNIES POINT
separates the £'s from the NEW PENCE**

3. David saved these coins.

   a He changed two of the coins for a £1 note. Which were they?
   b How many new pence remained?
   c Write in £'s how much money he has saved.

Doll £1·45   Football £2·85   Tricycle £3·12

B
The cost of the doll is
One pound and forty-five new pence **or**
One pound forty-five.

1. Read the price of each of the toys to your partner.
2. Write the prices in your book like this
   £1·45 = £1 and 45 new pence.
3. Write these prices
   a £1·68 = £☐ and ☐ new pence
   b £2·70 = £☐ and ☐ new pence
   c £5·15 = £☐ and ☐ new pence
   d £3·46 = £☐ and ☐ new pence
   e £7·09 = £☐ and ☐ new pence.
4. Write these prices as £'s only
   a £1 and 28 new pence
   b £4 and 20 new pence
   c £8 and 75 new pence
   d £3 and 24 new pence
   e £5 and 8 new pence.

Box of games £1·56

Toy garage £1·90

Camera £2·75

Car £2·26

22

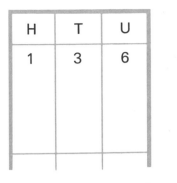

H	T	U
1	3	6

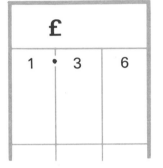

£		
1 ·	3	6

Money £'s and new pence

A

1 Turn back to page 19 and study Section **A** again.
2 Now draw these columns and write in these numbers
   a 136 b 278 c 350 d 108 e 206.
3 Write each number like this
   136 = ☐ hundred ☐ units = ☐ tens ☐ units.

B

1 Draw the columns and then write in these numbers of NEW PENCE
   a 136p b 278p c 350p d 108p e 206p.
2 Write each number of new pence as £'s, e.g. £1·36. Say each sum of money to your partner.
3 Draw more columns. Write in the following putting the figures in the correct columns
   a One pound forty-two b Two pounds sixty-eight
   c One pound twenty d Four pounds seventy
   e Three pounds five new pence f Five pounds
   g Six pounds ten new pence
   h Eight pounds eighty-five.
4 What is the value of the 6 in each of these sums of money
   a £1·06 b £6·45 c £5·60 d £2·06 e £4·62?
5 Write the following filling in the missing numbers of notes and 10p and 1p coins
   a £1·67 = £☐ ☐ TENS ☐p
   b £3·70 = £☐ ☐ TENS ☐p
   c £6·74 = £☐ ☐ TENS ☐p
   d £2·07 = £☐ ☐ TENS ☐p.
6 Write the following filling in the missing number of 10p and 1p coins which make up each amount
   a £2·46 = ☐ TENS ☐p
   b £3·25 = ☐ TENS ☐p
   c £1·80 = ☐ TENS ☐p
   d £4·05 = ☐ TENS ☐p.

Tiny Toys

Car £0·45

Van £0·76

Tractor £0·68

Crane £0·85

C

1 All the prices of the Tiny Toys are less than £1. How do you know?

> **REMEMBER**
> **0 should always be placed in the £'s column when there are no pounds.**

2 Which is
   a the most expensive b the least expensive toy?
3 Write a price label for each toy in new pence only.
4 Write these prices as new pence
   a £0·15 b £0·62 c £0·36 d £0·18.
5 Write these prices as £'s
   a 12p b 25p c 58p d 94p.

Money £'s and new pence

Kit for the 'Santa Maria'
£0·78

Kit for rubber powered plane
£0·85

Talking doll
£4·30

Kit for kite
£0·92

Hexagon kite
£1·26

Wrist watch
£4·10

Air pistol and target
£3·20

Medieval castle
£2·60

Thunderbird II
£0·68

Pair of roller skates
£1·74

1 Read the price of each article to your partner, for example
Thunderbird II costs 68 new pence.
A pair of roller skates costs one pound seventy-four new pence.

2 Write the names of the articles which cost
  a less than £1
  b between £1 and £2
  c between £2 and £3
  d between £3 and £4
  e more than £4.

3 Which of all the articles is
  a the cheapest
  b the most expensive?

4 Write the prices in order putting the lowest first.

£'s and new pence addition and subtraction

A

Look at the prices on the opposite page.
Draw this table in your book.

1 Make a list of the articles and the price of each.
2 Write the number of £1 notes, TENS and new pence coins required to pay for each article.

Article	Price	£1 notes	TENS (10p)	New pence (1p)
'Santa Maria'	£0·78	0	7	8
Kit for kite				
Hexagon kite				
Castle				
Plane kit				
Watch				
etc				

B

1 Susan has a £1 note. How much more will she need to buy
   a a hexagon kite   b a pair of roller skates?
2 John has saved £1. How much more must he save to buy
   a the castle   b the air pistol and target
   c the wrist watch?
3 Peter has a £1 note. How many new pence will he have left after buying
   a a kit for a kite
   b the rubber powered plane kit?

C

	£
Castle	2·60
Wrist watch	4·10
Thunderbird II	0·68
Total	·

1 This is the bill for three presents which Father bought for his children. Copy it.
   Make sure that you write the **figures** and the **pennies points** in the correct columns.
   Find the total cost of the presents.
2 In the same way write the prices and find the total cost of
   a the roller skates and the air pistol
   b the doll and the castle
   c the 'Santa Maria' kit, air pistol and plane kit.

D

	£
Money saved	2·88
Money spent	−1·26
Money left	·

1 David saved £2·88. He spent £1·26 on a kite.
   Copy the example. Make sure that you write the **figures** and the **pennies points** in the correct columns.
   Find how much money David had left.
2 In the same way find how much Jill had left from £4·50 after buying the doll.
3 Find the difference between
   a the prices of the doll and the air pistol
   b the prices of the castle and the hexagon kite
   c the prices of Thunderbird II and the plane kit.

£1·24

A

Copy the following and find the totals.
Make sure that the **figures** and the **pennies points** are in the correct columns.

	1 £	2 £	3 £	4 £	5 £
	1·24	2·32	4·00	3·46	0·76
	2·07	0·94	2·95	1·82	0·53
	+0·45	+1·60	+1·68	+1·55	+0·28

Write the answers only

	6 £	7 £	8 £	9 £	10 £
	0·72	2·04	3·05	1·66	0·95
	0·16	1·32	0·86	2·90	0·64
	+0·18	+0·80	+1·70	+0·45	+0·55

B

Copy the following and find the answers.
Make sure that the **figures** and **pennies points** are in the correct columns.

	1 £	2 £	3 £	4 £	5 £
	2·85	1·90	3·00	0·92	4·65
	−1·65	−1·46	−1·76	−0·68	−3·88

Write the answers only

	6 £	7 £	8 £	9 £	10 £
	3·48	2·05	5·00	4·24	3·20
	−2·46	−1·70	−2·90	−0·86	−1·55

C

1 Find the change
   a from a £1 note after paying for 1 pair of socks costing £0·46
   b from a £5 note after paying for 1 pair of shoes costing £3·85
   c from a £10 note after paying for a coat costing £5·25.

2 In each case write how the change could be given in £1 notes and 10p and 1p coins.

D

Collection for the blind and crippled children	
	£
Class 1	2·76
Class 2	1·47
Class 3	2·00
Class 4	0·97
Class 5	1·09

Answer the questions from the collection list.

1 Write the amounts of money in order putting the biggest first.

2 Find the difference in new pence between the collection
   a in Class 2 and Class 5
   b in Class 3 and Class 2.

3 How much more was collected in Class 1 than in Class 4?

4 Find the total amount collected.

26

Counting in sixes

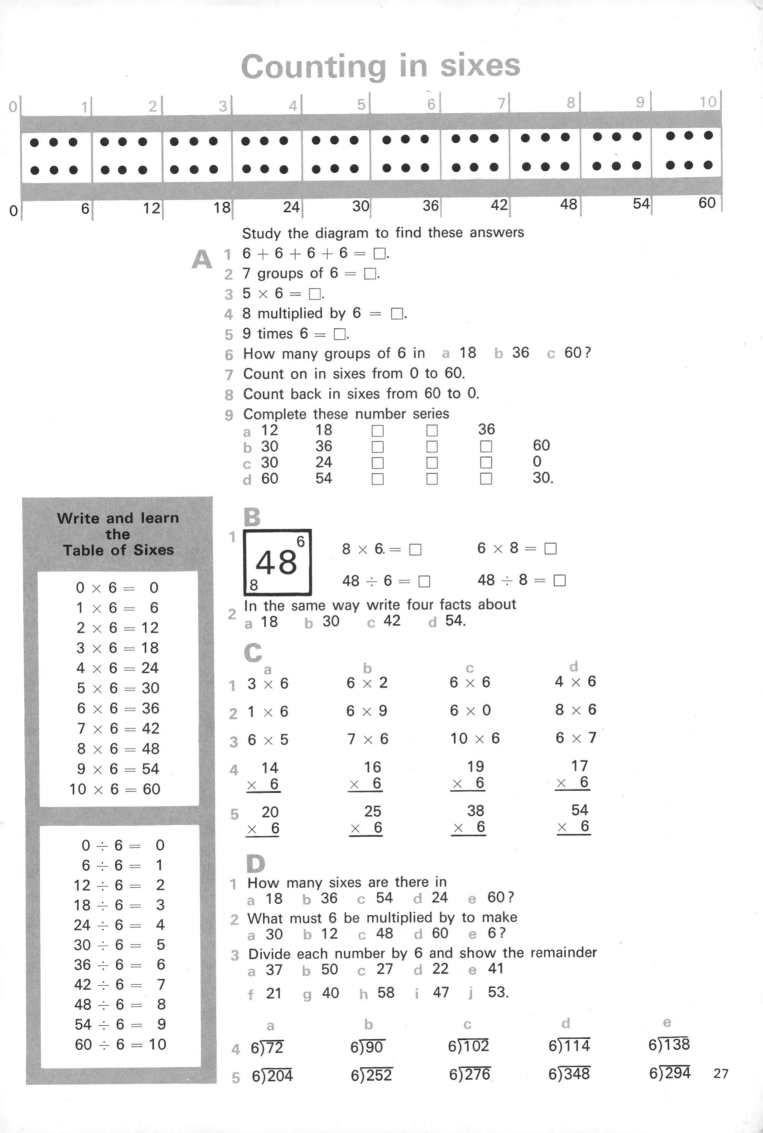

Study the diagram to find these answers

A
1. $6 + 6 + 6 + 6 = \square$.
2. 7 groups of $6 = \square$.
3. $5 \times 6 = \square$.
4. 8 multiplied by $6 = \square$.
5. 9 times $6 = \square$.
6. How many groups of 6 in   a 18   b 36   c 60?
7. Count on in sixes from 0 to 60.
8. Count back in sixes from 60 to 0.
9. Complete these number series
   - a   12   18 $\square$ $\square$ 36
   - b   30   36 $\square$ $\square$ $\square$ 60
   - c   30   24 $\square$ $\square$ $\square$ 0
   - d   60   54 $\square$ $\square$ $\square$ 30.

Write and learn the Table of Sixes

$0 \times 6 =$	0
$1 \times 6 =$	6
$2 \times 6 =$	12
$3 \times 6 =$	18
$4 \times 6 =$	24
$5 \times 6 =$	30
$6 \times 6 =$	36
$7 \times 6 =$	42
$8 \times 6 =$	48
$9 \times 6 =$	54
$10 \times 6 =$	60

$0 \div 6 =$	0
$6 \div 6 =$	1
$12 \div 6 =$	2
$18 \div 6 =$	3
$24 \div 6 =$	4
$30 \div 6 =$	5
$36 \div 6 =$	6
$42 \div 6 =$	7
$48 \div 6 =$	8
$54 \div 6 =$	9
$60 \div 6 =$	10

B

1.
$$\boxed{\begin{matrix} & 6 \\ 48 & \\ 8 & \end{matrix}}$$
   $8 \times 6. = \square$ $6 \times 8 = \square$

   $48 \div 6 = \square$ $48 \div 8 = \square$

2. In the same way write four facts about
   a 18   b 30   c 42   d 54.

C

	a	b	c	d
1	3×6	6×2	6×6	4×6
2	1×6	6×9	6×0	8×6
3	6×5	7×6	10×6	6×7
4	14×6	16×6	19×6	17×6
5	20×6	25×6	38×6	54×6

D

1. How many sixes are there in
   a 18   b 36   c 54   d 24   e 60?
2. What must 6 be multiplied by to make
   a 30   b 12   c 48   d 60   e 6?
3. Divide each number by 6 and show the remainder
   a 37   b 50   c 27   d 22   e 41

   f 21   g 40   h 58   i 47   j 53.

	a	b	c	d	e
4	$6\overline{)72}$	$6\overline{)90}$	$6\overline{)102}$	$6\overline{)114}$	$6\overline{)138}$
5	$6\overline{)204}$	$6\overline{)252}$	$6\overline{)276}$	$6\overline{)348}$	$6\overline{)294}$

27

Metric measures length

Measure these lines in centimetres (cm)

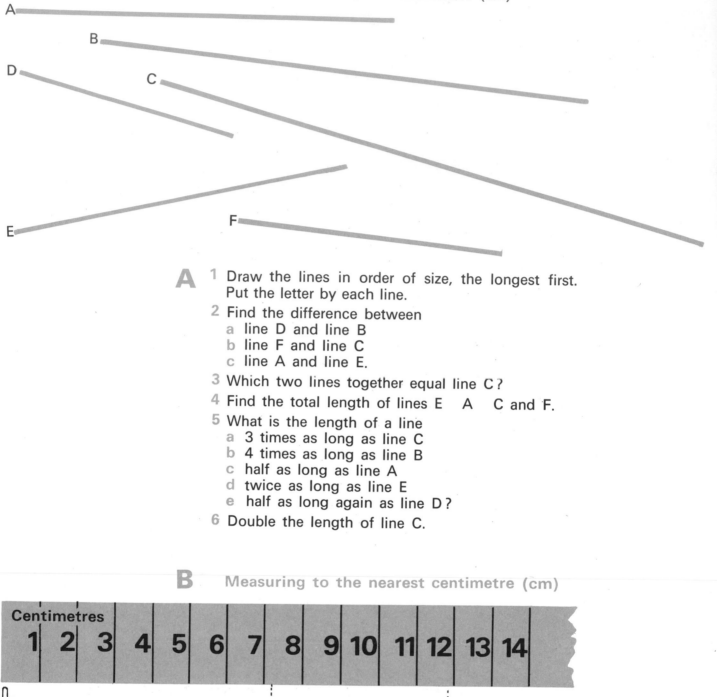

A 1 Draw the lines in order of size, the longest first. Put the letter by each line.
2 Find the difference between
  a line D and line B
  b line F and line C
  c line A and line E.
3 Which two lines together equal line C?
4 Find the total length of lines E A C and F.
5 What is the length of a line
  a 3 times as long as line C
  b 4 times as long as line B
  c half as long as line A
  d twice as long as line E
  e half as long again as line D?
6 Double the length of line C.

B Measuring to the nearest centimetre (cm)

1 Look at the length of the nail.
It is longer than 7 centimetres but shorter than 8 centimetres.
  a Which is the nearer measurement 7 cm or 8 cm?
  b Write
The length of the nail to the nearest cm is ☐ cm.
2 Now look at the length of the pencil. Write
  a The pencil is longer than ☐ cm but shorter than ☐ cm
  b The nearer measurement is ☐ cm
  c The length of the pencil to the nearest cm is ☐ cm.

28

Metric measures length

Centimetres
1 2 3 4 5 6 7 8 9 10 11 12 13 14 15 16 17 18

1 Look at the length of the nail in this diagram.
It is longer than ☐ centimetres but shorter than
☐ centimetres.

2 This time its length is exactly half way between
6 cm and 7 cm. In such cases the bigger number
is taken, for example
The length of the nail to the nearest cm is 7 cm.

3 Write the length of the pencil to the nearest cm.

4 Write the following lengths to the nearest cm.
Half-way between   a 9 cm and 10 cm
b 18 cm and 19 cm   c 24 cm and 25 cm.

5 Write a rule which you can remember for
measuring to the nearest cm.

D 1 Measure these lines to the nearest cm

A
B
C
D

2 Measure to the nearest cm the length and width of
a a page of this book
b a page in your exercise book
c sheets of paper of different sizes.
Keep a record of your work.

E Millimetres (mm)
Measuring to the nearest cm gives only an
approximate measurement. To get more accurate
measurements the centimetre is divided into 10
equal parts each called a MILLIMETRE (mm). The
picture shows a ruler marked in centimetres and
millimetres.

cm 1 2 3 4 5 6 7 8 9 10 11 12 13 14 15 16 17 18
mm 10 20 30 40 50 60 70 80 90 100 110 120 130 140 150 160 170 180

1 How many mm in
a 1 cm   2 cm   3 cm   5 cm   10 cm
b 20 cm   40 cm   70 cm   35 cm   54 cm?

2 **1 METRE = 100 CENTIMETRES**
How many millimetres in 1 metre?

3 See if you can measure the length of the lines in
Section **D 1** in millimetres. You must look carefully.

Metric measures length

A 1 Get a metre stick. Mark on it half a metre. Work with a partner and measure the length of your classroom in metres. For each length of the stick put a mark on the floor and count the metres as you go.

The diagram shows what you have to do.

2 Write   The length of my classroom is ☐ whole metres.

3 There is likely to be a piece at the end which has not been measured. Why?

4 Is this piece at the end
   a less than half a metre   b half a metre or more?

5 If the piece at the end is **less than half a metre** forget it.
   If the piece at the end is **half a metre or more** count to the next metre.
   Write   The length of my classroom to the nearest metre is ☐ metres.

6 In the same way, find the width of the classroom to the nearest metre.

Measuring in metres and centimetres

Measuring to the nearest metre gives an **approximate** measurement only. Usually more accurate measurements are required when CENTIMETRES are used to measure the piece at the end.

B 1 Measure the length and width of your classroom again. Write each answer as metres and centimetres.

2 Measure the length and width of corridors, the school hall, the playground, rooms at home, etc.
   a to the nearest metre
   b in metres and centimetres.
   Keep a record of your work.

		To the nearest metre	Measurement in m cm
Classroom	length		
	width		
Corridor	length		
	width		
School hall	length		
	width		

Metric measures length

Work with a partner

A

Draw this table in your book.

	Estimate cm	Measurement cm	Error cm

Make a list of six things the lengths of which are suitable to estimate and measure in **Centimetres**.
Choose things which you have not previously measured.
When you have estimated and measured the length of each to the nearest centimetre find your error.

B
1 Ask your partner to stand with his back to the wall. Mark his height as shown in the picture.
2 Measure his height to the nearest cm.
3 Estimate your own height, then let your partner measure it to the nearest cm.
By how much was your estimate wrong?
4 By how many cm are you taller or shorter than your partner?
5 Estimate the height of three more of your friends. Measure them and find your error in each case.
6 You now know the height of yourself, your partner and three friends.
Write the names in order of their heights putting the tallest first.
7 Go on making estimates of the heights of things in the classroom.
Then measure them and find the error in each case.

C Draw this table in your book.

	Estimate m cm	Measurement m cm	Error m cm

Make a list of six things the lengths of which are suitable to estimate and measure in **metres** and **centimetres**.
Choose things which you have not previously measured.
When you have estimated and measured the length of each to the nearest centimetre find your error.

Metric measures length

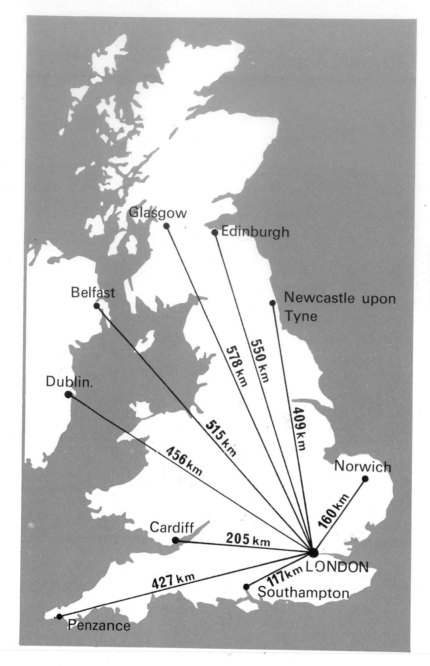

The metric measure for long distances is the KILOMETRE (km).

Distances between towns are stated in kilometres.

Speeds of motor cars, trains, aeroplanes are given in km per hour.

1 KILOMETRE = 1000 METRES

The map shows
the approximate distances in km
of certain towns from London
'as the crow flies'.

1 Which town on the map is
   a the greatest distance
   b the shortest distance from London?

2 Write the towns in order, putting the one nearest to London first.

3 Find the number of km in a return journey from London to
   a Cardiff
   b Norwich
   c Newcastle upon Tyne
   d Dublin.

4 Which is the greater distance from London
   a Cardiff or Norwich
   b Newcastle upon Tyne or Penzance
   c Glasgow or Edinburgh
   d Belfast or Dublin?
   In each case find the difference in km.

5 The distance from London to Edinburgh by road is 595 km.
   a By how many km is the road route further than the air route?
   b Why do you think the air route is the shorter?

6 The approximate distance by road from London to Southampton is 125 km.
   A man travelled this journey by car in 5 hours.
   Find his speed in km per hour.

7 The time taken for a flight from London to Dublin is 1½ hours.
   Find the average speed of the aircraft in km per hour.

8 The time taken for a flight from London to Edinburgh is 1 hour 15 minutes.
   Find the average speed of the aircraft in km per hour.

Counting in sevens

0	1	2	3	4	5	6	7	8	9	10
0	7	14	21	28	35	42	49	56	63	70

Study the diagram to find these answers

A

1 $7 + 7 + 7 + 7 = \square$.

2 6 groups of $7 = \square$.

3 $8 \times 7 = \square$.

4 5 multiplied by $7 = \square$.

5 10 times $7 = \square$.

6 How many groups of 7 in a 21 b 49 c 63?

7 Count on in sevens from 0 to 70.

8 Count back in sevens from 70 to 0.

9 Complete these number series

```
a  14    21    □    □    42
b  35    42    □    □    □    70
c  35    28    □    □    □     0
d  70    63    □    □    □    35.
```

Write and learn the Table of Sevens

$0 \times 7 = 0$
$1 \times 7 = 7$
$2 \times 7 = 14$
$3 \times 7 = 21$
$4 \times 7 = 28$
$5 \times 7 = 35$
$6 \times 7 = 42$
$7 \times 7 = 49$
$8 \times 7 = 56$
$9 \times 7 = 63$
$10 \times 7 = 70$

$0 \div 7 = 0$
$7 \div 7 = 1$
$14 \div 7 = 2$
$21 \div 7 = 3$
$28 \div 7 = 4$
$35 \div 7 = 5$
$42 \div 7 = 6$
$49 \div 7 = 7$
$56 \div 7 = 8$
$63 \div 7 = 9$
$70 \div 7 = 10$

B

1 $\boxed{42}^{\,7}_{\,6}$ $6 \times 7 = \square$ $7 \times 6 = \square$

$42 \div 7 = \square$ $42 \div 6 = \square$

2 In the same way write four facts about
  a 21 b 28 c 35 d 63.

C

	a	b	c	d
1	4×7	7×6	0×7	7×10
2	3×7	7×5	7×7	8×7
3	7×9	1×7	9×7	2×7
4	13 $\times 7$	16 $\times 7$	19 $\times 7$	17 $\times 7$
5	20 $\times 7$	25 $\times 7$	34 $\times 7$	46 $\times 7$

D

1 How many sevens are there in
  a 21 b 56 c 49 d 7 e 35?

2 What must 7 be multiplied by to make
  a 42 b 63 c 28 d 14 e 70?

3 Divide each number by 7 and show the remainder
  a 29 b 51 c 24 d 45 e 39
  f 19 g 60 h 76 i 68 j 48.

	a	b	c	d	e
4	7)84	7)140	7)105	7)119	7)133
5	7)203	7)168	7)224	7)189	7)294

Lines

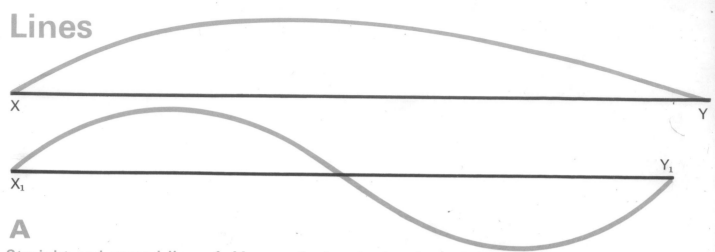

X   Y

X₁   Y₁

A

Straight and curved lines

1 Measure the length of each **straight** line XY and X_1Y_1.

2 Use a piece of thread. Measure each **curved** line XY and X_1Y_1 to the nearest $\frac{1}{2}$ cm. In each case, which is the shorter and by how much, the straight or curved line?

3 Now draw a line with two big curves in it. Measure the line to the nearest $\frac{1}{2}$ cm, using a piece of thread, and then draw a straight line of the same length.

4 Draw other curved lines. Then between the same points draw straight lines. Which is always the shortest distance between two points — the straight or the curved line?

B As the crow flies

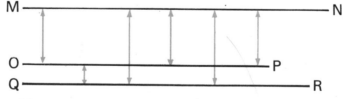

This is a map showing two towns, Dene and Eden.

1 Measure the distance on the map, to the nearest $\frac{1}{2}$ cm, from Dene to Eden   a by the road   b by the canal   c by the railway.

2 What is the distance in a straight line from Dene to Eden?

3 This distance is often called **as the crow flies.** Can you say why?

C Parallel straight lines

M ———————————————— N

O ———————————— P
Q ———————————— R

Here are three straight lines marked MN, OP and QR.

1 What is the length of each line?

2 At different points measure the distance between
   a lines MN and OP   b lines OP and QR   c lines MN and QR
   What do you find about the distance between parallel lines?

3 Draw parallel lines in your book and then make them longer at each end. Find by measuring that the distance between the lines is always the same.

> Write in your book.   **Parallel lines are the same distance apart throughout their length**

Lines

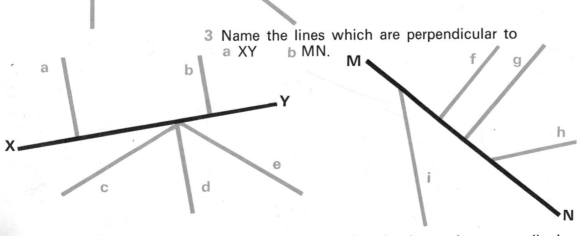

A

1 Which of these pairs of lines are **parallel?**

2 Railway lines must be parallel. Why?

3 Look at the edges of this page. Which of these are parallel?

4 Look round the classroom for examples of parallel lines.
Test them by measuring when you can.

B Perpendicular lines

1 Draw a line XY, 15 cm long. By using a **set square,** as shown in the picture, draw some lines at **right angles** to XY. Then do the same on the other side of XY.

All the lines you have drawn are perpendicular to XY because each line is at right angles to it

2 Draw a **vertical line** and two **sloping lines** as shown. Use your set square to draw at least three lines which are **perpendicular** on each side of each of your lines.

3 Name the lines which are perpendicular to
a XY   b MN.

4 Why must the walls of a house be perpendicular to the ground? The builder can make sure of this when building the walls. What does he use for this purpose?

Numbers from pictures

A

Drawing column and bar graphs.

Look again at pages 16 and 17 before making the following graphs.

1 To find the most popular TV programme
  a Make a record sheet and write a list of six popular TV programmes.
  b Ask each child in the class which one of the six is his favourite programme.
    Mark it on the record sheet.
  c Find the totals and then draw a graph in rows (**a bar graph**).
  d Write the programmes in order putting the most popular first.

2 In the same way find out and record the toys which the children in the class have, for example, an electric train, a doll's pram, a meccano set, etc. Make a list of at least six popular toys. Then draw a column graph to show the result of the count.

3 Draw other column or bar graphs which show
  a the favourite pudding at dinner time
  b the number of adults and children in each family in the class
  c the shoe sizes of the children in the class.

B

The diagram shows the number of children who stayed at school for dinner.

1 Each ⚲ stands for 1 child.

  How many stayed for dinner?

2 Suppose each ⚲ stands for 2 children.

  Find the total number shown in the diagram.

3 If each ⚲ stands for 5 children

  what is the total number then shown?

4 Find the total number when ⚲ stands for

  a 3 children   b 10 children.

5 In another class of the school 24 children stay for dinner. Make a diagram to show this number when

  ⚲ stands for 1 child.

6 Make a diagram to show this number when ⚲ stands for
  a 2 children   b 3 children   c 4 children.
  What do you notice about the diagrams?

7 Make a diagram to show 30 children when
  a ⚲ stands for 3 children
  b ⚲ stands for 5 children
  c ⚲ stands for 6 children.

Numbers from pictures

graphs

C

1 The diagram shows the number of children in another class who stayed at school for dinner. This time, instead of making small drawings, squared paper is used and one square stands for one child. The number scale helps you to count quickly.

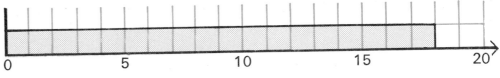

Read from the scale how many children stay for dinner.

2 In this example the number scale has been changed.

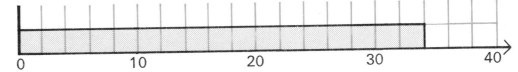

a One square stands for how many children?
b Read from the scale how many children stay for dinner.
c Using the same scale draw diagrams on squared paper to show   16 children   38 children.

3 Look at the scales in these diagrams

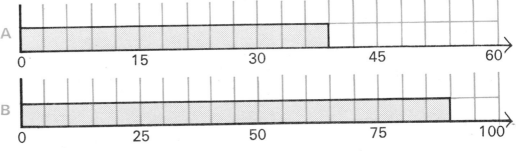

a How many children does one square represent in diagram A   in diagram B?
b How many children are shown in diagram A   in diagram B?

D

Philip and his partner made a count of the different makes of cars in a car park. They then drew this column graph.

1 Look at the horizontal axis. How many makes of cars are shown? Name them.

2 Look at the number scale on the vertical axis. One square stands for how many cars?

3 How many cars of each make are shown on the graph?

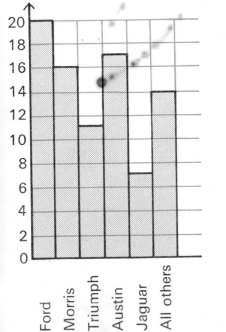

Counting in eights

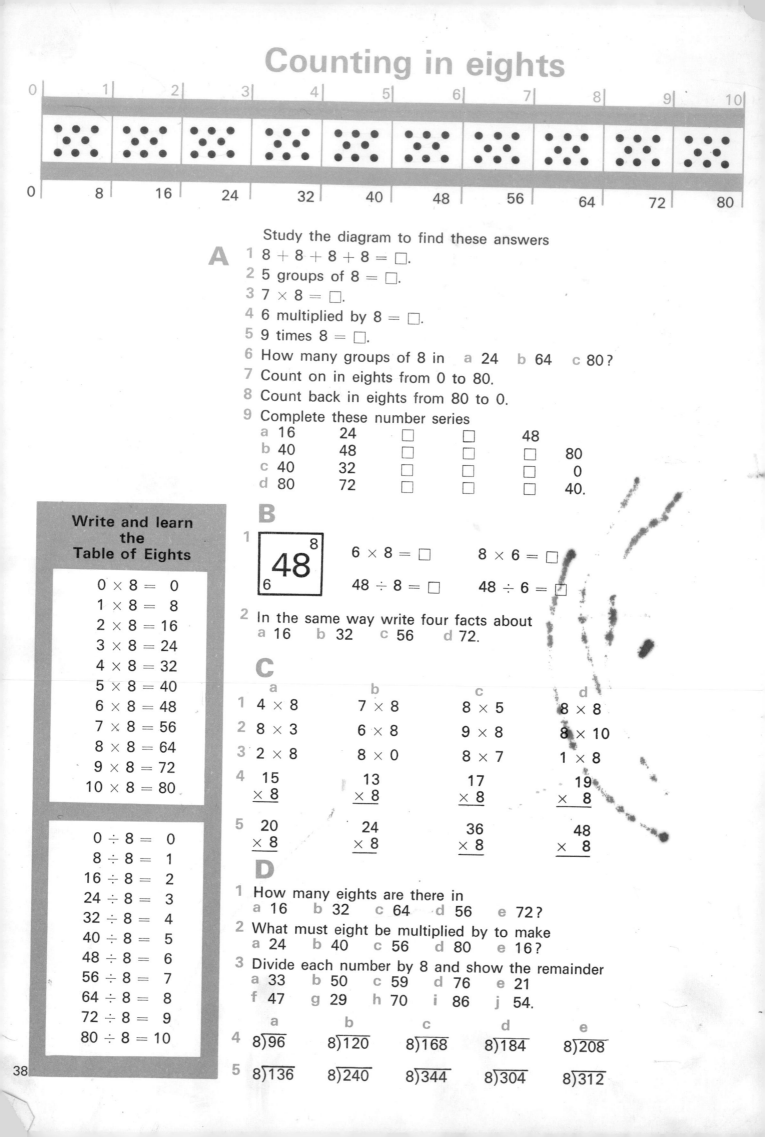

Study the diagram to find these answers

A
1. $8 + 8 + 8 + 8 = \square$.
2. 5 groups of $8 = \square$.
3. $7 \times 8 = \square$.
4. 6 multiplied by $8 = \square$.
5. 9 times $8 = \square$.
6. How many groups of 8 in   a 24   b 64   c 80?
7. Count on in eights from 0 to 80.
8. Count back in eights from 80 to 0.
9. Complete these number series

a 16	24	$\square$	$\square$	48
b 40	48	$\square$	$\square$	$\square$ 80
c 40	32	$\square$	$\square$	$\square$ 0
d 80	72	$\square$	$\square$	$\square$ 40.

Write and learn the Table of Eights

0×8	=	0
1×8	=	8
2×8	=	16
3×8	=	24
4×8	=	32
5×8	=	40
6×8	=	48
7×8	=	56
8×8	=	64
9×8	=	72
10×8	=	80

$0 \div 8$	=	0
$8 \div 8$	=	1
$16 \div 8$	=	2
$24 \div 8$	=	3
$32 \div 8$	=	4
$40 \div 8$	=	5
$48 \div 8$	=	6
$56 \div 8$	=	7
$64 \div 8$	=	8
$72 \div 8$	=	9
$80 \div 8$	=	10

B

1.

8
48
6

$6 \times 8 = \square$ $8 \times 6 = \square$

$48 \div 8 = \square$ $48 \div 6 = \square$

2. In the same way write four facts about
   a 16   b 32   c 56   d 72.

C

	a	b	c	d
1	4×8	7×8	8×5	8×8
2	8×3	6×8	9×8	8×10
3	2×8	8×0	8×7	1×8
4	15 $\times 8$	13 $\times 8$	17 $\times 8$	19 $\times 8$
5	20 $\times 8$	24 $\times 8$	36 $\times 8$	48 $\times 8$

D

1. How many eights are there in
   a 16   b 32   c 64   d 56   e 72?
2. What must eight be multiplied by to make
   a 24   b 40   c 56   d 80   e 16?
3. Divide each number by 8 and show the remainder
   a 33   b 50   c 59   d 76   e 21
   f 47   g 29   h 70   i 86   j 54.

a	b	c	d	e
4 $8\overline{)96}$	$8\overline{)120}$	$8\overline{)168}$	$8\overline{)184}$	$8\overline{)208}$
5 $8\overline{)136}$	$8\overline{)240}$	$8\overline{)344}$	$8\overline{)304}$	$8\overline{)312}$

38

Fractions
halves
quarters
and eighths

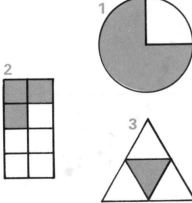

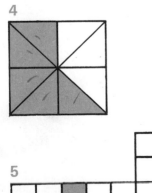

A

1 a Get some strips of paper of different lengths.
   Fold each one first into two equal parts, then
   again to make four equal parts.
  b What is each part called?
  c Fill in the missing numbers.

   1 = ☐ halves = ☐ quarters. $1 = \dfrac{\square}{2} = \dfrac{\square}{4}$

  d Cut off one part from each strip.
   What fraction remains?

2 a Get another strip of paper.
   Fold it into four equal parts, then into eight
   equal parts.
   Each part is called ONE EIGHTH $\frac{1}{8}$
  b Show this by shading $\frac{1}{8}$ of the strip.
  c Cut off $\frac{1}{8}$ of the strip. What fraction of the strip
   remains?

3 a Draw and cut out a large circle.
  b Show by folding how the circle can be divided
   into 8 equal parts.
  c Shade $\frac{1}{8}$ of the circle.
  d What fraction of the circle remains unshaded?

4 Cut out another circle.
   Fold it into eighths. Shade three eighths $\frac{3}{8}$.
   What fraction of the circle is unshaded?

5 Write these fractions using figures
  a five eighths   b seven eighths.

B   Look at the drawings below

a What part of each whole one is shaded?

b What part is not shaded?

C   Study the diagram, then fill in the following

1 One whole = ☐ halves = ☐ quarters = ☐ eighths.

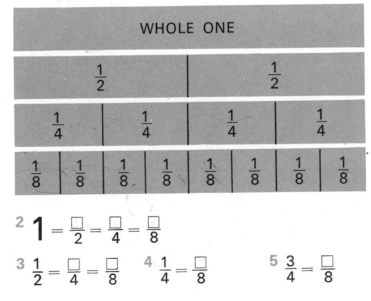

2 $1 = \dfrac{\square}{2} = \dfrac{\square}{4} = \dfrac{\square}{8}$

3 $\dfrac{1}{2} = \dfrac{\square}{4} = \dfrac{\square}{8}$ 4 $\dfrac{1}{4} = \dfrac{\square}{8}$ 5 $\dfrac{3}{4} = \dfrac{\square}{8}$

Now find the answers to the following

6 $\frac{1}{2} + \frac{1}{4}$ 12 $\frac{3}{4} + \frac{1}{8}$ 17 $\frac{3}{4} - \frac{1}{8}$

7 $\frac{1}{2} + \frac{1}{8}$ 13 $\frac{3}{8} + \frac{1}{2}$ 18 $1 - \frac{5}{8}$

8 $\frac{1}{4} + \frac{1}{8}$ 14 $\frac{1}{2} - \frac{1}{4}$ 19 $\frac{3}{8} - \frac{1}{4}$

9 $\frac{3}{4} + \frac{1}{8}$ 15 $\frac{1}{2} - \frac{1}{8}$ 20 $\frac{7}{8} - \frac{3}{4}$

10 $\frac{1}{8} + \frac{1}{8}$ 16 $\frac{1}{4} - \frac{1}{8}$ 21 $\frac{5}{8} - \frac{1}{2}$

11 $\frac{1}{4} + \frac{5}{8}$

Fractions
thirds
and sixths

A

1 The strip has been divided into three equal parts.

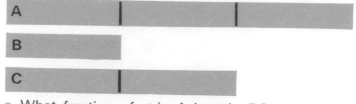

Each part is ONE THIRD $\frac{1}{3}$ of the whole strip.

2 Look at these strips.

A

B

C

a What fraction of strip A is strip B?
b What fraction of strip A is strip C?
c What fraction of strip C is strip B?

B

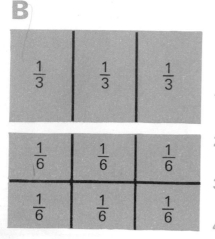

$\frac{1}{3}$	$\frac{1}{3}$	$\frac{1}{3}$
$\frac{1}{6}$	$\frac{1}{6}$	$\frac{1}{6}$
$\frac{1}{6}$	$\frac{1}{6}$	$\frac{1}{6}$

This strip has been folded first into 3 equal parts and then folded again to make 6 equal parts.

1 How many **thirds** in a **whole one?**   Write $1 = \frac{\square}{3}$

2 How many **sixths** in a **whole one?**   Write $1 = \frac{\square}{6}$

3 How many **sixths** equal **one third?**   Write $\frac{1}{3} = \frac{\square}{6}$

4 How many **sixths** equal **two thirds?**   Write $\frac{2}{3} = \frac{\square}{6}$

C a What part of each drawing below is shaded?

b What part is not shaded?

1

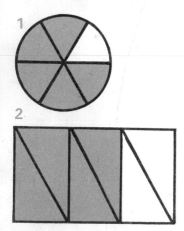

2

3

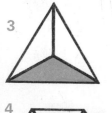

4

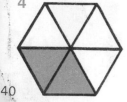

D Study the diagram, then find the answers.

WHOLE ONE					
$\frac{1}{2}$			$\frac{1}{2}$		
$\frac{1}{3}$		$\frac{1}{3}$		$\frac{1}{3}$	
$\frac{1}{6}$	$\frac{1}{6}$	$\frac{1}{6}$	$\frac{1}{6}$	$\frac{1}{6}$	$\frac{1}{6}$

1 How many **sixths** equal **one half?**   Write $\frac{1}{2} = \frac{\square}{6}$

2 Which is the biggest of these fractions $\frac{1}{2}$ $\frac{1}{6}$ $\frac{1}{3}$?

3 Put these fractions in order of size, the smallest first $\frac{2}{3}$ $\frac{5}{6}$ $\frac{1}{2}$

4 a $\frac{5}{6} + \frac{1}{6}$ b $\frac{2}{3} + \frac{1}{3}$ c $\frac{1}{3} + \frac{1}{6}$ d $\frac{2}{3} + \frac{1}{6}$

5 a $\frac{1}{2} + \frac{1}{6}$ b $\frac{1}{2} + \frac{1}{3}$ c $1 - \frac{1}{3}$ d $1 - \frac{1}{6}$

6 a $1 - \frac{2}{3}$ b $1 - \frac{5}{6}$ c $\frac{1}{3} - \frac{1}{6}$ d $\frac{2}{3} - \frac{1}{6}$

7 a $\frac{1}{2} - \frac{1}{3}$ b $\frac{1}{2} - \frac{1}{6}$ c $\frac{5}{6} - \frac{1}{2}$ d $\frac{5}{6} - \frac{2}{3}$

Find the value of

8 a $\frac{1}{4}$ of 28   b $\frac{3}{4}$ of 28   c $\frac{1}{4}$ of 40p   d $\frac{3}{4}$ of 40p

9 a $\frac{1}{3}$ of 24   b $\frac{2}{3}$ of 24   c $\frac{1}{3}$ of 36p   d $\frac{2}{3}$ of 36p

10 a $\frac{1}{6}$ of 18   b $\frac{5}{6}$ of 18   c $\frac{1}{6}$ of 30p   d $\frac{5}{6}$ of 30p

Fractions   fifths and tenths

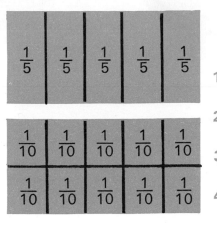

A

This strip has been folded first into 5 equal parts and then folded again to make 10 equal parts.

1 How many **fifths** in a **whole one?**   Write $1 = \dfrac{\square}{5}$

2 How many **tenths** in a **whole one?**   Write $1 = \dfrac{\square}{10}$

3 How many **tenths** equal **one-fifth?**   Write $\dfrac{1}{5} = \dfrac{\square}{10}$

4 How many **tenths** equal **two-fifths?**   Write $\dfrac{2}{5} = \dfrac{\square}{10}$

5 How many **tenths** equal **three-fifths?**   Write $\dfrac{3}{5} = \dfrac{\square}{10}$

6 How many **tenths** equal **four-fifths?**   Write $\dfrac{4}{5} = \dfrac{\square}{10}$

B
a What part of each drawing below is shaded?
b What part is not shaded?

1
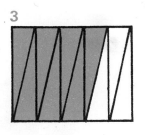

2
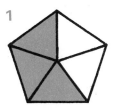

3
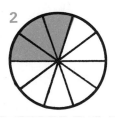

4
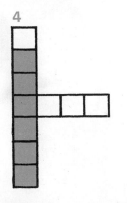

C
Study the diagram, then find the answer.

| WHOLE ONE |
| $\frac{1}{2}$ | $\frac{1}{2}$ |
| $\frac{1}{5}$ $\frac{1}{5}$ $\frac{1}{5}$ $\frac{1}{5}$ $\frac{1}{5}$ |
| $\frac{1}{10}$ $\frac{1}{10}$ $\frac{1}{10}$ $\frac{1}{10}$ $\frac{1}{10}$ $\frac{1}{10}$ $\frac{1}{10}$ $\frac{1}{10}$ $\frac{1}{10}$ $\frac{1}{10}$ |

1 How many **tenths** equal **one-half?**   Write $\dfrac{1}{2} = \dfrac{\square}{10}$

2 Choose from each group of fractions the biggest and the smallest.

  a $\frac{1}{5}$ $\frac{1}{2}$ $\frac{1}{10}$ b $\frac{1}{2}$ $\frac{2}{5}$ $\frac{3}{10}$
  c $\frac{7}{10}$ $\frac{4}{5}$ $\frac{1}{2}$ d $\frac{3}{5}$ $\frac{1}{2}$ $\frac{9}{10}$

3 a $\frac{3}{5} + \frac{2}{5}$ b $\frac{1}{5} + \frac{4}{5}$ c $\frac{7}{10} + \frac{3}{10}$ d $\frac{1}{10} + \frac{9}{10}$

4 a $\frac{1}{5} + \frac{3}{5}$ b $\frac{2}{5} + \frac{1}{5}$ c $\frac{7}{10} + \frac{1}{10}$ d $\frac{3}{10} + \frac{3}{10}$

5 a $\frac{1}{10} + \frac{1}{5}$ b $\frac{3}{5} + \frac{1}{10}$ c $\frac{3}{10} + \frac{2}{5}$ d $\frac{1}{10} + \frac{4}{5}$

6 a $\frac{1}{2} + \frac{1}{5}$ b $\frac{1}{2} + \frac{2}{5}$ c $\frac{1}{2} + \frac{1}{10}$ d $\frac{1}{2} + \frac{3}{10}$

7 a $1 - \frac{3}{5}$ b $1 - \frac{7}{10}$ c $1 - \frac{9}{10}$ d $1 - \frac{2}{5}$

8 a $\frac{1}{2} - \frac{1}{10}$ b $\frac{9}{10} - \frac{1}{2}$ c $\frac{3}{5} - \frac{3}{10}$ d $\frac{1}{5} - \frac{1}{10}$

Find the value of

9 a $\frac{1}{5}$ of 40   b $\frac{3}{5}$ of 40   c $\frac{1}{5}$ of 25p   d $\frac{4}{5}$ of 25p

10 a $\frac{1}{10}$ of 70   b $\frac{3}{10}$ of 70   c $\frac{1}{10}$ of 50p   d $\frac{7}{10}$ of 50p

11 Which coin has the same value as
  a $\frac{1}{10}$ of £1   b $\frac{1}{10}$ of a TEN   c $\frac{1}{10}$ of a FIVE?

12 How many centimetres in $\frac{1}{10}$ of a metre?

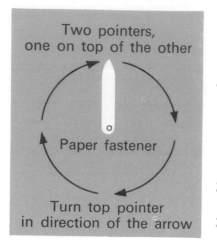

Two pointers, one on top of the other

Paper fastener

Turn top pointer in direction of the arrow

Angles

A

1 To make an angle board.
  a Cut out two narrow cardboard pointers.
  b Place one pointer on top of the other.
  c Pin them together at one end to a piece of cardboard, using a paper fastener, as shown in the picture.

2 Turn the **top pointer only** through a right angle. Make a drawing of the position of the pointers.

3 Turn the **top pointer only** through another right angle and again draw the position of the pointers.

4 Turn the **top pointer only** through another right angle and again draw the position of the pointers.

5 Turn the **top pointer only** through another right angle and again draw the position of the pointers.

6 a Where is the top pointer now?
  b Through how many right angles has it turned?

7 You have four drawings which should look like these

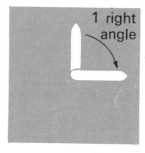
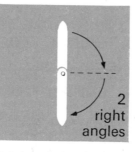
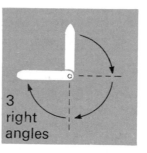
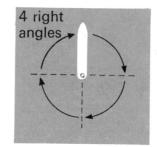

8 Think of the hands of a clock when both of them point to 12. What time is it when the **little hand only** turns through
  a 1 right angle   b 2 right angles
  c 3 right angles   d 4 right angles?

B

1 Take your angle board again and practise moving the pointers to make angles **less** than one right angle. These are **acute** angles (acute means sharp).

2 Now practise making angles which are greater than one right angle but less than two right angles. These are **obtuse** angles (obtuse means blunt).

3 Which of these angles are
  a acute angles   b right angles
  c obtuse angles?

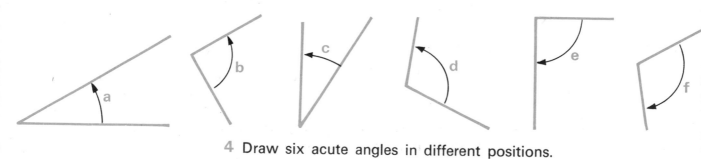

4 Draw six acute angles in different positions.
5 Draw six obtuse angles in different positions.

Angles direction

A

Right turn, left turn, about turn

In the picture, Tom is facing the front of the class. Through how many right angles will he turn if

1 He turns to the **right**?
2 He turns to the **left**?
3 He turns about and faces in the **opposite** direction?
4 He turns round completely?
5 What fraction of one whole turn is
   a one right angle   b two right angles
   c three right angles?

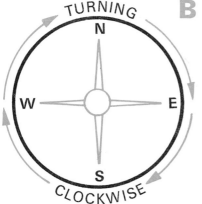

B

North, south, east and west

Ask your teacher for a **compass**, which is used to find direction. The pointer of the compass shows **North**. Then the other compass directions **South, East** and **West** can always be found.

1 Print **North** on a card. Use a compass to place the card in the north part of the classroom.
2 Stand facing **North**.
   In which direction are you facing if
   a you turn to the **left** through one right angle
   b you turn to the **right** through one right angle
   c you turn about through two right angles?
3 Stand facing **East**. Turn in a **clockwise** direction through two right angles. In which direction are you facing?
4 Stand facing **South**. Turn clockwise until you are facing **East**. Through how many right angles have you turned?
5 Stand facing **West**. Turn in a clockwise direction through four right angles. In which direction are you now facing?

C

1 From which direction does the sun rise? In which direction does it set?
2 Fix a pole in the ground and find in which direction the shadow points
   a in the morning   b at midday
   c in the evening.

D

1 This is an aeroplane flight plan. Name the directions in which the plane has travelled.

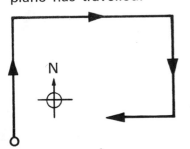

E

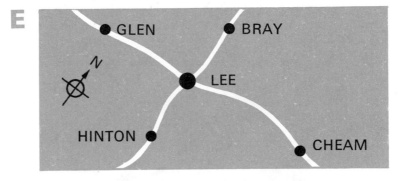

This is a map showing the position of five villages. In what direction from Lee is

1 Glen   2 Bray   3 Hinton   4 Cheam?

43

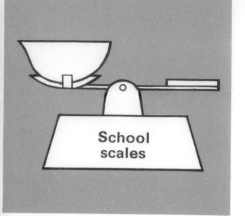

School scales

Metric measures weight

A

In Book 1 you practised weighing using
1 kilogramme (1 kg)
$\frac{1}{2}$ kilogramme ($\frac{1}{2}$ kg)

1 Get a 1 kg weight.
  a Feel it in your hand.
  b Weigh 1 kg of sand, earth or potatoes.

2 Collect three things which you think weigh 1 kg. Weigh each one on the scales and find out if its weight is more or less than 1 kg.

3 Get a $\frac{1}{2}$ kg weight.
  a Feel it in your hand.
  b Weigh $\frac{1}{2}$ kg of sand, earth or potatoes.

4 Collect three things which you think weigh $\frac{1}{2}$ kg. Weigh each one on the scales and find out if its weight is more or less than $\frac{1}{2}$ kg.

B

If smaller quantities than 1 kg and $\frac{1}{2}$ kg have to be weighed, smaller weights are required.

These smaller weights are always counted in GRAMMES (g).

1 a Read what is printed on this label on a small tin of mustard.
  b Find out the meaning of **net weight**.
  c What is the weight of mustard in the tin?

2 Write the weight of the contents marked on the labels.

COLMAN'S MUSTARD

Net weight 50 g

57
TOMATO SOUP

Net weight
300 g

SALAD CREAM

Net weight
200 g

TABLE SALT

Net weight
450 g

JOHNSON'S
HOME MADE
MARMALADE

Net weight
250 g

3 The net weight of a large packet of corn flakes is 450 g. The net weight of a small packet is 220 g. Find the difference between their weights.

Metric measures weight

A

The gramme weight

1 Ask your teacher to show you a 1 gramme weight.
Feel it in your hand.
What do you notice about its weight?

2 Place the 1 gramme weight on the scale pan of the school scales.
Watch what happens.
Is it heavy enough to move the scale pan?
You will now understand why the 1 gramme weight has no use for weighing ordinary things in shops. It is, however, a very important weight when small quantities have to be measured in science. A special balance has to be used. You can perhaps see a metric balance and also some of the weights which are even smaller than 1 gramme.

B

This diagram shows some of the weights in grammes supplied with school scales.

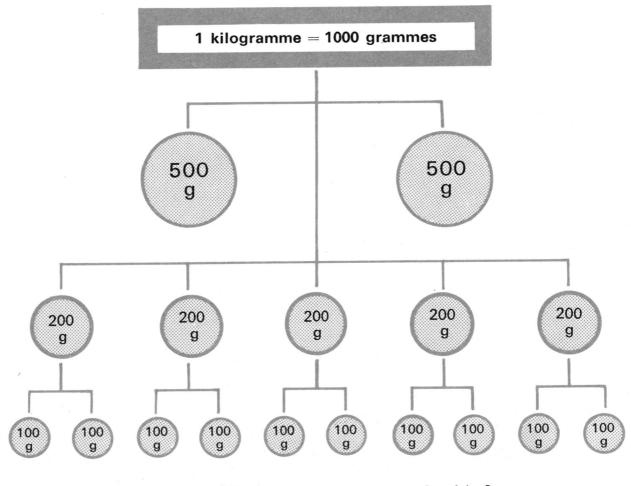

1 How many 500 gramme weights are equal to 1 kg?
Write   1 kilogramme = ☐ × 500 g.

2 How many 200 gramme weights are equal to 1 kg?
Write   1 kilogramme = ☐ × 200 g.

3 How many 100 gramme weights are equal to 1 kg?
Write   1 kilogramme = ☐ × 100 g.

45

Metric measures weight

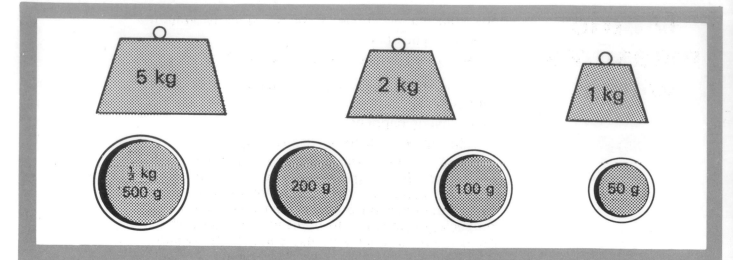

A

The picture shows the weights which can be used with scales.

1 Which of the weights would you use to weigh
   a 3 kg   b 6 kg   c 8 kg   d 7 kg?
   e Two of the same weights will be needed to
   weigh 4 kg and 9 kg. Which is it?

2 Which of the weights would you use to weigh
   a 300 g   b 600 g   c 700 g   d 800 g?
   e Two of the same weights will be needed to
   weigh 400 g and 900 g. Which is it?

3 Which weights would you use to weigh
   a 250 g   b 550 g   c 850 g   d 450 g
   e 950 g?

4 Find how much each of these parcels weighs when
   the weights on the pan are

   Parcel A   2 kg   1 kg   200 g   50 g

   Parcel B   5 kg   500 g   200 g

   Parcel C 2×2 kg $\frac{1}{2}$ kg   100 g   50 g

   Parcel D   5 kg 2×2 kg 2×200 g   50 g.

B Sometimes weights are placed on both scale pans as shown in the drawings.

1 Find the weight of each parcel.
2 A parcel weighs 50 g more than 650 g.
   What is the weight of the parcel?
3 By how much is a parcel weighing 1 kg 300 g
   less in weight than another parcel weighing 2 kg?

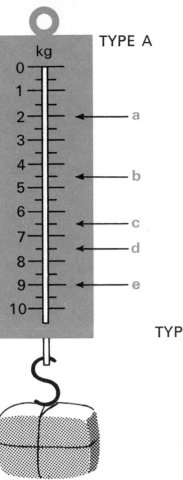

TYPE A

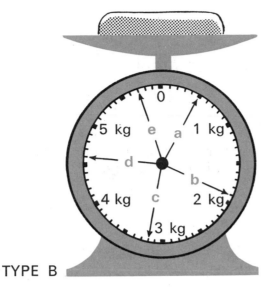

TYPE B

Metric measures weight

There are different kinds of weighing machines other than scales and weights. The pictures show two types of **spring balance.** Get similar spring balances of each type and find out how they work. Observe how the pointer moves along the scale to show the weight.

A

Look at the scale on type A.

1 How many kg can be weighed?

2 Into how many parts is each kg divided?

3 What weight in grammes is shown by each part?

4 Read the weight of objects as shown by the pointers **a, b, c, d and e.**

5 Answer the questions above from the scale on type **B.**

When you go shopping for Mother look out for other kinds of weighing machines.
Look carefully at the scale on each.

B

Estimating weights

1 Weigh 1 kg of sand and put it in a bag. Mark it 1 kg.

2 Now weigh 500 g, 700 g and 1½ kg of sand into separate bags and mark each one.

3 Close your eyes, pick up each bag in any order and call out its weight. Do this many times until you get the right answer every time.

4 Now weigh bags of sand each holding
100 g   200 g   300 g and 400 g.
Do the same as before.

5 Collect a number of things of different weights, stones, bricks, parcels, etc.
Estimate the weight of each to the nearest 500 g.
Then weigh each one as accurately as you can.
Find your error in each case.

Object	Estimate		Actual		Error	
	kg	g	kg	g	kg	g

Metric measures
capacity

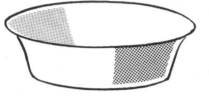

A

Collect some large vessels like those shown in the pictures. You will also need the litre and half-litre measures.

1 Pour 1 litre of water into the bowl.
   Measure with your ruler as accurately as possible the depth of the water.
2 Now pour 1 litre of water into the bucket and measure its depth.
3 Pour 1 litre of water into each of the other vessels and measure the depth in each.
4 The amount of water is the same each time. Why is its depth different?
5 By looking at the depth of water in the vessels, estimate in litres the amount each will hold. Now check your estimates by using the litre measure.

B

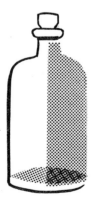

1 a Get a milk bottle, fill it with water and find how much it holds.
   b Collect other bottles and find out which hold 1 litre and which hold $\frac{1}{2}$ litre or less.
2 Get a medicine bottle, a cup and an egg cup.
   Fill the medicine bottle with water.
   How many bottlefuls are needed to fill the $\frac{1}{2}$ litre measure?
3 Find how many
   a cupfuls
   b eggcupfuls are needed to fill the $\frac{1}{2}$ litre measure.
   The amount such small containers hold is measured in **millilitres**. One millilitre (ml) is about a thimbleful.

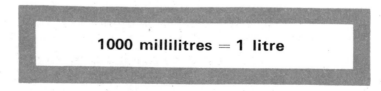

1000 millilitres = 1 litre

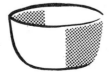

4 Get a 100 millilitre measure and find in millilitres how much the cup, the eggcup and the medicine bottle will hold.

Counting in nines

| 9 | 18 | 27 | 36 | 45 | 54 | 63 | 72 | 81 | 90 |

Study the diagram to find these answers

A
1. $9 + 9 + 9 + 9 = \square$.
2. 6 groups of $9 = \square$.
3. $8 \times 9 = \square$.
4. 7 multiplied by $9 = \square$.
5. $9 \times 9 = \square$.
6. How many groups of 9 in   **a** 27   **b** 45   **c** 90?
7. Count on in nines from 0 to 90.
8. Count back in nines from 90 to 0.
9. Complete these number series

    a 18   27 $\square$ $\square$ 54
    b 45   54 $\square$ $\square$ $\square$ 90
    c 45   36 $\square$ $\square$ $\square$ 0
    d 90   81 $\square$ $\square$ $\square$ 45.

Write and learn the Table of Nines

$0 \times 9 =$	0
$1 \times 9 =$	9
$2 \times 9 =$	18
$3 \times 9 =$	27
$4 \times 9 =$	36
$5 \times 9 =$	45
$6 \times 9 =$	54
$7 \times 9 =$	63
$8 \times 9 =$	72
$9 \times 9 =$	81
$10 \times 9 =$	90

$0 \div 9 =$	0
$9 \div 9 =$	1
$18 \div 9 =$	2
$27 \div 9 =$	3
$36 \div 9 =$	4
$45 \div 9 =$	5
$54 \div 9 =$	6
$63 \div 9 =$	7
$72 \div 9 =$	8
$81 \div 9 =$	9
$90 \div 9 =$	10

B

1.
$$\begin{array}{|c|} \hline 9 \\ 45 \\ 5 \\ \hline \end{array}$$

$5 \times 9 = \square$ $9 \times 5 = \square$

$45 \div 9 = \square$ $45 \div 5 = \square$

2. In the same way write four facts about
   a 27   **b** 54   **c** 72   **d** 63.

C

	a	b	c	d
1	4×9	6×9	9×3	9×0
2	8×9	9×5	7×9	9×10
3	9×2	9×9	9×1	9×7
4	14×9	16×9	18×9	15×9
5	20×9	24×9	33×9	46×9

D

1. How many nines are there in
   a 36   **b** 54   **c** 81   **d** 27   **e** 63?
2. What must 9 be multiplied by to make
   a 18   **b** 45   **c** 72   **d** 90   **e** 9?
3. Divide each number by 9 and show the remainder
   a 20   **b** 46   **c** 30   **d** 66   **e** 17
   f 85   **g** 78   **h** 61   **i** 57   **j** 98.

	a	b	c	d	e
4	$9\overline{)117}$	$9\overline{)144}$	$9\overline{)162}$	$9\overline{)135}$	$9\overline{)171}$
5	$9\overline{)270}$	$9\overline{)630}$	$9\overline{)369}$	$9\overline{)207}$	$9\overline{)477}$

49

Shapes

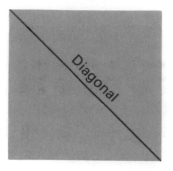

Diagonal

squares and rectangles

A

In Book 1 you learnt how to draw squares and rectangles using a ruler and a set square.

1 Draw three squares and mark them X, Y and Z. Square X has sides 6 cm long, square Y has sides 10 cm long and square Z has sides 15 cm long. Colour in each square.

2 Measure the square in the diagram, draw one the same size, colour it and cut out the square carefully.

3 Now draw a line from one corner to the opposite corner and cut along this line.

4 You now have two shapes. Look at each one. Each shape has ☐ sides and ☐ angles. Such a shape is called a **triangle.**

5 Fit one triangle on the other. Do they fit?

6 Draw another square the same size. Cut it another way to make two triangles. Fit one on the other. Do they fit exactly?

7 What part of the whole square is each of the triangles?

8 Repeat this exercise with other squares. Do you get the same results?

9 Write the name given to the line joining one corner to the opposite corner of a square.

B

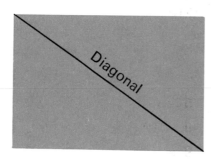

Diagonal

1 Draw three rectangles and mark them L, M and N. Rectangle L has sides 5 cm long and 4 cm wide. Rectangle M has sides 9 cm long and 7 cm wide. Rectangle N has sides $4\frac{1}{2}$ cm long and 12 cm wide. Colour each rectangle.

2 Measure the rectangle in the diagram and draw one the same size. Colour it and cut it out carefully.

3 Now draw a diagonal and cut along the line.

4 How many sides and angles has each shape?

5 What is each shape called? Do they fit exactly?

6 Draw another rectangle the same size. Cut it along the other diagonal. Find out again if the shapes can be made to fit.

7 What part of each rectangle is each triangle?

8 Do the same again with rectangles L, M and N. Do you get the same results? How many diagonals can be drawn in any square or rectangle?

9 Find a way to divide a square into two equal rectangles.

10 Find a way to divide a rectangle into two equal rectangles.

Shapes

squares and rectangles

A

1 Draw, and then cut out this square.

2 Draw the two diagonals and cut along the lines.

3 You have cut the square into four parts.
  Each part is a triangle. How do you know?

4 Place the four triangles one on top of the other.
  What do you find?

5 What part of the whole square is one triangle?
  Make another square, using two of the triangles.

B

1 Draw, and then cut out the rectangle.

2 Draw the two diagonals. Cut along the lines.

3 How many parts have you?

4 What shape is each part?

5 Place these shapes one over the other.
  What do you find?

C

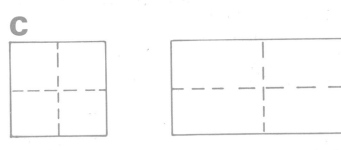

1 Here is a way of folding a square or rectangle into
  four equal parts.
  Try this for yourself.
  What four shapes have you made from
  a the square   b the rectangle?

2 Get some coloured sticky paper.
  Cut out some squares and rectangles the same
  size as each of those above.
  Use these whole shapes, halves or quarters to
  make other shapes.

  First copy those below and stick them in your
  book.
  Then think of other shapes to make.

Table race tables 2 to 10

2 minutes for one column

25 minutes for the page

1	2	3	4	5	6	7	8	9	10
2	4	6	8	10	12	14	16	18	20
3	6	9	12	15	18	21	24	27	30
4	8	12	16	20	24	28	32	36	40
5	10	15	20	25	30	35	40	45	50
6	12	18	24	30	36	42	48	54	60
7	14	21	28	35	42	49	56	63	70
8	16	24	32	40	48	56	64	72	80
9	18	27	36	45	54	63	72	81	90
10	20	30	40	50	60	70	80	90	100

Before starting each race practise several times with a partner.

Then work quickly, column by column, using strips of paper.

Write the answers only.

Multiplication tables

	A	B	C	D	E
1	5×10	3×8	4×6	6×3	3×7
2	6×7	2×3	3×0	2×5	5×0
3	2×2	2×10	2×4	8×6	4×8
4	3×6	4×7	5×7	5×9	2×6
5	4×9	5×8	4×4	6×6	3×3
6	3×5	4×3	7×6	7×8	7×4
7	8×5	7×7	8×8	5×5	8×9
8	2×9	8×7	10×9	9×7	7×1
9	9×3	6×10	5×6	5×4	6×9
10	9×8	9×9	0×9	1×8	9×5

Division tables

	F	G	H	I	J
1	$30 \div 3$	$14 \div 2$	$42 \div 7$	$40 \div 8$	$27 \div 3$
2	$16 \div 2$	$15 \div 3$	$12 \div 3$	$0 \div 3$	$9 \div 3$
3	$24 \div 4$	$16 \div 4$	$40 \div 4$	$15 \div 5$	$20 \div 5$
4	$30 \div 5$	$40 \div 5$	$18 \div 6$	$48 \div 6$	$54 \div 6$
5	$24 \div 6$	$60 \div 6$	$21 \div 7$	$70 \div 7$	$32 \div 8$
6	$54 \div 9$	$18 \div 9$	$72 \div 9$	$24 \div 8$	$63 \div 7$
7	$64 \div 8$	$56 \div 7$	$36 \div 6$	$90 \div 9$	$100 \div 10$
8	$45 \div 5$	$0 \div 9$	$28 \div 7$	$63 \div 9$	$36 \div 9$
9	$72 \div 8$	$42 \div 6$	$27 \div 9$	$56 \div 8$	$45 \div 9$
10	$36 \div 4$	$35 \div 7$	$81 \div 9$	$49 \div 7$	$48 \div 8$

Turn back to pages 4 and 5.   Work the tests.   Try to beat the clock.

Number
multiplication practice
tables 2 to 9

First work Group **A.** Mark the answers and correct any mistakes.
Then work Group **B.** Do the same with each group.
Check by dividing the answers.

A

| 1 | 44
× 2 | 2 | 41
× 8 | 3 | 73
× 3 | 4 | 91
× 9 | 5 | 122
× 4 |

B

| 1 | 80
× 7 | 2 | 60
× 5 | 3 | 70
× 6 | 4 | 101
× 8 | 5 | 302
× 3 |

C

| 1 | 26
× 3 | 2 | 73
× 5 | 3 | 82
× 9 | 4 | 124
× 4 | 5 | 347
× 2 |

D

| 1 | 104
× 7 | 2 | 109
× 6 | 3 | 207
× 4 | 4 | 405
× 2 | 5 | 109
× 9 |
| 6 | 240
× 3 | 7 | 130
× 7 | 8 | 120
× 8 | 9 | 190
× 5 | 10 | 150
× 6 |

E

| 1 | 54
× 7 | 2 | 73
× 9 | 3 | 65
× 8 | 4 | 77
× 6 | 5 | 86
× 9 |
| 6 | 289
× 3 | 7 | 187
× 4 | 8 | 158
× 6 | 9 | 117
× 8 | 10 | 179
× 5 |

F

1 Find the product of   a 27 and 9   b 64 and 8.
2 Find the answers to the following first by addition
  then by multiplication
  a 68 + 68 + 68 + 68
  b 79 + 79 + 79 + 79 + 79.
3 Write the names of the months
  a which have 30 days. Find the total number of days.
  b which have 31 days. Find the total number of days.
4 The milkman delivers daily to school 7 crates each
  holding 24 bottles.
  a How many bottles each day?
  b Find the number of bottles delivered in a school
    week.
5 For the school concert there were 195 seats for
  sale each night from 28th May to 31st May.
  If all the seats were sold how many people came
  to the concert?
6 8 children sat at each table for school dinner.
  How many children stay if 28 tables are filled?

REMEMBER
**The answer to a
multiplication sum
is called
the PRODUCT**

Number
division practice tables 2 to 9

First work Group **A**. Mark the answers and correct any mistakes.
Then work Group **B**. Do the same with each group.
Check by multiplying the answers.

A

| 1 $6)\overline{42}$ | 2 $4)\overline{36}$ | 3 $7)\overline{63}$ | 4 $3)\overline{96}$ | 5 $2)\overline{68}$ |

B

| 1 $6)\overline{44}$ | 2 $9)\overline{75}$ | 3 $5)\overline{39}$ | 4 $8)\overline{60}$ | 5 $7)\overline{54}$ |

REMEMBER

Show remainders as in this example

9 rem. 2
$6)\overline{56}$

C

| 1 $2)\overline{186}$ | 2 $3)\overline{159}$ | 3 $7)\overline{287}$ | 4 $4)\overline{368}$ | 5 $9)\overline{630}$ |
| 6 $8)\overline{568}$ | 7 $6)\overline{426}$ | 8 $5)\overline{350}$ | 9 $7)\overline{560}$ | 10 $9)\overline{459}$ |

D

| 1 $5)\overline{335}$ | 2 $3)\overline{231}$ | 3 $2)\overline{198}$ | 4 $6)\overline{372}$ | 5 $4)\overline{276}$ |
| 6 $7)\overline{294}$ | 7 $9)\overline{576}$ | 8 $8)\overline{688}$ | 9 $5)\overline{395}$ | 10 $6)\overline{474}$ |

E

| 1 $8)\overline{856}$ | 2 $4)\overline{832}$ | 3 $7)\overline{735}$ | 4 $3)\overline{918}$ | 5 $9)\overline{972}$ |

F

1 $6)\overline{639}$	2 $4)\overline{837}$	3 $3)\overline{929}$	4 $2)\overline{617}$	5 $5)\overline{546}$
6 $7)\overline{379}$	7 $8)\overline{410}$	8 $6)\overline{218}$	9 $9)\overline{402}$	10 $7)\overline{528}$
11 $5)\overline{746}$	12 $7)\overline{949}$	13 $9)\overline{907}$	14 $8)\overline{873}$	15 $6)\overline{782}$

G

1 How many sevens are there in   a 210   b 476?
2 Find the number which when multiplied by 9 gives the answer 765.

REMEMBER

In division the amount is called the QUOTIENT

3 When a number has been divided by 6 the quotient is 49 and remainder is 3. What is the number?
4 Share 200 sweets among 7 children. Find the number each child receives and the number which remains.
5 Is this answer correct
   $39 \times 6 = 234$?
   Write these answers only
   a $6 \times 39 = \square$
   b $234 \div 6 = \square$
   c $234 \div 39 = \square$.
6 a One quarter ($\frac{1}{4}$) of 272
   b Three quarters ($\frac{3}{4}$) of 96
   c One third ($\frac{1}{3}$) of 450
   d One sixth ($\frac{1}{6}$) of 192
   e One tenth ($\frac{1}{10}$) of 700.

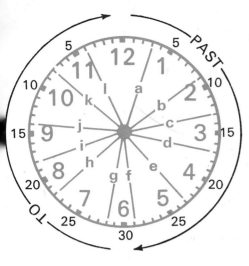

Time to a minute

A

This clock diagram will help you to tell the time to a minute.

Each of the pointers shows the **minute hand** of the clock in a different position.

Find by counting

1 how many minutes PAST the hour are shown by the pointers **a, b, c, d, e** and **f**

2 how many minutes TO the hour are shown by the pointers **g, h, i, j, k** and **l**.

B

Find the time by each of the clocks shown below.

Write the time of each clock in two different ways.

Here is the first one done for you

a 22 minutes past 2 in the morning

b 2.22 a.m.

Morning

Afternoon

C

Some watches and clocks have a **seconds hand** which travels round a small dial as shown in the picture.

There are 60 seconds in a minute.

How many seconds are there in

a $\frac{1}{2}$ minute   **b** $\frac{1}{4}$ minute   **c** $\frac{3}{4}$ minute?

> **60 seconds = 1 minute**
> **60 minutes = 1 hour**
> **24 hours = 1 day**

STOP WATCH

Time to a minute

A

A stop watch measures short periods of time in minutes and seconds.

1 Get a stop watch. Find out how to start and stop it, how to read the minutes and seconds shown on the dial.

2 How many minutes and seconds are shown .on the dial in the picture?

3 Work with a partner and time these exercises, changing about in turn.
Use a stop watch or a watch showing seconds.
a Count 1 2 3 4 up to 60.
Did you finish in one minute?
Try again until you can count second by second to a minute.
b How many words can you write in a minute?
c Turn to page 13, Section **A**.
How many examples can you work in a minute?

4 First estimate how long it takes your partner to change into gym shoes.
Then check your estimate by timing him.

5 In the same way estimate how long it will take
a to walk from the classroom to the playground
b to walk round the sides of the playground
c to run the length of the playground.
Check each of your estimates, using the stop watch.
Think of other such exercises to practise with your partner.

B

Reading and writing time

1 Write each of these times in the shortest way you can
a twenty-six minutes past eight in the morning
b in eleven minutes time it will be noon
c a quarter past three in the afternoon
d my bedtime is at ten minutes to eight.

2 Write each of these times in words
a 7.25 a.m.   b 10.40 a.m.
c 12.02 p.m.   d 5.45 p.m.

3 Write these times in minutes and seconds
a $3\frac{1}{2}$ minutes   b $2\frac{3}{4}$ minutes
c $5\frac{1}{4}$ minutes   d $3\frac{1}{6}$ minutes.

C

1 Write the number of minutes which each programme lasts.

2 Find the number of minutes between
a 9.15 a.m. and 9.45 a.m.
b 4.08 p.m. and 4.31 p.m.
c 7.15 a.m. and 8 a.m.
d 2.35 p.m. and 3 p.m.
e 9.45 a.m. and 10.05 a.m.
f 11.49 a.m. and 12.06 p.m.
g 4.25 p.m. and 5.10 p.m.

TV programmes	
4.40	Cartoon — Tom and Jerry
4.55	Blue Peter
5.20	Tales from Europe
5.40	The Magic Roundabout
5.50	The News
6.00	Regional News

Money multiplication

A To remind you

Fill in the missing numbers of £'s, TENS and NEW PENCE

£		
2 • 4	6
0 • 8	4
0 • 3	0
0 • 0	8
0 • 0	6½

1 2 • 4 6 = £☐ ☐ TENS ☐p
2 0 • 8 4 = £☐ ☐ TENS ☐p = ☐p
3 0 • 3 0 = £☐ ☐ TENS ☐p = ☐p
4 0 • 0 8 = £☐ ☐ TENS ☐p
5 0 • 0 6½ = £☐ ☐ TENS ☐p

Write these sums of money as £'s
6 a 17p b 32p c 56p d 5p e 4½p f 20p.

> **REMEMBER**
> **When writing sums of money as £'s**
> **e.g. £3·45**
> **the 'p' for new pence is NOT used.**

B

1 Turn back to page 14.
  Work examples **A1, 4, 6, 7 and 10.**
2 Father bought 4 ice creams at 5p each.
  Find the total cost as shown in the examples.
3 Find the cost of
  a 8 bars of chocolate at 7p each
  b 5 cakes at 4½p each.
  (Show the working in the two ways)
4 Susan bought 4 packets of biscuits at 17p each.
  Find the total cost as shown in the examples.
5 Find the cost of
  a 6 tins of paint at 13p each
  b 3 metres of cloth at 32p per metre.
  (Show the working in the two ways)

```
  5p          £0 • 05
 ×4              ×4
 ─────        ─────
   p          £ •
```

```
 17p          £0 • 17
 ×4              ×4
 ─────        ─────
   p          £ •
```

C

Work the following. Remember the 0 in the £'s place.

1 £0·04   2 £0·06   3 £0·08   4 £0·06½   5 £0·07½
     ×4   ×7   ×9   ×6   ×3

6 £0·15   7 £0·15   8 £0·36   9 £0·20   10 £0·28
     ×5   ×6   ×2   ×4   ×3

Mark the answers and correct any mistakes.
Then write each answer as new pence only.

D

Study these examples

20p × 5 100p = £1·00	£0·20 × 5 £1·00	57p × 3 171p = £1·71	£0·57 × 3 £1·71

Work the following

1 £0·36   2 £0·23   3 £0·45   4 £0·14   5 £0·17
     ×4   ×6   ×3   ×9   ×8

Work the following and give the answers   a in pence   b in pounds

6 48p   7 65p   8 70p   9 34p   10 83p
    ×5   ×4   ×9   ×7   ×6

Money division

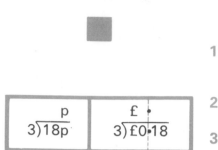

$$3\overline{)18p} \quad 3\overline{)£0·18}$$

A

Turn back to page 15.
Work examples **A1, 4, 6, 7 and 10**.

1 Write these sums of money as £'s
   a 18p   b 35p   c 63p
   d 84p   e 90p   f 64p.

2 David bought 3 bars of chocolate for 18p.
   Find the cost of one bar as shown in the examples.

3 a 5 loaves cost 35p. Find the cost of one loaf.
   b 7 metres of wire cost 63p.
     Find the cost of 1 metre.
     (Show the working in the two ways)

4 a $4\overline{)£0·12}$ b $6\overline{)£0·48}$ c $8\overline{)£0·56}$

  d $9\overline{)£0·63}$ e $5\overline{)£0·40}$ f $7\overline{)£0·42}$

B

$$4\overline{)64p} \quad 4\overline{)£0·64}$$

1 Mother bought 4 tins of fruit for 64p.
  Find the cost of 1 tin as shown in the examples.

2 a 6 packets of sweets cost 84p.
    Find the cost of one packet.
  b 5 metres of ribbon cost 90p.
    Find the cost of 1 metre.
    (Show the working in the two ways)

3 a $3\overline{)£0·69}$ b $2\overline{)£0·48}$ c $4\overline{)£0·68}$

  d $8\overline{)£0·96}$ e $6\overline{)£0·84}$ f $5\overline{)£0·85}$

Mark the answers and correct any mistakes.
Then write each answer as new pence only.

C

Work the following. Remember the 0 in the £'s place.

	a	b	c	d	e
1	$2\overline{)£1·26}$	$4\overline{)£1·68}$	$5\overline{)£2·50}$	$7\overline{)£2·17}$	$9\overline{)£3·60}$
2	$3\overline{)£1·35}$	$6\overline{)£2·52}$	$4\overline{)£3·48}$	$8\overline{)£2·64}$	$5\overline{)£2·70}$
3	$2\overline{)£1·94}$	$4\overline{)£1·08}$	$8\overline{)£3·60}$	$5\overline{)£2·05}$	$9\overline{)£2·97}$

D

Work the following

	a	b	c	d	e
1	$2\overline{)£2·84}$	$3\overline{)£6·96}$	$4\overline{)£8·48}$	$6\overline{)£6·06}$	$8\overline{)£8·80}$
2	$3\overline{)£4·23}$	$2\overline{)£3·80}$	$5\overline{)£6·55}$	$7\overline{)£9·80}$	$9\overline{)£10·89}$
3	$4\overline{)£5·32}$	$3\overline{)£4·74}$	$6\overline{)£7·32}$	$5\overline{)£6·80}$	$7\overline{)£8·75}$

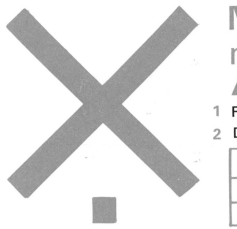

Money
multiplication and division

A

1 Find the cost of a small and a large loaf of bread.

2 Draw a table like the one below. Fill it in to make a **ready reckoner.**

Number of loaves	1	2	3	4	5	6	7	8	9	10
large	p									
small	p									

From the ready reckoner find

a the number of large loaves and the change from 25p   38p   60p

b the number of small loaves and the change from 15p   28p   40p.

B

1 $39 \times 4 = 156$
Write these answers only

a $4\overline{)156}$

b $39p \times 4 = £$

c $4\overline{)£1·56}$

d $£0·39 \times 4$

e $39\overline{)156}$

2 $28p \times 6 = £1·68$
Write these answers only

a $6\overline{)168}$

b $£0·28 \times 6$

c $6\overline{)£1·68}$

d 28×6

e $28\overline{)168}$

C

1 A bat costs 6 times as much as a ball. If the ball costs 34p how much does the bat cost?

2 4 boys paid equal shares to repair a broken window which cost £2·76.
How much did each boy pay?

3 A railway fare is 74p. Find the total cost of 3 full fares and a half for a child.

4 Share 70p equally among 4 children.
How much each?

5 Find the change Mother will receive out of a £5 note after paying for 7 metres of cloth at 58p per metre.

6 A pair of gloves costs 95p.
a Find the cost of 3 pairs.
b These were paid for in £1 notes, TENS and new pence. How many of each?

D

Work the following

1	2	3	4	5
£1·32 ×3	£1·34 ×2	£1·08 ×7	£1·90 ×4	£1·04 ×6
6	7	8	9	10
£2·45 ×2	£1·53 ×4	£1·16 ×9	£1·25 ×8	£2·46 ×5

E

Find the answers and the remainders

1 $3\overline{)£0·82}$ 2 $5\overline{)£0·76}$ 3 $6\overline{)£0·95}$ 4 $4\overline{)£1·33}$ 5 $8\overline{)£1·63}$

The remainder is always a number of new pence.
Can you see why?

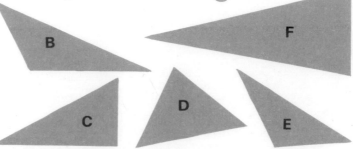

Shapes triangles

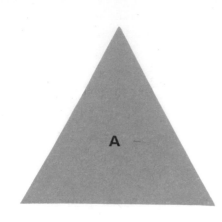

Look at each of these shapes
A 1 Count the number of sides in each shape.
2 Count the number of angles.
These shapes are called TRIANGLES.
3 Write
A TRIANGLE is a shape with ☐ sides and ☐ angles.

4 How many triangles can you find in each of these drawings?

5 Look around you at home, at school and in the streets. Make drawings of things which are triangles.

1 Draw this table.
Measure the sides of each triangle below.
Write the measurements in the table.

2 What can you find out about the lengths of the sides in
a triangle A
b triangle B
c triangle C
d triangle D?

Triangle	Length of sides (cm)		
	a	b	c
A			
B			
C			
D			

B

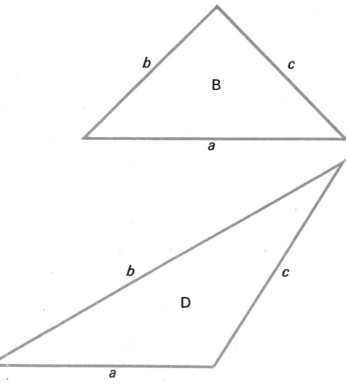

Shapes triangles

height

base   base

height

A 1 Measure the base of each triangle.

2 The height of a triangle is perpendicular to the base.
Measure the height of each triangle.

3 Measure to the nearest ½ cm the height of each triangle, A, B, C and D on the opposite page (Section **B**).

B

> REMEMBER **There are three kinds of angles.**
> **An angle can be**
> a **a right angle**
> b **an acute angle — less than a right angle**
> c **an obtuse angle — greater than a right angle but less than two right angles**

Use a set square to measure each of these angles. Name them.

1   2   3   4   5

C Look again at the triangles on the opposite page (Section **B**).

1 Use a set square to measure the angles in triangle A. Name them.

2 Measure and name the angles in triangle B.

3 Measure the angles in triangle C.
Name one of the angles. Then name the other two.

4 Measure the angles in triangle D.
Name one of the angles. Then name the other two.

5 Draw three triangles in different positions each having a right angle.

6 Draw three triangles in different positions each having an obtuse angle.

7 Draw three triangles in different positions each having three acute angles.

8 Why cannot you draw triangles which have
a two right angles   b two obtuse angles?

9 Triangles are named from the angles
right-angled   acute-angled   obtuse-angled.

Name the triangles on the opposite page in Sections **A and B**.

61

Plans

A

This is the plan of a box with the lid closed. It is the actual size.

1 Find by measuring
   a the length of the box   b the width of the box.

2 Draw the plan in your book, using a ruler and set square.

3 If you had to make the plan smaller you could halve the length and the width. Draw the plan half-size. Place this drawing beneath the other.

4 If you had to make the plan still smaller, you could again halve the length and the width. What would be the length and width of the drawing then?

5 Draw the plan in this way making it one-quarter size. Place this drawing beneath the other two.

**Look at your drawings.
Notice that the drawings become smaller but the shapes remain the same.**

6 Can you say why each of the shapes **a, b and c**, must be wrong for this plan?

7 The plan of a picture frame is drawn $\frac{1}{4}$ of the actual size.
   a Measure the outside length and width of the frame on the plan.
   b What is the actual length and width?
   c Measure the inside length and width.
   d Find the actual inside length and width.

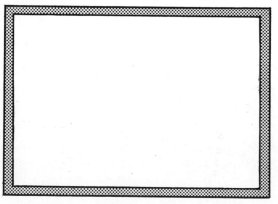

B   Look again at the plan at the top of the page. This time it is the plan of a room. It is drawn to the scale 1 cm to 1 metre, which means 1 cm on the plan stands for 1 metre of the length or width.

1 How long is the room?

2 How wide is the room?

3 Write the length and width of the plan of the room in cm.

4 A room measures 17 metres long and 13 metres wide. Draw a plan of the room to the scale 1 cm to 1 metre.

Plans

C

Look again at the plan at the top of the opposite page (Section **A**). This time it is a plan of a table top. It is drawn to the scale of 1 cm to 10 cm, which means 1 cm on the plan stands for 10 cm on the table.

1 How long is this table?
2 How wide is the table?
3 Draw a plan of a table top which measures 100 cm long and 55 cm wide, using the scale 1 cm to 10 cm.

D

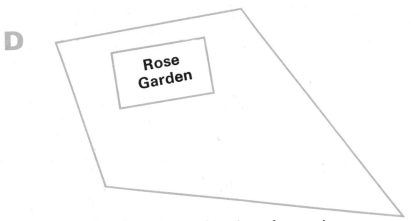

The drawing shows the plan of a garden.

1 Measure each of the sides.
2 The plan is drawn to the scale of 1 cm to 10 metres.
   Find the actual length of each side of the garden.
3 What is the actual length and width of the rose garden?
4 If the drawing was a plan of a field drawn to the scale 1 cm to 50 metres, find the actual length of each side of the field.

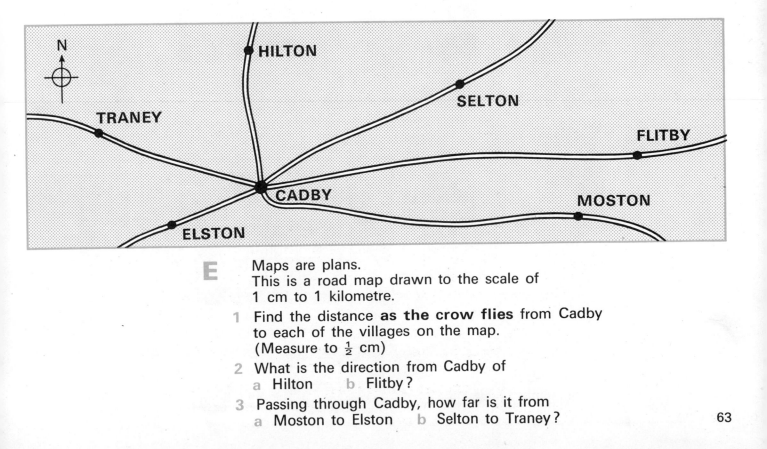

E

Maps are plans.
This is a road map drawn to the scale of 1 cm to 1 kilometre.

1 Find the distance **as the crow flies** from Cadby to each of the villages on the map.
   (Measure to ½ cm)
2 What is the direction from Cadby of
   a Hilton   b Flitby?
3 Passing through Cadby, how far is it from
   a Moston to Elston   b Selton to Traney?

63

Plans and maps

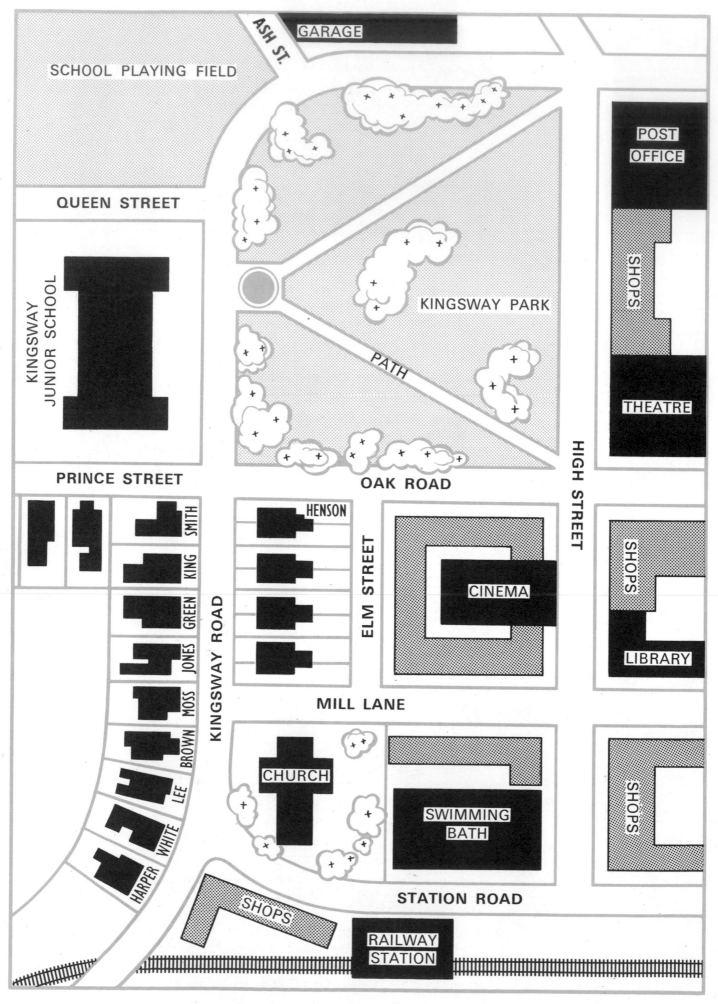

Plans and maps

The drawing on the opposite page is a plan of the Kingsway Junior School and the streets and buildings nearby.

This kind of plan is usually called a map.

A

1 Write the names of all the streets and roads shown on the map.

2 Some houses are detached (they stand by themselves).
Others are semi-detached (they are in twos).
How many houses are on Kingsway Road?

3 What other places are shown on the map?

4 Which of these children lives nearest to the school
Tom Lee   Betty Jones   Sally Smith?

5 Which of the three children lives farthest from the school?

6 From Tom's classroom window he can see grass and trees. Why?

B

1 Mr Smith's house is No. 1.
Mr King's house is No. 3.
Write the names of the people who live on that side of the road and the number of each house.

2 Address an envelope to Janet Moss and one to Samuel White.

3 Mr Henson lives at 2 Kingsway Road.
What is the number of the house at the corner of Mill Lane?

4 Which houses are opposite to Mr Green's house?

5 Who are Mrs White's next-door neighbours?

6 Which roads form the boundary of the playing field?

7 Coming out of Mill Lane, which way will you turn along Kingsway Road to get to the garage?

8 When Fred Harper comes home from school, which roads are on his left?

C

1 Describe a journey from the school to the
a church   b cinema.

2 Mary goes from school to buy some stamps.
Which is the shortest way?

3 Tom walks from the Post Office to the station.
Name the buildings he passes
a on his right   b on his left.

4 John paces Oak Road. It measures 100 paces.
How long is Mill Lane?

5 Is Station Road longer or shorter than Oak Road?

6 How does the railway get by Kingsway Road?

7 Now draw a careful map of the streets and buildings near your own school.

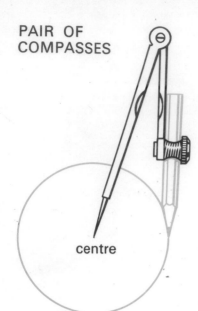

Shapes circles

A

Learn to use a **pair of compasses** to **draw circles.**

1 Make sure that the pencil is screwed in tightly.

2 Open the compasses and fix the point firmly in the paper.

3 Hold the compasses lightly at the joint using thumb and first finger.

4 Turn the compasses first in one direction and then in the other to complete the circle.

5 Practise drawing circles of different sizes.

6 What do you do to make the circle bigger or smaller?

centre

7 Copy these circles.
You can make them as big as you wish.

B

1 Draw a large circle and mark the centre.

2 Cut out the circle and fold it into two equal parts.

3 Fold it again. Into how many parts is it now folded?

4 Open it. Through which point do the crease marks pass?

5 Join the ends of the crease marks.

6 Name the shape you have made.
Test it with the ruler and set square.

7 Draw other circles of different sizes.
Cut them and fold them as before.
Join the ends of the crease marks.
Do you get a square each time?

C

1 Draw a large circle and mark the centre.

2 Cut out the circle and fold it in half.

3 Fold it in half again and then again.
Into how many parts is it now folded?

4 Open it. Through which point do all the crease marks pass?

5 Join the ends of the crease marks.

6 You have drawn a new shape.
How many sides and angles has the shape?
It is called an **octagon.**

7 Do this exercise again, using circles of different sizes.
Do you get the same result each time?

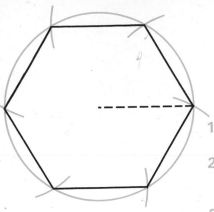

Shapes circles

A

Draw a large circle and mark the centre.
Do not alter the width of the compasses.
Mark round the circle as in the diagram.

1 How many times can you do this?
Join the marks you have made.

2 You have drawn another new shape.
How many sides and angles has the shape?
It is called a **hexagon**.

3 Do this exercise again using circles of different sizes.
Do you get the same shape each time?

B

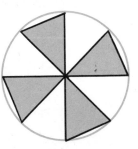
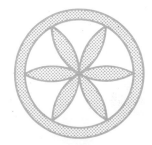

Copy these patterns.
Then see if you can make some more, using compasses and ruler.

C

Drawing circles of given size
Look at the picture.

1 Open the compasses to a distance of 3 cm.

2 Now draw a circle and mark the centre.
Draw many lines from the centre to the edge of the circle.

3 Measure each of these lines.
What do you find?

> **One of these lines
> is called a radius of the circle.
> Two or more are called radii.**

4 Draw four circles, the radius of each measuring
a 2 cm   b 4 cm   c 5 cm   d 3½ cm.
Take each circle and measure from the edge, through the centre, to the edge.
What do you find?

> **In each case the measurement
> is called a diameter.**

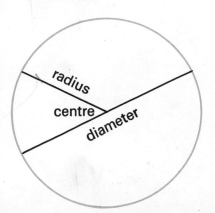

Look at the diagram.
Learn and remember the new words which describe parts of a circle.

3-D Shapes

brick

A Get some boxes of the same shape as those above and a brick.

1 a Count the number of faces on each.
Don't forget the top and bottom.
b Name the shape of each face.
c What can you discover about the opposite faces?

2 On each count the number of
a edges
b corners.

3 Draw the boxes and the brick in your book.

Then underneath draw this table and fill it in to remind you of what you have discovered.

Name	Number of corners	Number of edges	Number of faces	Shape of faces
Match box				
Corn flake box				
Pencil box				
Milk straw box				
Brick				

These box shapes are called **rectangular solids.**
Can you see why?

These measurements can be made on a rectangular solid.

1 LENGTH
2 WIDTH or BREADTH
3 HEIGHT or THICKNESS

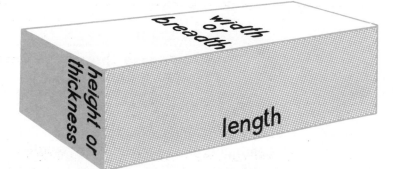

3-D Shapes   A

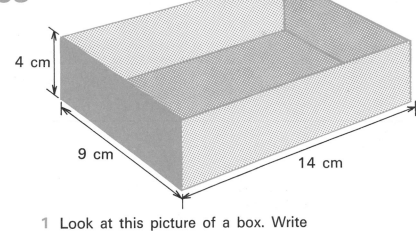

4 cm

9 cm

14 cm

1 Look at this picture of a box. Write
  a its length
  b its width or breadth
  c its height or thickness.

2 How many edges on the box measure
  a 14 cm   b 9 cm   c 4 cm?

3 Now measure the length, the width and the height of all the rectangular solids you have collected. Measure as accurately as you can to the nearest centimetre.

Draw this table in your book.
Enter the measurements of all the 3-D shapes you have collected.

	Length	Width or Breadth	Height or Thickness
Match box Brick Milk straw box etc			

B

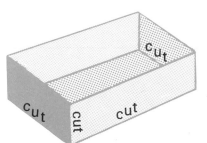

1 Get a match box without a top.
2 Use a sharp knife to cut along the four edges shown in the picture.
3 Open the box and lay it flat on a sheet of paper.
4 Draw round the edge of the shape and you will then have a picture like this

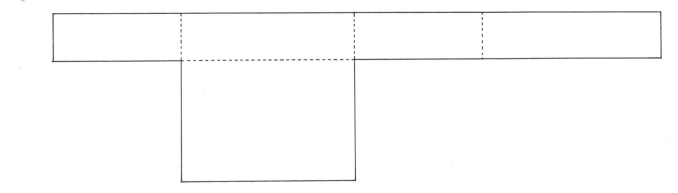

You can see how the box is made.
Try to make one choosing your own measurements.

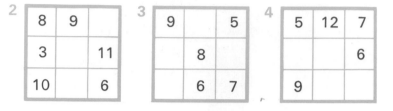

Number

A

1 This is called a **magic square**. If you add each row of figures down, across or diagonally the answer is always the same. Try it.
What is the answer each time?

Copy these magic squares and fill in the missing numbers.

2
8	9	
3		11
10		6

3
9		5
	8	
	6	7

4
5	12	7
		6
9		

B

1 What is the value of the 8 in each number
   a 708   b 893   c 380?

2 How many 10's in
   a 930   b 726   c 308?

3 Find the number which does not belong in each of these series
   a 56   49   42   37   28
   b 24   32   40   48   58
   c 90   81   72   64   54

4 Find the value of x
   a $x - 9 = 16$ b $17 + x = 3 \times 9$
   c $4 \times 12 = 6 \times x$ d $\frac{54}{x} = 9$

5 Put these fractions in order, the largest first
   $\frac{1}{8}$ $\frac{1}{4}$ $\frac{1}{3}$ $\frac{1}{10}$ $\frac{1}{2}$ $\frac{1}{6}$ $\frac{1}{5}$

6 a $\frac{3}{4} + \frac{1}{8}$ b $\frac{3}{10} + \frac{1}{2}$ c $1 - \frac{3}{4}$ d $\frac{2}{3} - \frac{1}{6}$

C

Find the numbers which are missing in each of these examples

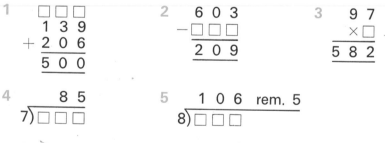

1
```
  □ □ □
    1 3 9
  + 2 0 6
  ─────────
    5 0 0
```

2
```
    6 0 3
  - □ □ □
  ─────────
    2 0 9
```

3
```
      9 7
    × □
  ─────────
    5 8 2
```

4
```
        8 5
  7)□ □ □
```

5
```
      1 0 6  rem. 5
  8)□ □ □
```

D

The column graph shows how many children went to the library on certain days.

1 How many days are given on the horizontal scale?

2 Look at the vertical scale. How many children does one small division stand for?

3 How many children attended on each of the four days?

4 By how many is the biggest number greater than the least?

5 Add together all the attendances and divide the total by 4 (the number of days).
The answer is the **average** attendance. What is it?

6 Copy the graph on squared paper and show that 180 went on Friday and 340 on Saturday.

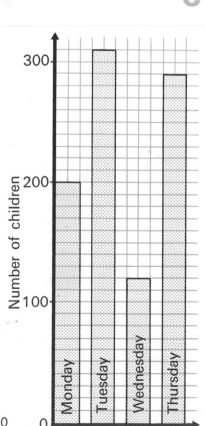

School Outing	
Meet at school	8.45 a.m.
Bus departs	9.10 a.m.
Bus arrives back	7.15 p.m.

Cost of Outing

Fare 64p return

Lunch 35p   Tea 18p

A

Two brothers and their sister went on the school outing.

1 Write as £'s
   a the cost for each child
   b the cost for the three children.

2 Each child was given 50p to spend apart from the cost of the outing.
   On returning home Ann had $27\frac{1}{2}$p left, Philip $13\frac{1}{2}$p and David $9\frac{1}{2}$p. How much did each child spend?

3 From the timetable find
   a the waiting time at school in the morning
   b the time from the departure of the bus to its arrival home.

4 If it takes the children 20 minutes to walk from home to school at what time did they
   a leave home in the morning
   b reach home in the evening?

B

SMITH Grocer	£
Butter	0·46
Cheese	0·24$\frac{1}{2}$
Sugar	0·13$\frac{1}{2}$
Tea	0·36

LEE Butcher	£
Ham	0·55
Leg of lamb	0·84
Steak	0·62
Sausages	0·20$\frac{1}{2}$

1 Total each of these bills.

2 Mother paid them both at the same time. Find their total cost.

3 How much change had she from a £5 note?

4 This is the bill Peter received in a supermarket after buying four packets of sweets.
   Write in new pence
   a the cost of each item   b the total cost.

£0·02
£0·03$\frac{1}{2}$
£0·06$\frac{1}{2}$
£0·08

5 Write these prices as £'s
   a 7p   b 9$\frac{1}{2}$p   c 4$\frac{1}{2}$p   d 18$\frac{1}{2}$p   e 30p.

C

1 Find the cost of
   a 6$\frac{1}{2}$ metres at 8p per metre
   b 3$\frac{1}{2}$ metres at 24p per metre
   c $\frac{3}{4}$ metre at 84p per metre
   d 7 metres at 6$\frac{1}{2}$p per metre.

2 Write as £'s and new pence the cost of
   a 1$\frac{1}{2}$ metres at 70p per metre
   b 5$\frac{1}{2}$ metres at 32p per metre
   c 14 metres at 9$\frac{1}{2}$p per metre
   d 10 metres at 20$\frac{1}{2}$p per metre.

3 1 kg = 1000 grammes.
   What fraction of 1 kg is
   a 500 g   b 200 g   c 100 g?

4 $\frac{1}{2}$ kg (half-kilo) of bacon costs 35p.
   Find the cost of
   a 1 kg b 200 g c 100 g d 700 g e 400 g.

5 1$\frac{1}{2}$ kg beef costs £1·92. Find the price for half-kilo.

71

Metric measures

A Measure these shapes.
Then draw them using a ruler,
a set square or compasses.
Cut out each drawing
and see if it fits.

B Estimating distances by pacing
Work with a partner in the playground

start ├─────┼─────┼─────┼─────┼─────┼─────┼─────┼─────┼─────┼─────┤

10 paces

1 Mark a starting line and from it take 10 ordinary
walking paces.

2 Mark the distance and then measure it to the
nearest metre.
Write   10 paces = □ metres approximately.

3 If the playground is 80 paces long and 50 paces
wide, what is its approximate length and width in
metres?

4 Find by pacing
a the approximate length and width of your
school playground
b the approximate length of streets in the
neighbourhood.

C Work with a partner.

1 In the playground measure a distance of 50 metres.

2 Estimate in seconds how long it will take you
a to walk   b to run this distance.

3 Use a stop watch to find the exact time for each.

4 At this rate how long would it take you to walk or
to run 100 metres?

5 Get a **Book of Records** and find the world's
record time to run
a 100 metres   b 1000 metres (1 km).
Find the record times for swimming these
distances.

Metric measures

A

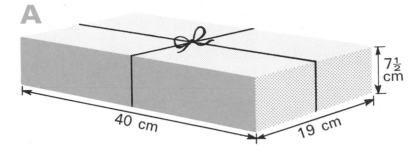

The drawing shows a parcel tied with string.

1 Find the length of string used allowing 19 cm for knots.

2 If the parcel weighed 10 kg find out the cost of the postage.

B

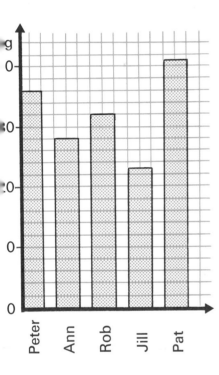

The column graph shows the weight in kilogrammes (kg) of five children.

1 Write the names of the children in order of their weights, putting the heaviest first.

2 Look at the vertical scale on the graph. What does one division stand for?

3 By how many kg is
  a Peter heavier than Jill
  b Jill lighter than Ann
  c Pat heavier than Rob?

4 Find the weight of each child.

5 Add the weights and divide the total by 5. The answer is the **average** weight.

6 Which of the children are
  a above the average weight
  b below the average weight?

C

This is a picture of the petrol gauge on Father's car.
The pointer shows what fraction of the tank is full.

1 The tank on Father's car holds 60 litres. Find
  a how many litres there are in the tank
  b how many litres are required to fill it.

2 Father bought petrol at the petrol station. The pumps then read as shown.
  a How many litres did Father buy and how much did it cost at 8p per litre?
  b How many more litres could be put into the tank to fill it?

73

Lines
Angles
Shapes

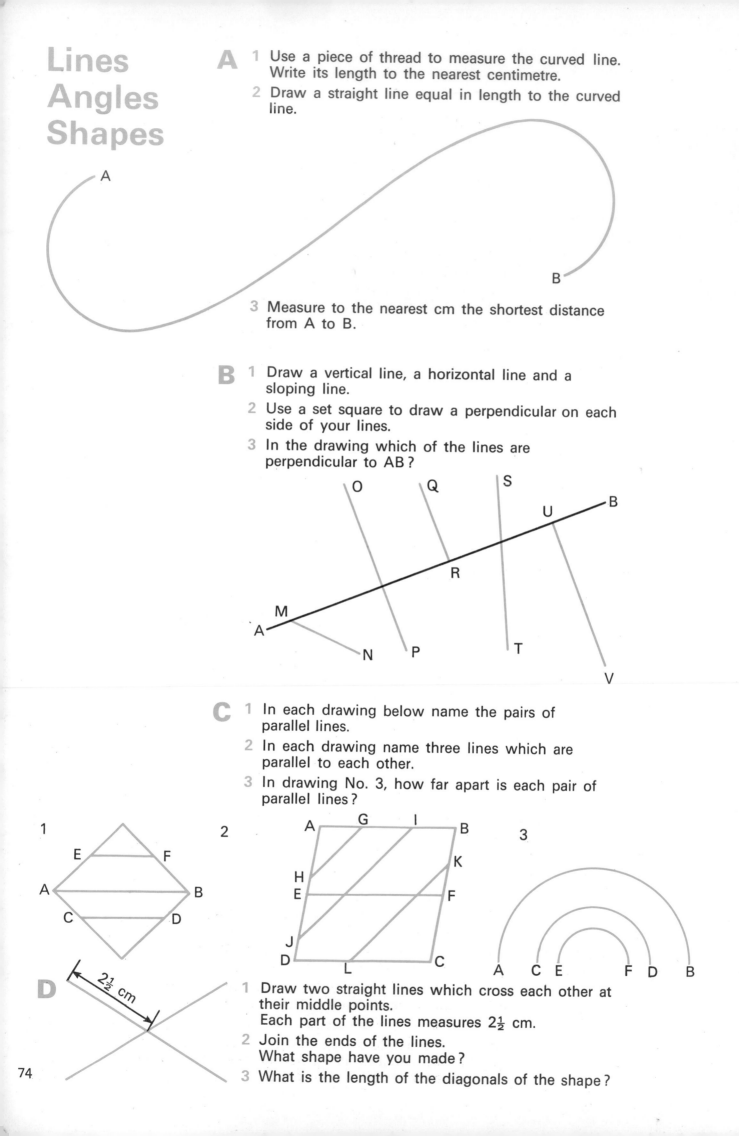

A

1 Use a piece of thread to measure the curved line. Write its length to the nearest centimetre.

2 Draw a straight line equal in length to the curved line.

3 Measure to the nearest cm the shortest distance from A to B.

B

1 Draw a vertical line, a horizontal line and a sloping line.

2 Use a set square to draw a perpendicular on each side of your lines.

3 In the drawing which of the lines are perpendicular to AB?

C

1 In each drawing below name the pairs of parallel lines.

2 In each drawing name three lines which are parallel to each other.

3 In drawing No. 3, how far apart is each pair of parallel lines?

1   2   3

D

1 Draw two straight lines which cross each other at their middle points.
   Each part of the lines measures 2½ cm.

2 Join the ends of the lines.
   What shape have you made?

3 What is the length of the diagonals of the shape?

Lines Angles Shapes

A

1 Use a ruler and a set square to measure and copy this drawing.
2 Complete the drawing to make a triangle with a base of 6 cm.
3 What is the height of the triangle?
4 Measure the two sides of the triangle.
5 In the same way draw another triangle but double the base and the height.
6 Measure the two sides.
What do you discover about their lengths?

B

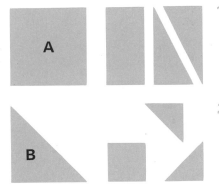

1 The square marked A has been cut into three pieces, as shown.

Draw any size of square and show, by drawing lines in it, how this can be done.

2 The triangle marked B has been cut into three pieces as shown.

Draw any sized triangle of this kind and show, by drawing lines in it, how this can be done.

C

1 Choose from the given angles below those which are
a acute angles   b right angles   c obtuse angles.
2 Name the angles which you think are the same size.

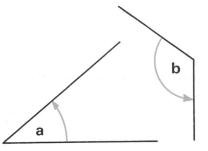

D

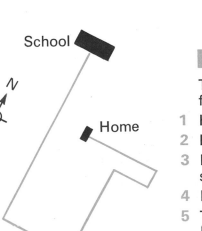

This is a plan showing the journey Anne makes from school to home.

1 How many right-angled turns does she make?
2 How many turns to the left, to the right?
3 In which direction, North, South, East or West, is she walking when she leaves school?
4 In which other directions does she walk?
5 The plan is drawn to a scale of 1 cm to 100 metres. How far does Anne walk on her journey home? Write the answer as km and metres.

Shapes and space area

A These are five different shapes.

Count the number of squares which cover the space in each.

What do you discover about the space in each shape?

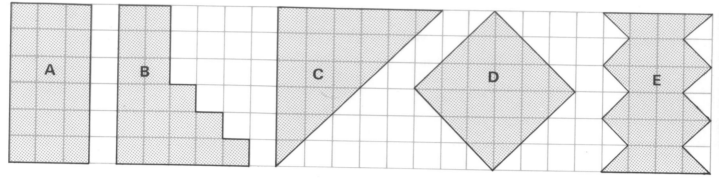

B Which is
a the largest   b the smallest of these shapes?
Describe how you found the answer.

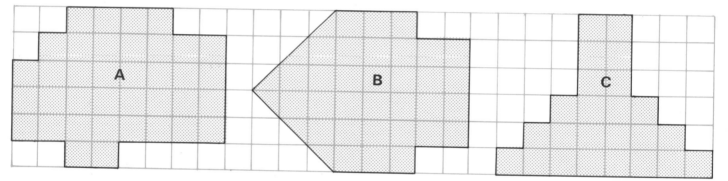

C You have measured the length of lines in **centimetres**.

square centimetre   cm²

The space in shapes can be measured in **square centimetres**.

The number of sq. cm in a shape is called its **area**. Find the area of each of these shapes by counting the square centimetres.

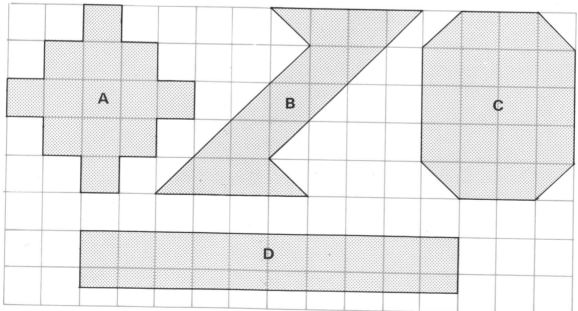

Imperial measures
length

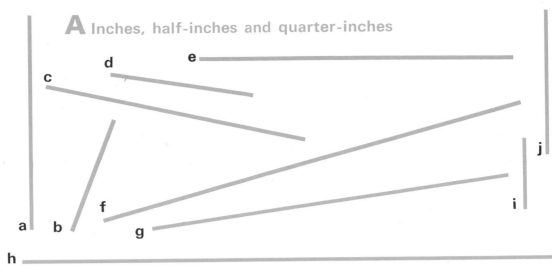

Draw this table in your book.

Lines	Estimate	Measure	Error
Horizontal			
Vertical			
Sloping			

1 Make a list of the horizontal lines, then the vertical lines and then the sloping lines.

2 Estimate the length of each line.

3 Now measure the length of each line.

4 Find the difference between your estimate and the measurement in each case.
If your estimate is too long put + in front.
If your estimate is too short put − in front.

Look at the measurements of the lines, then answer the following

5 Which two lines together make　a 10″　b 5″?

6 Which line is $1\frac{1}{2}$″ longer than line **i**?

7 Which line is twice the length of line **c**?

8 Which line is half the length of line **j**?

B Measuring length to the nearest inch

1 Measure this line.

It is longer than 4″ but shorter than 5″.
Which is the nearer measurement 4″ or 5″?
Write
The line is ☐ inches long to the nearest inch.

2 Measure these lines to the nearest inch
a
b
c
d

Imperial measures length

1 Measure this line.

It is longer than 5½″ but shorter than 6″.
Which is the nearer measurement 5½″ or 6″?
Write
The line is ☐ inches long to the nearest half-inch.

2 Measure these lines to the nearest half-inch

a

b

c

d

3 Collect several things which are less than 1 foot long.

Make a list and then measure each one to the nearest half-inch.

4 The line below is not a straight line. It is a curve.
It cannot be drawn or measured with a ruler. Why?

Use a piece of thread to measure it to the nearest half-inch.
Draw other curves and measure them
a to the nearest inch
b to the nearest half-inch.

D

Make a record of the estimates and measurements you are now going to make.
Find the error in each case.

1 Estimate in inches
a the length and width of the top of your desk
b the height of the chair seat
c the width of the cupboard.
Use a ruler to measure them to the nearest inch.

2 Estimate in feet and inches
a the height of your chair back
b the length and width of the teacher's table.
Use a foot ruler to measure them in feet and inches to the nearest inch.

3 Estimate in yards
a the length and width of the school hall
b the length and width of the playground.
Use a long tape to measure them to the nearest yard.

Keep practising making estimates and measuring.

Imperial measures length

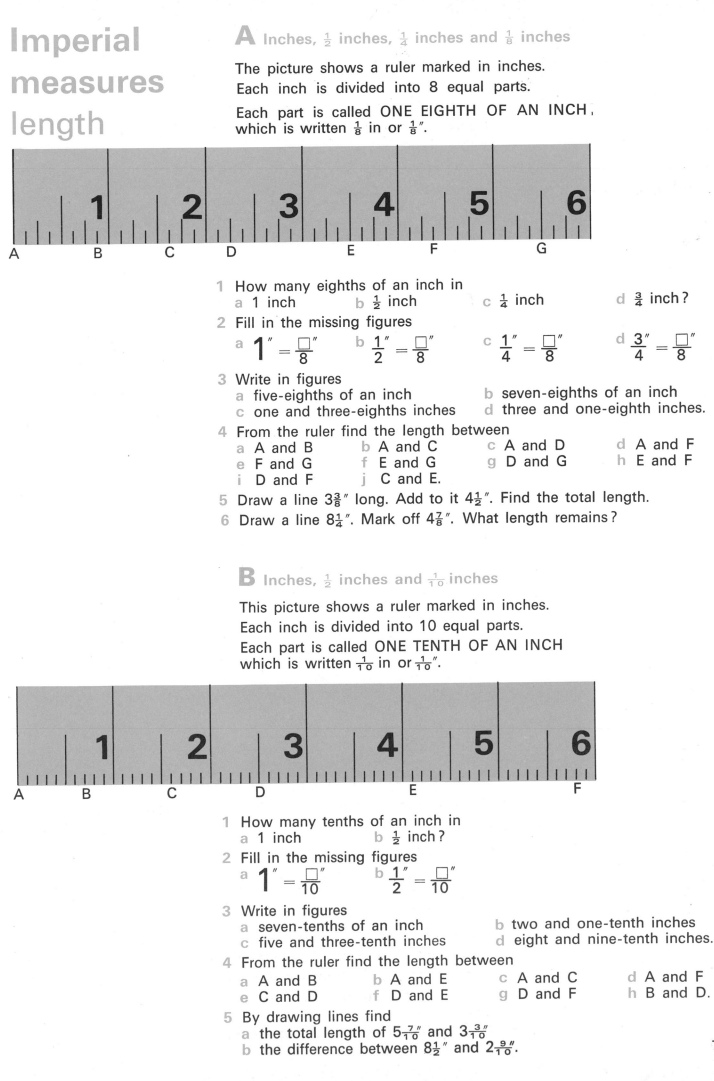

A Inches, $\frac{1}{2}$ inches, $\frac{1}{4}$ inches and $\frac{1}{8}$ inches

The picture shows a ruler marked in inches.
Each inch is divided into 8 equal parts.

Each part is called ONE EIGHTH OF AN INCH,
which is written $\frac{1}{8}$ in or $\frac{1}{8}$".

1 How many eighths of an inch in
  a 1 inch   b $\frac{1}{2}$ inch   c $\frac{1}{4}$ inch   d $\frac{3}{4}$ inch?

2 Fill in the missing figures
  a $1'' = \frac{\square''}{8}$ b $\frac{1''}{2} = \frac{\square''}{8}$ c $\frac{1''}{4} = \frac{\square''}{8}$ d $\frac{3''}{4} = \frac{\square''}{8}$

3 Write in figures
  a five-eighths of an inch   b seven-eighths of an inch
  c one and three-eighths inches   d three and one-eighth inches.

4 From the ruler find the length between
  a A and B   b A and C   c A and D   d A and F
  e F and G   f E and G   g D and G   h E and F
  i D and F   j C and E.

5 Draw a line $3\frac{3}{8}$" long. Add to it $4\frac{1}{2}$". Find the total length.

6 Draw a line $8\frac{1}{4}$". Mark off $4\frac{7}{8}$". What length remains?

B Inches, $\frac{1}{2}$ inches and $\frac{1}{10}$ inches

This picture shows a ruler marked in inches.
Each inch is divided into 10 equal parts.
Each part is called ONE TENTH OF AN INCH
which is written $\frac{1}{10}$ in or $\frac{1}{10}$".

1 How many tenths of an inch in
  a 1 inch   b $\frac{1}{2}$ inch?

2 Fill in the missing figures
  a $1'' = \frac{\square''}{10}$ b $\frac{1''}{2} = \frac{\square''}{10}$

3 Write in figures
  a seven-tenths of an inch   b two and one-tenth inches
  c five and three-tenth inches   d eight and nine-tenth inches.

4 From the ruler find the length between
  a A and B   b A and E   c A and C   d A and F
  e C and D   f D and E   g D and F   h B and D.

5 By drawing lines find
  a the total length of $5\frac{7}{10}$" and $3\frac{3}{10}$"
  b the difference between $8\frac{1}{2}$" and $2\frac{9}{10}$".

79

Imperial measures length

A

1 Measure the length of each of these lines as accurately as possible using eighths or tenths of an inch.

You must first find on which edge of the ruler the divisions are marked.

a ————————————————————————
b ——————————————————————————
c ————————————————————
d ———————————————————————————
e —————————————————————
f ————————————————

2 Write the lines in order of their lengths putting the longest first.

3 Write each measurement in eighths or tenths only.

The first one is done for you

Line **a** $4\frac{3}{10}'' = 43$ tenths $= \frac{43}{10}''$

REMEMBER **1 yard = 3 feet = 36 inches**
1 foot = 12 inches

B

1 How many inches in
   a $\frac{1}{2}$ ft   b $\frac{1}{4}$ ft   c $\frac{3}{4}$ ft?

2 Write these measurements in feet only
   e.g. $2' 6'' = 2\frac{1}{2}$ ft
   a 1 ft 3 in   b 2 ft 9 in
   c 5 ft 6 in   d 4 ft 3 in.

3 How many inches in
   a $\frac{1}{2}$ yd   b $\frac{1}{4}$ yd   c $\frac{3}{4}$ yd?

4 Write these measurements in yards only
   a 1 yd 18 in   b 3 yd 1 ft 6 in
   c 2 yd 9 in   d 3 yd 2 ft 3 in.

5 How many inches in
   a 2 ft   b $1\frac{1}{4}$ ft   c $2\frac{1}{2}$ ft
   d $1' 5''$ e $1' 10''$ f $2' 11''$
   g 2 yd   h 1 yd 8 in   i $1\frac{3}{4}$ yd?

C

1 Find the total length in ft and in
   a $9'' + 11''$
   b $5'' + 8'' + 10''$
   c $6\frac{1}{2}'' + 11'' + 4\frac{1}{2}''$.

2 How much short of 1 foot is
   a $7''$ b $8\frac{1}{2}''$ c $5\frac{3}{4}''$?

3 From $1' 3''$ take $8''$.

4 Take $9''$ from $1' 7''$.

5 Find the difference between $1' 10''$ and $2' 6''$.

6 Double $10\frac{1}{2}''$. Write the answer in ft and in.

7 Half as much again as $1' 4''$. How many inches?

8 Divide $2' 6''$ into 3 equal parts.

Imperial measures
length

A

1 Find the total length of
3 ft 6½ in, 10½ in and 2 ft 9 in.

2 What is the difference in inches between
3 yd and 2 yd 17 in?

3 The distance all round a square is 18 inches.
How long is each side?

4 Four wooden rods each 5′ 3″ long are placed end
to end. Find their total length.

5 Mother buys a piece of cloth 1¼ yd long.
She cuts off 40″. How much is left?

6 The width of an oblong board is ¼ of its length.
It is 3′ 4″ long. How wide is it?

7 A water tank 3′ 6″ high is a quarter full of water.
How deep is the water?

8 The distance round an oblong is 3′ 6″.
The width of the oblong is 9″. Find its length.

B

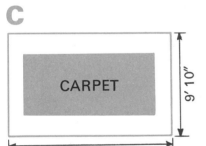

	Height	
	Feet	Inches
Mother	5	3½
Father	6	1
John	4	7½
Elizabeth	5	5
Alison	4	3¾

The heights of each person in a family are given
in the table.

1 Who is the tallest in the family?

2 Who is third in order of height?

3 By how much is Father taller than Mother?

4 By how much is Alison shorter than John?

5 Elizabeth has grown 1¼″ each year in the last two
years. How tall was she two years ago?

6 How much must John grow to be as tall as his
Father?

C

CARPET

9′ 10″

12′ 9″

This is the plan of a room in David's house.
A plan is the picture seen from above.

1 By how much is the room longer than it is wide?

2 The carpet measures 3½ yd long and 2 yd wide.
  a What is the length and width of the carpet in feet?
  b Find the distance all round the carpet in yards.

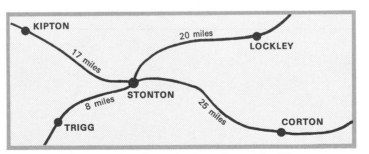

D

This is a map showing the roads and villages near
to **Stonton.**

1 How many miles is it from Kipton to Corton,
passing through Stonton?

2 As the crow flies, from Kipton to Corton is
35 miles. How much nearer is this than by road?

3 Tom's father walked to Trigg from Stonton at
4 miles per hour. How long did it take him?

4 Tom cycles from Stonton to Lockley in 2 hours.
  a What is his speed in miles per hour?
  b At the same speed how long will it take from
  Stonton to Corton?

Imperial measures weight

Pair of scales

Weights supplied with scales

14 lb (1 stone)   8 oz ($\frac{1}{2}$ lb)
7 lb ($\frac{1}{2}$ stone)   4 oz ($\frac{1}{4}$ lb)
4 lb   2 oz ($\frac{1}{8}$ lb)
2 lb   1 oz
1 lb (16 oz)

A

1 Which of the weights will be used to weigh
   a 13 oz   b 2 lb 6 oz   c 13 lb
   d 5 lb 11 oz   e 1 st 8 lb?

2 How much do things weigh when these weights are needed to balance the scale pan

   a 1 lb   8 oz   2 oz   b 7 lb   4 lb   8 oz
   c 4 lb   2 lb   4 oz   d 7 lb   1 lb   4 oz   2 oz
   e 1 st   7 lb   4 lb   f $\frac{1}{2}$ st   2 lb   1 lb?

B

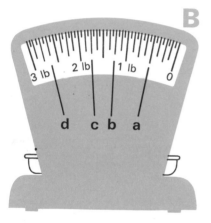

The picture shows a spring balance often used by the grocer or the butcher. Things are put on a scale pan at the front and the customer can read the weight through a glass panel at the back. A pointer moves to show the weight.

1 What is the greatest number of lb which can be weighed on this spring balance?

2 Into how many parts is each lb space divided?

3 What weight is shown by each small division?

4 Read the weight of each object as shown by pointers **a, b, c and d.**
   Write the answer in each case in lb and oz.

C

Estimating weight

1 a Weigh 1 lb of sand and put it into a bag. Mark it 1 lb.

  b Now weigh 1$\frac{1}{2}$ lb   2 lb   2$\frac{1}{2}$ lb   3 lb of sand into separate bags and mark each one.

  c Close your eyes, pick up each bag in any order and call out its weight.

  d Do this many times until you give the right answer every time.

2 Now weigh bags of sand each holding
   $\frac{1}{4}$ lb   6 oz $\frac{1}{2}$ lb   12 oz.
   Do the same with these as in the previous exercise. Practise until you get the right answers.
   Look around the classroom and find some things which you think weigh
   a 1 lb   b 2 lb   c $\frac{1}{2}$ lb   d $\frac{1}{4}$ lb   e 1 oz.
   Weigh each one to see if you are right.
   If not, find out how far out you were.

3 Get from your teacher a number of objects of different size — stones, bricks, books, parcels, etc.

Draw some columns in your book like those shown here. Feel the weight of each object in turn and estimate its weight to $\frac{1}{4}$ lb.
Then weigh it.
Write your answers in the columns.

	Estimate		Actual		Error
	lb	oz	lb	oz	oz
Stone					
Brick					
Book					
Parcel					

82

Imperial measures weight

A

1 How many ounces in
 a 1 lb 3 oz b 1 lb 9 oz c 1 lb 14 oz
 d 2¼ lb e 1¾ lb f 2 lb 7 oz?

2 Write these ounces as lb and oz
 a 20 oz b 29 oz c 31 oz d 40 oz.

3 How many lb in a 1½ st b 1 st 10 lb c 2 st 3 lb?

4 How many cwt in a ½ ton b ¾ ton c 1 ton 13 cwt
 d 1¼ tons e 2 tons 7 cwt?

5 Write as tons and cwt a 28 cwt b 36 cwt c 42 cwt.

B

1 Make 1½ lb heavier by 7 oz.

2 Make 1 lb 4 oz lighter by 5 oz.

3 ¼ lb × 7.

4 Divide 2 lb 4 oz by 6.

5 7 lb + 1 lb 3 oz.

6 What is the difference between 1¼ lb and 13 oz?

7 Three times 7 oz = ☐ lb ☐ oz.

8 ☐ lb ☐ oz ÷ 4 = 7 oz.

9 Find ½ of 1 lb 5 oz.

10 Double the weight 1 lb 10 oz.

11 Share 1½ lb sweets equally among 4 boys. How many ounces each?

12 The grocer weighed a piece of bacon by putting
 ½ oz weight with it in one pan and ½ lb and ¼ lb
 weights in the other pan. How much did the bacon weigh?

13 Write in lb and oz the total weight of ten ¼ lb packets of tea.

14 How many 2 oz weights will balance
 a three ¼ lb weights b a 2 lb weight?

15 Find the cost of the following
 a ¼ lb @ 24p per lb b 1 lb 8 oz @ 18p per lb
 c 12 oz @ 36p per lb.

16 David weighs 5 st 9 lb and Jill 4 st 7 lb.
 a By how many lb is David heavier than Jill?
 b Susan weighs 8 lb heavier than Jill. Find Susan's weight.
 c Who is the heavier and by how many lb, David or Susan?

17 On a lorry there are 3½ tons of coal in 1 cwt bags.
 How many bags are there?

C

At the Post Office a very fine spring balance is
used to weigh letters to find what stamp is needed.
Look at this one.

1 How many parts to each ounce are shown?

2 What is the name of each part?

3 Read the weight of each letter as shown by
 pointers **a, b, c and d.**

4 Find out the postage rates for letters.
 What is the cost of the stamp for each letter?

Imperial measures capacity

A

Get these liquid measures
1 GALLON   1 QUART   1 PINT

1 By pouring water from one measure to another find
a how many pints in 1 quart
b how many quarts in 1 gallon
c how many pints in 1 gallon.

> **REMEMBER**
> **2 pints (pt) = 1 quart (qt)**
> **4 quarts   = 1 gallon (gal)**
> **8 pints   = 1 gallon**

2 How many pints in
a $\frac{1}{2}$ gal   b $\frac{1}{4}$ gal   c $\frac{3}{4}$ gal?

3 How many pints in
a 3 qt   b $1\frac{1}{4}$ gal   c 1 gal 1 qt?

4 What fraction of 1 gal is
a 2 pt   b 6 pt   c 1 pt   d 1 qt?

B

Collect six different containers.

Estimate how much each container holds.

Use the measure you think best to find the capacity of each container as accurately as you can.

See how near your estimate is to the right answer.

Practise estimating and measuring at home using other containers.

C

Get a school milk bottle.

1 Find how much water the bottle holds.

2 How many
a tablespoonfuls   b dessertspoonfuls
c teaspoonfuls
will fill the bottle?

3 How many of each of these measures in 1 pint?

school milk bottle

teaspoon

dessertspoon

tablespoon

D

The table shows the number of pints of milk which were delivered daily for a week.

1 Find the total number for each family.

2 What is the price per pint of milk?

3 Find the weekly milk bill for each family.

	Sun	M	Tu	W	Th	F	Sat
Jones	1	1	2	1	2	1	1
Brown	2	2	2	2	1	2	2
Smith	3	–	1	2	2	1	1
Black	2	2	3	1	1	1	2

THE COMPLETE IDIOT'S GUIDE® TO

Raising a Puppy

by Liz Palika

with color photos © 1999 by Winter/Churchill, www.dogphoto.com

alpha books

A Division of Macmillan General Reference
1633 Broadway, 7th Floor, New York NY 10019

Copyright © 1999 by Liz Palika

Macmillan Publishing books may be purchased for business or sales promotional use. For information please write: Special Markets Department, Macmillan Publishing USA, 1633 Broadway, New York, NY 10019.

International Standard Book Number: 1-58-245040-4
Library of Congress Catalog Card Number: 98-45938

01 00 99   8 7 6 5 4 3 2 1

Interpretation of the printing code: the rightmost number of the first series of numbers is the year of the book's printing; the rightmost number of the second series of numbers is the number of the book's printing. For example, a printing code of 99-1 shows that the first printing occurred in 1999.

Printed in the United States of America

Contents at a Glance

Appendices

Contents

Appendices

Foreword

Whether you're just starting to look for a puppy or already have one at home, you'll find this book to be invaluable. Liz Palika has packed this Guide with loads of important health tips and training techniques. With over 20 years experience as a trainer, she has a knack for conveying information that's easy to understand and training techniques that are practical and easily implemented.

The steps in raising a great puppy begin even before your pet comes home. In the first chapters, you'll find helpful information to guide you in the decision-making process. Liz brings up important issues you need to consider before making your adoption choice. As she says, "Your expectations will affect the relationship with your pet." This means you need to plan ahead by giving some thought to the physical and behavioral aspects of the dog that will become a part of your family. Remember, you don't have the luxury of choosing relatives, so indulge yourself when picking your pet.

A little forethought can help set the relationship up to succeed. For example, dogs with longhair coats require extra grooming time. Dogs of working breeds can require immense amounts of exercise. Big dogs have higher grocery and veterinary bills. Toy breeds are very social and will readily return all of the love you give them, but fare poorly on backpacking trips. Check out Chapter 2 for more important information on breed differences.

Need information about your pup's health care? Well, look no further. The well-researched chapters on health care provide essential information. All the important medical topics you need to know about are included: vaccinations, veterinary visits, spay/neutering, intestinal worms, fleas, nutrition and more. You're also provided with facts about proper care for preventing health problems, what signs to be familiar with when problems develop and how to handle emergencies.

What about puppy behavior? Well, bringing a puppy into your home can be a wonderfully enriching experience, or it can seem like a visit to Dante's Inferno. To get the job done right with a minimum of hassles and headaches, you're going to need some help. But you'll find that depending on friends and associates for that help can be very confusing. If you don't know now, you'll soon discover that *everyone*, even if the person never lived with a dog, has his or her own individual ideas on how it should be done. You'll get all types of advice. Some will be quite sensible, while other advice will verge on the bizarre and even inhumane. This is one of the biggest reasons you will find this book to be very helpful. The information in this Guide is consistent, humane and makes sense. There are plenty of great ideas on how to prepare your home for your pet, good information on housetraining, as well as sage advice on how to puppy-proof your home and deal with the inevitable chewing problems.

A puppy's adult personality is determined by a combination of its breed characteristics, its individual genetics and the experiences it has during the early months of life. All things considered, it's the pup's early experience that is probably the most significant. No time in the relationship with your dog is more important than puppyhood. That's when you make it or break it in determining what the pet you'll be spending the next 12 to 18 years with will be like. This places an awesome responsibility on your shoulders. Socialization and handling compliance are vital issues that must be addressed early in the pup's life.

Raising a puppy the right way requires the proper tools. And you'll find them all right here. You'll appreciate Liz Palika's years of experience as she takes you through important training issues. When you finish reading this book, you will have all the tools necessary to breeze through puppyhood. Okay, so it's not really possible to breeze through raising any puppy, but at least you won't get stuck in a never ending Twilight Zone of house soiling and destructive chewing. To successfully survive puppyhood, I've always felt you need good information and a good sense of humor. Well, here's the information. You just need to supply the sense of humor.

Wayne Hunthausen, DVM

Dr. Wayne Hunthausen is a veterinary behavior consultant who works with pet owners and veterinarians throughout North America. He currently serves on the Practitioner Board for Veterinary Medicine, the Behavior Advisory Board for Veterinary Forum and the Editorial Board of Feline Practice and Canine Practice. In 1996, he helped found the Interdisciplinary Forum for Applied Animal Behavior and serves on its organization committee. He has served as the president, secretary-treasurer and executive board member of the American Veterinary society of Animal Behavior.

Introduction

I have been teaching dog training classes for more than 20 years, and throughout that time people have asked me the same questions over and over. Many of these questions are directly related to normal puppy behavior:

➤ Why does my puppy nip me?

➤ Why does he chase the kids?

➤ Why doesn't he sleep through the night?

Other questions have to do with training:

➤ Why does my puppy fight the leash?

➤ Why doesn't she come when I call her?

➤ How can I stop her from dashing through every open door?

Many other questions are about problem or destructive behaviors:

➤ Why does he chew on everything?

➤ Why is he digging up my backyard?

➤ My neighbors say he barks when I'm not home. What can I do?

Many puppy owners also have questions about how to care for their puppy:

➤ Why are vaccinations so important? What vaccinations should my puppy get and when?

➤ Can I feed a grocery store or generic puppy food? It's much cheaper!

➤ How should I trim her toenails? How can I clean her ears? How often can I bathe her?

In this book I have compiled all of the answers to the thousands of questions that puppy owners have asked me throughout the years. I am a firm believer in the adage, "There is no such thing as a stupid question." If it was important enough for you to ask, then the answer is just as important!

I'll give you all of the information a new puppy owner needs, from how to choose the right puppy for your family, to housetraining, to obedience training, to health care, to activities that are fun for you and your pup.

I really want you to enjoy your puppy. And that means understanding him, training him, taking good care of him and doing things with him. I know puppies can be a handful, but when you understand why they do things, and know how to teach them what the limits are, you'll both have a much happier time together.

For More Information

Since this book is for everyone who loves dogs, it is written so everyone can understand it. If you are an experienced dog owner, don't take offense at the basic material you may think everyone knows. Everyone doesn't! But keep reading, because there is information here for everyone, from the first-time dog owner to the long-time fancier.

I'll begin by helping you decide what type of dog will be right for you. Then we'll talk about where to get a puppy, and what to do on her first day home. We'll look at housetraining, basic obedience training and, at the end, some fun trick training. I'll also tell you how you can use training and a little ingenuity to solve most of the problems puppies get into.

I'll look at many aspects of your puppy's health. I'll give you advice on how to choose the best veterinarian, and tell you when your puppy should be seeing the doc. And, although I hope youíll never need it, I'll tell you what to do in an emergency.

Finally, I'll talk about how your puppy fits into your life and your community. I'll tell you about some of the fun things you can do with a pup. It's a lot of ground to cover, but we'll get to it all!

You'll find four different little boxes throughout the book. I'll use them to highlight really important points in the text and offer additional information.

Paws for Thought

These boxes contain little tidbits of information that can help your understanding of the subject we're discussing at the moment.

Breed Bits

This is information that's specific to one particular breed.

G-r-r-r!

These boxes highlight something very important that you need to watch out for. Pay particular attention!

Puppy Tails

This is the place where I get to tell you interesting stories, historical highlights or extra information.

And the Thank-Yous

As always, I have to thank my husband Paul for his patience—his never-ending patience! When he comes home from work and I tell him, "Guess what? That vacation we were talking about is on hold again. I have a book contract," he just shakes his head, asks me if I have enough time and sighs. He sighs a lot! I don't think he had any idea what he was getting into when he married me 24 years ago. Thank you, Paul!

I must also thank my sister, Mary, and my good friends, Petra and Kerry. They have taken over teaching my classes when I'm too busy writing or when I'm off to a dog show. They have helped me with book signings, photo shoots and everything else associated with my various dog-related activities. Thanks again; I couldn't do it without you!

Part 1
So You Want a Puppy

If you have decided you would like to own a dog, you aren't alone. More than 50 million Americans share their homes with at least one dog. But wanting a dog isn't enough. Do you have the time to spend raising a puppy? Are you willing to make changes in your house to make it safe? Are other family members also happy about having a dog in the house? If you get a dog, what kind do you want? Worldwide, there are more than 400 different breeds—which one would make you happy?

Once you're sure a dog is right for you, we'll take a look at how a puppy comes into the world and what makes each puppy a unique individual. Each puppy is shaped by his breed heritage, the genes passed to him by his parents, his mother's care and the loving, affectionate care given by his breeder. All of these things together create an individual puppy just waiting for you. So, how do you find this puppy? I'll tell you how!

Chapter 1

Are You Ready for a Puppy?

In This Chapter

➤ Do you have time for an active, inquisitive puppy?

➤ Can a puppy be safe in your house and yard?

➤ Is your family ready for puppyhood?

➤ Are you a creature of habit? A puppy will change that

➤ Is your bank account ready for a puppy?

➤ A puppy has its good points, too

So, you want a puppy. Puppies are so adorable—soft little balls of fur, so helpless and yet so full of personality—that it's hard not to take one home. You aren't alone in wanting to own a puppy. The American Veterinary Medical Association estimates 52 million dogs live in American homes. That's a lot of puppy love!

However, the decision to add a puppy to your life is not one to be made lightly, or worse yet, on impulse. You should evaluate your needs, including the time commitment involved and the financial obligations. Your family must also be consulted, because if they live in the house with the puppy, their needs and desires must be considered. Adding a puppy to your family is taking on a 12- to 14-year commitment. Before you make any decision, make sure it's the right one!

How Busy Are You?

A puppy will require a substantial time commitment from you. In the first few days after being taken away from his mom and littermates, a puppy will be lonely and possibly afraid. You (and other family members) will need to spend time with the puppy to reassure him that he is loved and safe. If you can bring the puppy home on a Friday night and spend most of the weekend with him, that would be perfect.

Bonding with the puppy also takes time. This time is well spent, because it is that bond—the close relationship we have with dogs—that makes dog ownership so special. Often, puppy owners tell me their new puppy prefers to spend time with their older dog rather than with the people in the family. What happened was that the new puppy spent more time with the older dog, and as a result, bonded more strongly with the dog. To make sure your puppy bonds strongly with you and not your older dog, your neighbor or the cat, for the first few weeks after you bring home a puppy you will need to spend a lot of time with him.

You will also need time to start teaching your puppy. Housetraining, of course, is a necessity, and it certainly takes time. Teaching your puppy what to chew on (and what not to chew on), as well as other household rules, also requires time.

You will want to start training your puppy as soon as you bring him home. The basic obedience commands, such as sit, walk on a leash nicely and come, are important to ensure good behavior later. You will want to enroll yourself and your puppy in a puppy kindergarten training class, and will have homework to practice from the class. All of which take time.

You will also need to schedule time for daily grooming sessions, including brushing, combing and flea and tick control. Weekly grooming sessions are needed for bathing the puppy and trimming toenails. Some breeds require less grooming than others, but all need the basics.

Breed Bits

A long, fuzzy Bouvier des Flandres puppy will need a good half-hour grooming session each day—minimum!

You must also allot time for exercise. Many behavior problems result from too much energy and not enough exercise. In the beginning, of course, play times will be simple and short. However, as your puppy grows, his stamina and endurance will increase and his exercise needs will increase as well.

As your puppy grows up, you will need to rethink your time with him. You won't need to spend time housetraining because (hopefully!) he will be well housetrained. He will also understand the household rules and will be well behaved when left alone. But you may want to teach him something else. How about dog games, sports and activities? You may want to teach him to catch a Frisbee, play flyball, pull a wagon or do tricks. You may decide to get involved in therapy dog volunteer work. All of these activities, which are great for you and your puppy, take time.

Even if you don't decide to do anything beyond basic training with him, he'll still need training reviews, exercise time, walks, grooming, play sessions, and plain old love and attention from you regularly, all of his life. If you don't want to spend time with your dog, why would you want a dog?

Where Do You Live?

If you rent your home, will your landlord allow you to own a dog? In most states it is perfectly legal for landlords to forbid pet ownership. They can also limit pet ownership to dogs of a certain size or weight, or limit the number of pets you may have. Home ownership associations can do the same thing.

What will your neighbors say when you bring home a dog? You may think it's none of their business, but they can make life very difficult for you, your family and your dog if they are unhappy with the situation. Sometimes it helps to prepare a neighbor ahead of time. Ask your neighbor what his favorite breed of dog is, what good memories he has of dogs, and mention you are thinking about getting one. Ask if he knows of a good dog trainer. Let your neighbor know that you want to make sure your new dog won't be a problem. My grandma said, "You can catch more flies with honey than you can with vinegar." Dealing with neighbors sometimes requires a great deal of honey!

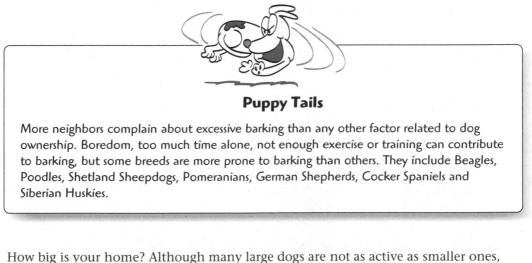

Puppy Tails

More neighbors complain about excessive barking than any other factor related to dog ownership. Boredom, too much time alone, not enough exercise or training can contribute to barking, but some breeds are more prone to barking than others. They include Beagles, Poodles, Shetland Sheepdogs, Pomeranians, German Shepherds, Cocker Spaniels and Siberian Huskies.

How big is your home? Although many large dogs are not as active as smaller ones, they do take up physical space. If a St. Bernard is sprawled across your living room floor, will you still have room to walk? Do you have room for the puppy, his bed, toys, bowls, grooming supplies and the other necessities of puppy life?

Is your house nicely decorated? Are your furnishings very important to you? If you like a very clean, immaculate house, you should rethink your desire to get a puppy. Puppies make a mess—that's all there is to it. Puppies will have housetraining accidents,

Breed Bits

St. Bernards are very big dogs, usually between 26 and 28 inches tall at the shoulder. They are heavyset, big-boned substantial dogs.

spill their food, slobber water all over the floor and track dirt in from outside. Your puppy will come in from playing in the rain and shake dirty water all over, and will bring you—as a present—a dirty stick with dead leaves. He may also bring you a pinecone covered in mud and sticky with sap or a very dead, decomposing mouse, not to make you angry but to share it with you.

Your puppy will also break things—not intentionally, of course. Things will get chewed on and knocked down. Dogs' tails have been known to clear a coffee table in one swipe. It's amazing how powerful a tail can be!

Does your home come with a yard? A securely fenced yard does make puppy ownership easier. With a secure yard, you can let the puppy play outside when you need time alone. Housetraining is also easier with a yard. However, apartment dwellers can still have a puppy. It will just take more time, a consistent routine and more effort on your part.

Puppies can cause problems in the yard, too, though. Do you take pride in your exotic plant collection or your nicely landscaped lawn? If so, don't let a puppy anywhere near it! However, a nice yard and a puppy can co-exist; simply fence off a certain portion of the yard for the puppy. Make a dog run and let the puppy have free access to that area, while the rest of your yard is protected.

Dogs can live just about anywhere. They are infinitely adaptable. However, some situations will require more work or more ingenuity from you. If you want a puppy, you can make it work.

There's something else to consider, too. Many communities have laws concerning dog ownership. Some cities and counties have enacted breed-specific laws that make ownership of certain breeds illegal. Rottweilers, Pit Bulls and German Shepherds have been the targets of several of these laws. Usually these laws have been enacted because of a serious situation, often a severe dog bite case involving a specific breed. Although it seems strange—to dog owners, anyway—to condemn an entire breed because of one or two incidences, it happens. Make sure you know the laws of your community before you get a puppy.

Who Will Be Living with the Puppy?

Does everyone in the family want this new puppy? If some family members (or room-mates) are less than pleased at the prospect of a puppy, the dog will suffer for it. One person's animosity, lack of caring, anger, neglect or abuse could severely traumatize the dog. Everyone must be in agreement before you bring home the puppy.

Are there young children in your family? Often the parents of young children get a puppy so that the dog and kids can grow up together. This is fine, as long as you are prepared for the consequences. Young kids and puppies are made to grow up together—they are very much alike—but there are some problems that parents must be ready to deal with. For example, a young puppy often looks at a young child as an equal, a playmate, and will play with the child as he does with another puppy. That means he will chase, jump on and grab the child with his teeth. That, of course, can scare and hurt a child. Parents must be ready to supervise playtimes and make sure the puppy never takes advantage. Parents often tell me having a puppy is just like having another child!

Paws for Thought

Many widows and widowers get a new puppy after losing their spouse. A dog gives them something to care for, love and shower with affection. A dog also relieves the terrible loneliness the surviving spouse feels after losing a loved one.

Will this puppy be living with a senior citizen? A puppy can add a lot of joy and laughter to a senior's life, as long as the senior citizen is able to deal with the energy level of a puppy. Many seniors also hesitate to discipline a puppy, even when the discipline is well deserved. They tell me, "I've raised my family; now I just want a friend and companion." In these situations, sometimes it's better if the senior adopts an adult dog rather than a puppy. However, if the senior citizen is healthy, active and able to do what is needed for a puppy, well then, go for it!

Do you live alone? Many single adults own dogs, and although this situation can work very well, it does require dedication from the dog owner. In a two-adult household (with or without kids) there is more than one person to care for the puppy and spend

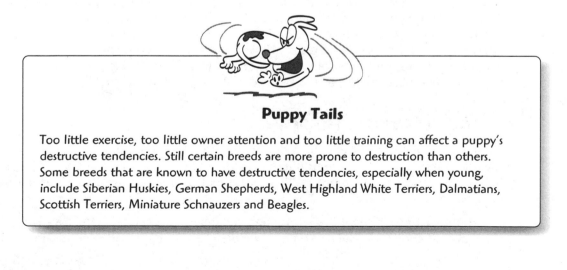

Puppy Tails

Too little exercise, too little owner attention and too little training can affect a puppy's destructive tendencies. Still certain breeds are more prone to destruction than others. Some breeds that are known to have destructive tendencies, especially when young, include Siberian Huskies, German Shepherds, West Highland White Terriers, Dalmatians, Scottish Terriers, Miniature Schnauzers and Beagles.

Kids and puppies can be a perfect match, if you choose the right puppy and supervise the relationship.

time with him. However, in a single-person home, that person is responsible for everything. This takes some dedication. If you work long hours (nine or more each day) and spend a great deal of time away from home, don't get a puppy. However, if you work from home or work close to home and can spend time with the puppy, great! The puppy will be a wonderful companion for you.

Will this new puppy be coming into a household where there are already other pets? If you have a dog or two, adding a puppy will probably be very easy; you've done this before and know what to expect. In addition, your dogs are already socialized to other dogs, so problems should be minimal. However, if you are adding a puppy to a house with resident cats, problems could (and probably will) ensue. Make sure you are willing to spend the time and effort to teach everyone how to get along.

Can You Afford a Puppy?

Buying a puppy from a breeder or adopting one from the local humane society is only the first financial obligation your puppy will incur. For the first year of your puppy's life, it will seem as if your money is disappearing into one of those black holes astronomers talk about.

Your puppy will need supplies—a leash and collar, a bed or kennel crate, toys and chewies, and good food—all of which cost money. Your puppy will need several

Puppy Tails

Tigger is a 17-year-old tiger-striped cat who has helped raise six dogs. He teaches the puppies to respect cats. If a puppy chases him, Tigger bops him on the nose—without claws first, but with claws if the puppy persists. However, once the puppy starts treating him with respect, Tigger becomes the puppy's friend as well as his teacher. Tigger curls up with the puppy, washes his face, and encourages the puppy to wash Tigger's face.

vaccinations and will need to be checked over by a veterinarian to make sure he's healthy. When he's old enough, he will need to be neutered (the girls will be spayed). He will also need to be licensed.

You may have to spend some money to shore up your backyard fence to make sure it's puppy-proof. Or you may want to build a dog run so that you can protect your backyard. Many dog owners wish they had invested in their local home building center's stock before getting their puppy!

In addition, you will need to be ready for emergencies. What happens if your puppy cuts himself and needs stitches? Or gets stung by a bee and has an allergic reaction? Off to the veterinarian you go, checkbook in hand!

Puppies do cost money—not just to buy, but to maintain. You need to be aware of all the potential costs before bringing home the puppy, because it isn't fair to deny the puppy proper care just because you didn't realize how much it would cost.

Will You Enjoy Living with a Puppy?

Many potential dog owners don't realize how much a puppy will change their lifestyle. A new puppy isn't like a new houseplant; you can't add it to your home and expect everything else to remain the same. A new puppy will require you to change some things.

You will have to be more aware of objects, since puppies love to chew. You won't be able to leave your shoes in the middle of the floor; you'll have to put them away. You will have to close doors behind you, close closet doors and put up baby gates to keep the puppy out of trouble.

You will have to puppy-proof your house and put away valuable knickknacks that you don't want the puppy to break. You will have to be aware of what the puppy can get into. You will also have to watch the puppy to make sure he doesn't get into trouble.

Having a puppy will require you to spend time with him, be aware of him and be watchful.

Puppy Tails

In 1903, the famous sports cartoonist Tad Dorgan made a drawing of a sausage in a roll, drawing the sausage as a Dachshund. That's where we get the term "hot dog."

You will also have to be forgiving. If your puppy chews on your shoes because you left them in the middle of the floor, it's not the puppy's fault. It's your fault for leaving them there. Yes, you can say "no" when you take the shoes away, but don't scold him any more than that. Next time, make sure you don't leave them there for him to chew on.

The same thing applies to housetraining. If your puppy asks to go outside and you are too busy to respond or don't pay attention, you cannot scold the puppy for the resulting puddle. It's your job to pay attention, especially when a puppy is involved. An older dog will have better bladder control and will often wait until he can get your attention, but when a puppy needs to go outside, he needs to go out *now*!

A puppy is a wonderful addition to your life *if* you are aware of the changes it will make and *if* you are ready to make those changes. When given a chance, a wanted, loved and treasured puppy will grow up to be your best friend.

There Are Good Points to Puppy Ownership

So far we have discussed many of the negative aspects of puppy ownership. But puppyhood is certainly not all hard work, messes and money. There are lots of great things about having a puppy.

Puppies are cute. I don't think there is anything quite as cute as an eight-week-old puppy. That round, full belly with a leg at each corner is adorable. How can you not love the wet tongue, fuzzy coat, floppy paws, soft ears and wagging tail that quivers at your every word?

What about puppy breath? There is nothing in the world like the milky smell of a puppy's breath. Some people like the smell of a (human) baby's head, while other people love the smell of a new car. Me, I love puppy breath!

Puppies can cause big changes in everyone's life. Before you add a puppy to your family, make sure everybody wants a puppy.

A puppy is also a way of touching other people. When you take a puppy (and later, a dog) for a walk, you will find yourself talking to your neighbors, meeting new people and having fun with the neighborhood kids. People like dogs and will talk to you about your dog.

A puppy will also make you laugh, and that's good medicine! We've known for years that laughter makes us feel better, and now even health care professionals are telling us that laughter is genuinely good for us. Watching a puppy play is great fun. Everything is a toy to be chewed on, growled at and shaken to death. While doing all this, the puppy is adorably clumsy and uncoordinated, tripping over his own feet.

I also feel a sense of wonder about the world around me when watching a puppy. It's easy in our busy world to forget to look around and really see what's happening. But to a young puppy, everything is new and exciting. When watching a puppy discover the world, you can renew your own sense of wonder. Watch a puppy investigate a grasshopper, chase a butterfly or smell a flower. Watch the puppy sit still sniffing the scents on a breeze. What a wonderful world we live in!

A puppy is also a promise of things to come. When I get a new puppy I always fall in love with him, but I am also thinking of the adult dog that puppy will become and our future together. Will we go camping together and explore new places? Will we train in a new dog sport? Will this puppy be like Ursa was and wash my face when I cry at a sad movie? Will he be like Dax and bring me toys when he wants attention? What characteristic will he have that will make him unique? I look forward to the new relationship we will forge together, because this new puppy will become my new best friend. What a wonderful promise!

The Least You Need to Know

➤ Puppies require a great deal of time. If you want to get a puppy, you will need to set aside that time.

➤ Before you get a puppy, look at your living situation and make sure a puppy will fit in.

➤ Everyone in the household must want the puppy and be able to handle it.

➤ A puppy is a financial obligation; make sure you can afford to give the puppy the care he needs.

➤ A puppy will love you unconditionally but will also mess up your house and disrupt your routine. Can you deal with that?

➤ This new puppy will be a source of laughter, joy and wonder, and when he grows up he will be your new best friend.

Big or Small, Longhaired or Short?

All domesticated dogs are related. They all belong to the same scientific species *Canis familiaris,* and as such, can breed with each other and produce fertile offspring. This singular species is made up of more varied and diverse breeds than any other species known to humanity. There are tiny dogs weighing no more than two pounds and gigantic dogs weighing more than 200 pounds. There are dogs that herd sheep on grassy meadows, dogs that swim to retrieve waterfowl and dogs that originated in desert lands. Some have long, silky, flowing coats; some have short, slick coats; others have coarse, curly coats. There are even dogs with no hair at all except a little puff on the head and legs.

What Is Important to You?

Before you get a puppy, it's important to decide what canine characteristics are important to you, because your expectations will affect the relationship you have with your new dog. Some people love to spend hours combing out a long, silky coat, while other people would prefer a wash-and-wear dog. Active people may not be bothered by—and might even prefer—an energetic dog, while other dog owners would prefer a more laid-back personality. Let's make sure you understand some of your choices before you fall in love with a breed that's not right for you.

Long Hair or Short?

Coat types vary incredibly among breeds. Australian Shepherds and Collies have a medium-length silky coat that is easy to brush and care for. It will rarely mat, and dirt will fall out of it. However, these dogs do shed, and twice a year they shed heavily. German Shepherds, also a herding breed, have a shorter outer coat (than Australian Shepherds or Collies), but they have a thick, heavy undercoat. A German Shepherd's coat never mats, but it sheds very heavily twice a year and a little bit all the time.

The Irish, English and Gordon Setters have a gorgeous long, flowing coat that is absolutely stunning, but this coat comes with a price. It needs to be combed daily or it will mat—and it is capable of matting horribly! Afghan Hounds also have a long, silky coat that needs regular, thorough combing. Old English Sheepdogs have an entirely different type of coat. This thick, heavy coat needs constant grooming or it will turn into one big, horrible *mat!* This is a coat that requires time and effort to keep it looking nice.

Labrador Retrievers, Doberman Pinschers, Boxers, Weimaraners, Pointers and Smooth Fox Terriers have a short, slick coat that isn't long enough to tangle or mat. However, don't make the mistake of thinking this short coat doesn't shed; it does, and twice a year these breeds shed heavily. The hair that is shed is short instead of long—just the right length for working its way into your sofa cushions.

Many other breeds, including Poodles and Cocker Spaniels, have hair that grows constantly and needs regular grooming and haircuts. If you cannot cut the dog's hair yourself, make sure you take the cost of professional grooming into consideration before getting one of these breeds. As a general rule, most of these breeds should get a haircut or professional grooming every four to six weeks. In between, you will need to keep them combed, dematted and brushed.

Grooming costs vary, depending upon the area where you live, the economy and the breed of dog you have. However, as an average, grooming for a Cocker Spaniel will cost between $20 and $40. An Old English Sheepdog's shampoo, brush, comb and haircut may run between $40 and $60.

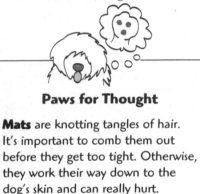

Paws for Thought

Mats are knotting tangles of hair. It's important to comb them out before they get too tight. Otherwise, they work their way down to the dog's skin and can really hurt.

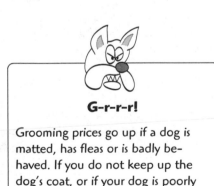

G-r-r-r!

Grooming prices go up if a dog is matted, has fleas or is badly be-haved. If you do not keep up the dog's coat, or if your dog is poorly trained, expect to pay more.

A Lhasa Apso requires considerable grooming. This puppy owner knew that before she decided to add a Lhasa to her family.

Breeds that Need Regular Grooming and Haircuts

Bichons Frises	English Cocker Spaniels
Bouviers des Flandres	English Springer Spaniels
Lhasa Apsos	Welsh Springer Spaniels
Maltese	Airedale Terriers
Old English Sheepdogs	Scottish Terriers
Pekingese	Silky Terriers
Toy, Miniature and Standard Poodles	West Highland White Terriers
Pomeranians	Welsh Terriers
Miniature, Standard and Giant Schnauzers	Wire Fox Terriers
Shih Tzus	Yorkshire Terriers
Cocker Spaniels	

Breed Bits

Border Collies are considered to be one of the best herding breeds alive. However, a good herding dog is not necessarily a good pet. Border Collies are very active, like to play, need to work and are intelligent enough to get into lots of trouble. Don't get one unless you can keep her active and stimulated.

Coat types are purely a personal preference. Some people like the look and feel of a short, slick coat, while others like to snuggle up to a furry, silky-coated friend. Make sure you will be comfortable with the feel of a specific breed's coat, as well as the upkeep and grooming that particular coat will require.

Excitability, Activity Level and Playfulness

There is nothing more annoying to a calm, laid-back person than someone who is bouncing around, ready for activity at any moment. I know, because I am one of those couch potato people. However, one of my best friends (the human kind) is a high energy, ready-to-go person. To maintain our friendship, I simply avoid her when I want some couch time.

Dogs also have differences in personality and activity levels. Some breeds are known for being more active, while others are more laid back. The key to a successful relationship is to match your personality and activity level with your canine.

Excitability

Excitability is usually referred to as the dog's ability to "come alive" when something happens, such as the doorbell ringing. Some breeds are more easily excited than others. The following table is a generalization, of course, because individual dogs have different levels of excitability.

Some Easily Excited Breeds	Some Not So Easily Excited Breeds
Chihuahuas	Akitas
Shih Tzu	Alaskan Malamutes
Fox Terriers	Bloodhounds
Jack Russell Terriers	Bulldogs
Scottish Terriers	Chow Chows
West Highland White Terriers	Newfoundlands
Yorkshire Terriers	Rottweilers
Silky Terriers	St. Bernards

Activity Level

Excitability does not necessarily mean a breed also has a high activity level, although the two do often go hand in hand. A high activity level means this breed is more active, whether or not something specific is going on that might make a dog want to run around. Some owners—like my active friend—prefer a dog that is more active, whereas I prefer a dog that is more relaxed, like me.

Some Active Breeds	Some Laid-Back Breeds
Border Collies	Akitas
Miniature Pinschers	Alaskan Malamutes
Miniature Schnauzers	Basset Hounds
Pomeranians	Bloodhounds
Cocker Spaniels	Bulldogs
Shetland Sheepdogs	Chow Chows
Shih Tzu	Golden Retrievers
Fox Terriers	Great Danes
Jack Russell Terriers	Newfoundlands
Silky Terriers	Pugs
West Highland White Terriers	St. Bernards

Desire to Play

Most dog owners like to play with their dogs. It could be throwing the tennis ball or playing hide-and-seek or tossing a Frisbee. People with a high energy level usually enjoy an active dog that likes to play a lot. However, laid-back people like me would be driven to distraction by a dog that needs to play all the time. A family with several children may need a dog that likes to play a lot, but a senior citizen with health problems might prefer a dog that is less active and less driven to play.

Some Breeds that Need to Play More	Some Breeds that Need to Play Less
Australian Shepherds	Akitas
Border Collies	Basset Hounds
German Shepherds	Bloodhounds
Golden Retrievers	Bulldogs
Irish Setters	Chihuahuas
Labrador Retrievers	Dachshunds
Toy, Miniature and Standard Poodles	Greyhounds
Shetland Sheepdogs	Pekingese
English Springer Spaniels	St. Bernards

Paws for Thought

Within a wolf pack, the subordinate members show affection to the more dominant members. In your family, a puppy will show affection to you. As she grows up, she will continue showing you affection as long as you remain the dominant figure in her eyes.

Demand for Affection

Some breeds crave being with their owner as much as possible. When these dogs are not with their owner, especially for hours at a time, behavior problems can result. These breeds are good for people who want a close relationship with their dog, or who like a dog that looks upon them as someone to worship. These dogs want to be your shadow, to follow you from room to room and to touch you as much as possible. Other breeds do not need such close ties and will do better when alone for long hours at a time. These breeds have a tendency to be more standoffish. That doesn't mean they won't love you and want to be with you. It just means they won't be quite so demanding about it.

Some Breeds that Like to Be Close	Some Breeds that Are a Little Standoffish
Australian Shepherds	Afghan Hounds
Bichons Frises	Akitas
Cocker Spaniels	Basset Hounds
German Shepherds	Bloodhounds
Golden Retrievers	Bulldogs
Maltese	Chow Chows
Toy, Miniature and Standard Poodles	Rottweilers
Shetland Sheepdogs	St. Bernards
Shih Tzu	Siberian Huskies

Protectiveness

Many people get a dog for protection. Perhaps a neighbor's home was burglarized, or maybe one of the family members travels a lot and the people remaining at home would like some additional security. In any case, many breeds were designed to be protective. However, there is often a fine line between protectiveness and aggression. If you would like a dog for protection, make sure you are also willing to do the training needed to keep the dog under control, so that its protectiveness doesn't turn into dangerous aggression.

Some breeds known to be good watchdogs without necessarily being aggressive:

Standard Poodles	Scottish Terriers
Miniature Schnauzers	West Highland White Terriers
Airedale Terriers	Welsh Corgis

Some breeds that are willing to back up their bark with actual protective behavior:

Akitas	German Shepherds
Australian Shepherds	Great Danes
Boxers	Rottweilers
Doberman Pinschers	

Some breeds that simply don't care to be watchdogs and would, in fact, probably lead the burglar to the good silver:

Alaskan Malamutes	Bulldogs
Newfoundlands	Golden Retrievers
Basset Hounds	Labrador Retrievers
Bloodhounds	Siberian Huskies
Brittanies	

Trainability

To me, this is the most important factor in my relationship with a dog. For me to have a good relationship with a dog, I need to be able to train it. I also want the dog to be able to learn, to retain that learning and to want to work for me. I am not comfortable with a dog that doesn't want to please me. However, not everyone needs this type of relationship; some dog owners don't want to spend a lot of time training a dog. Before you choose a breed, decide what your goals are for the dog and if training plays a big part in your expectations. If it does, don't choose a breed that doesn't train well. If it doesn't, you may not want a breed that will always be looking for a job to do.

Paws for Thought

Breeds that are more resistant to training are not stupid. They are simply more interested in pleasing themselves than you. They are capable of learning very well; you just need to figure out how to teach and motivate these dogs.

Breeds that Train More Easily and Wish to Please You	Breeds that Train Less Easily and Wish to Please Themselves
Akitas	Basset Hounds
Australian Shepherds	Beagles
Border Collies	Bulldogs
Doberman Pinschers	Chow Chows
German Shepherds	Dachshunds
Golden Retrievers	Dalmatians
Standard Poodles	Lhasa Apsos
Rottweilers	Pekingese
Shetland Sheepdogs	Pugs
Welsh Corgis	Yorkshire Terriers

What Is a Breed?

As dogs became domesticated, the people who lived with them found that dogs could help them in all kinds of tasks. Perhaps one hunter found that his male dog had great scenting abilities and could follow the trail of game with ease. When a neighboring hunter had a female dog who could also use her nose quite well, they arranged for these two to breed. The resulting puppies could also follow a game trail well. By breeding together dogs that shared the same skills, abilities were shaped into different breeds.

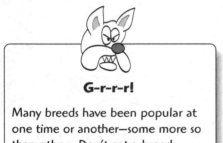

G-r-r-r!

Many breeds have been popular at one time or another—some more so than others. Don't get a breed simply because it's popular. Instead, make sure the characteristics of a particular breed are right for you.

Dogs were also bred to create or emphasize physical characteristics. For example, all Rottweilers are black, with tan or rust markings in specific places. All Rottweilers have a short, coarse, dense coat and the ears do not stand up, as do German Shepherds' ears.

As breeds became known by specific names, people who liked the same breed joined together in clubs or associations. These clubs developed a standard for each breed. This standard is a written description of the breed, and describes a perfect dog of that breed by looks, physical conformation, how it moves, its temperament and its working abilities. These standards are what keep a Rottweiler looking like a Rottweiler and a Greyhound looking like a Greyhound.

People who wished to breed one of these dogs could then use this standard to evaluate their dog and the dog they wished to breed it to. A dog that compared poorly to the ideal described in the standard was removed from the breeding program. When dog shows began, this standard was used by the judges to evaluate the dogs competing. Today dog show judges still use each breed's standard as the ideal against which they judge.

Puppy Tails

Sometimes people mate dogs of different breeds in hopes of creating a new breed. In fact, many breeds were once a mixture of several other breeds. However, it takes many years of hard work, study and research to create a new breed. The new breed is not recognized as such by the organizations that register purebred dogs until it can be bred again and again for generations—and breed true to its standard.

Why So Many Breeds?

The American Kennel Club (AKC) recognizes more than 140 different breeds of dogs. Worldwide, there are more than 400 known breeds, each distinct in its own way. Why are there so many?

Most breeds developed in a specific region, and often these regions were far removed from other populated areas. Modern transportation has made traveling easier today, but years ago people rarely traveled far from home. If a shepherd needed a herding dog, he used the dogs available locally. Therefore, each corner of the world developed its own breeds. Herding dogs were developed all over the world, and they all share similar herding instincts, but they may differ in size, color, coat length or physical conformation. The same applies to guard dogs, tracking dogs, sighthounds, retrievers and the many other types of working dogs.

With modern transportation, these different breeds of dogs have found fans all over the world. Hungarian herding dogs can be found in California, and British herding dogs work sheep in Idaho. Japanese guard dogs live like kings in New York City, while German working dogs train in China. Travel is easier, but the various breeds have, for the most part, remained true to their ancestors.

These puppies are similar in size right now, but very quickly the Newfoundland will outgrow the Labrador Retriever and the Australian Shepherd.

Pointing Out the Sporting Breeds

The sporting breeds are those breeds originally designed to help fowl (wild bird) hunters. These various breeds found the birds, pointed to them using their body posture, flushed out the birds and retrieved shot birds on land and from the water. These dogs were vital in helping put food on the table.

Breed Bits

The Labrador Retriever has been the most popular breed in America for several years. These happy, loyal, intelligent dogs are also used as guide dogs for the blind and service dogs for the disabled.

The pointers—German Shorthaired Pointers, German Wirehaired Pointers, Vizslas, Weimaraners, Wirehaired Pointing Griffons and Pointers—were bred to run in the fields all day long, find the birds, point to them (using body language), and then retrieve the shot birds. They are very high-energy dogs. In a pet home these dogs need a lot of exercise. Two jogging sessions a day and a good, vigorous game of tennis ball fetch would be realistic. These dogs were bred to work independently, and training can sometimes be a challenge.

The retrievers—Chesapeake Bay Retrievers, Golden Retrievers, Labrador Retrievers, Curly-Coated Retrievers and Flat-Coated Retrievers—were bred to work close to the hunter, taking directions and retrieving shot fowl. These dogs take to training easily, usually want to please, need to be close to people and can suffer if left alone for too many hours each day. They do have a lot of energy and will need at least one good, vigorous exercise session per day, although two sessions would be even better.

The Irish, English and Gordon Setters are lovely dogs, very regal and majestic in appearance. These breeds were developed to run the fields, point out fowl, flush them and retrieve the shot birds. They are intelligent and trainable. However, their high-energy needs can make them a challenge to own. They need vigorous exercise at least twice a day; three times would be even better.

The spaniels are the smallest members of the sporting group. They are Brittanies, American Water Spaniels, Clumber Spaniels, Cocker Spaniels, English Cocker Spaniels, English Springer Spaniels, Field Spaniels, Irish Water Spaniels, Sussex Spaniels and Welsh Springer Spaniels. These are friendly, people-oriented dogs that were bred to flush and retrieve birds. They usually take well to training, although they can be easily distracted. They do have high energy levels, and daily vigorous exercise is a must.

Paws for Thought

All of the spaniel breeds need regular grooming that includes a haircut. If you are unable to do this yourself, a trip to the groomer will be a regular financial obligation—usually $20 to $40 a month.

Sniffing Out the Hounds

There are three types of hounds—scenthounds, which use their nose to find game; sighthounds, which hunt by using their eyesight; and the large gamehounds, which are very strong physically and can thus hunt larger game. The hounds are, and have been, hunters, and have helped to provide food for their humans' tables throughout history. Many of the hounds were also used to control vermin, find escaped criminals or lost children and, like the Greyhounds, for sport racing.

The scenthound family is made up of Basset Hounds, Beagles, Bloodhounds, the various types of Coonhounds and Foxhounds, Dachshunds, Otterhounds, Harriers, and Petits Bassets Griffons Vendéens (quite a mouthful!). These are rugged hunters, bred to use their scenting abilities and to ignore physical discomfort while working. These skills can, unfortunately, sometimes cause problems in pets. Although physically stoic and able to take the punishment children often dish out (even inadvertently), hounds do not always understand the need for obedience training.

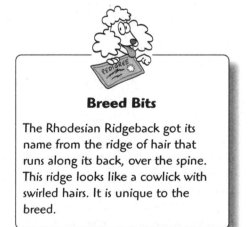

Breed Bits

The Rhodesian Ridgeback got its name from the ridge of hair that runs along its back, over the spine. This ridge looks like a cowlick with swirled hairs. It is unique to the breed.

The sighthounds are elegant, light-boned breeds designed to chase down their prey. The Afghan Hound, Basenji, Greyhound, Borzoi, Ibizan Hound, Pharaoh Hound, Saluki and Whippet are long-legged, deep-chested, narrow-waisted breeds that love nothing better than a fast run. All of the sighthounds share the ability to hunt their prey visually. These dogs like to run so much that often they are not reliable off leash, and cannot be trusted to come back when their owner calls them to come. Obviously, this can be a problem. These dogs must also be well socialized to other pets, especially cats and pet rabbits, so that they do not hunt the family pets!

The large gamehounds are the Rhodesian Ridgebacks, Scottish Deerhounds, Irish Wolfhounds and Norwegian Elkhounds. These are sturdy, powerful, fearless dogs that were bred to hunt larger game. These breeds are known to be independent and somewhat aloof at times. Training can be challenging, but is absolutely necessary.

Keep the Working Breeds Busy

These breeds were designed to work for humans, and many have done so for centuries. They were bred to do a specific job, and as pets they still need to work. A bored working dog is a dog that will get into trouble. The working breeds need training and a sense of purpose to be happy. These are, for the most part, loyal, dedicated, intelligent dogs.

The guard dogs were bred to protect property and livestock. These dogs were often left alone to do their job, and needed to have the intelligence and courage to work without a handler. They need training, socialization and an owner who is as loyal and courageous as the dog is. These breeds include the Akita, Bullmastiff, Great Dane, Great Pyrenees, Komondor, Kuvasz, Mastiff and Rottweiler.

G-r-r-r!

Sled dogs have a thick double coat and often cannot tolerate very hot weather. Make sure these dogs have a cool place to relax during the heat of the summer, and exercise them early in the morning or later at night.

Several breeds were designed to protect their owners. The Doberman Pinscher, Boxer, and Giant and Standard Schnauzers were bred to work for and protect people. These are intelligent, loyal dogs that, without socialization, can become dangerous so-called "one person" dogs. Therefore, these dogs need early socialization and training. These breeds also need vigorous exercise daily.

The sled and draft dogs were bred to pull loads behind them. The sled dogs, obviously, pulled sleds in the snow. The Alaskan Malamute, Samoyed and Siberian Husky's physical prowess and skills were often vital to their owners' survival. Able to run for hours at a time in punishing conditions, these dogs still love to run, especially in cold weather and snow. They need lots of exercise; two or three times a day is not too much!

Bernese Mountain Dogs and Greater Swiss Mountain Dogs are draft dogs. They were bred to pull wagons—often very heavy wagons full of milk containers. These breeds are trainable and very loyal. Exercise is needed, but not as much as the sledding dogs require.

The rescue dogs—the Newfoundland, St. Bernard and Portuguese Water Dog—were bred to find, physically help and rescue people. The St. Bernard was primarily used in the snow to find stranded travelers or avalanche victims, while the Portuguese Water Dog and Newfoundland saved swimmers and boaters. These are physically powerful dogs that need early training.

A Gathering of Herding Dogs

Herding dogs are active, intelligent dogs that like to keep busy. They either work alone, making their own decisions, or work under the direction of a shepherd. These dogs need a leader, and if one isn't available they will step into that position—much to the detriment of the people in their family! Herding dogs are, as a general rule, easy to train. They can also be very protective of both their people and their property.

The breeds used to herd sheep include Australian Shepherds, Bearded Collies, Border Collies, German Shepherd Dogs, Old English Sheepdogs, the Belgian Sheepdog breeds, Canaan Dogs, Collies, Pulis and Shetland Sheepdogs. The sheep dogs are quick, active and smart. Vigorous, daily exercise is a must, as is early training and socialization.

The cattle herders include Australian Cattle Dogs, Kelpies, Briards, Bouviers des Flandres and the Corgis. These dogs are tougher in personality than the sheep herding dogs. They are also able to take physical punishment, since cattle are rougher and tougher than sheep. Cattle herding dogs need early training and socialization, and regular exercise. The owner must be a strong leader, or behavior problems will ensue.

G-r-r-r!

Many herding dogs are prone to nipping. When the sheep or cattle do not move where the dogs want them to go, the dog will nip at the animal's heels. Unfortunately, that often translates into nipping people. Early training can correct this tendency.

Challenging the Terriers

Terriers are active, free-spirited dogs that are always looking for something to do. Training is always needed, although it can sometimes be a challenge because these dogs are also very independent.

Many of the terrier breeds were developed to hunt vermin. Rats and mice could threaten an entire community's food if they weren't controlled, and terriers were often more successful at keeping the vermin at bay than cats were. These dogs were used in homes, in businesses and on farms. Today some of these terrier breeds are still used to

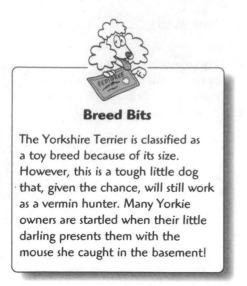

control rodents, but most are simply pets. As pets, these dogs need lots of exercise and lots of play. If they are left alone too much, terriers can be very destructive.

Some of the vermin catchers are Airedales, Australian Terriers, Bedlington Terriers, Border Terriers, Cairn Terriers, Dandie Dinmont Terriers, Fox Terriers, Irish Terriers, Jack Russell Terriers, Kerry Blue Terriers, Lakeland Terriers, Manchester Terriers, Miniature Schnauzers, Norfolk Terriers, Norwich Terriers, Scottish Terriers, Sealyham Terriers, Skye Terriers, Soft Coated Wheaten Terriers, Welsh Terriers and West Highland White Terriers.

Some of the terriers were bred as fighters. The Pit Bull Terrier, American Staffordshire Terrier, Miniature Bull Terrier and Bull Terrier were bred to fight bulls or other dogs. Although bull fighting is rarely seen today, unfortunately illegal dog fighting is still going on. These dogs are strong and fearless, and need early training and socialization, especially to other dogs. However, they take well to training and can make great pets.

Playing with the Toy Breeds

These dogs are the easiest to spoil. Most of them are very small—often tiny—and are impossibly cute. However, these are still dogs with the same instincts and drives as their bigger cousins. In fact, many toy breeds are miniature versions of sporting and working dogs. For example, the Papillons, with their lovely butterfly ears, are from the spaniel family, and many would still like to hunt even though they are physically too small to do so safely.

All of the toy breeds need early training and socialization. Without it, many of these breeds get yappy and some get snappy. The owners of toy breeds also need training so that they understand how not to spoil their intelligent little dogs.

Exercise is also necessary, although obviously not as much as the bigger dogs need. A good walk around three or four residential blocks or a retrieving game up and down the hallway is fine.

The toy breeds include Affenpinschers, Brussels Griffons, Cavalier King Charles Spaniels, Chihuahuas, Chinese Cresteds, English Toy Spaniels, Italian Greyhounds, Japanese Chin, Maltese, Toy Manchester Terriers, Miniature Pinschers, Papillons, Pekingese, Pomeranians, Toy Poodles, Pugs, Shih Tzus, Silky Terriers and Yorkshire Terriers.

Leisure Time with the Non-Sporting Breeds

Many of these breeds were originally bred to do a job, but are no longer doing that work. For example, Schipperkes were barge dogs; today they are companions and treasured pets. Dalmatians ran with the horses and coaches in a time long before cars were invented; today they ride on fire engines and live in our homes.

All of the non-sporting breeds were bred to work, and all accept training, although some seem to do better than others. The American Eskimo Dog, Bichon Frise, Keeshond, Standard and Miniature Poodles and the Standard Schnauzer all will do well in training and socialize easily as puppies. Bulldogs, Chow Chows, Lhasa Apsos, Finnish Spitz, Shiba Inus and Schipperkes are known for having a mind of their own, and training can often be quite a challenge.

Exercise is also important for many of these breeds, especially the more athletic breeds such as the American Eskimo Dog, the Dalmatian, the Poodles and the Shiba Inu. The Bulldog and Chow Chow are not particularly athletic, and mild exercise is all they need.

Other non-sporting breeds include the Boston Terrier, the Chinese Shar-Pei, the French Bulldog, the Tibetan Spaniel and the Tibetan Terrier.

What About Mixed Breed Dogs?

A friend of mine will own nothing but mixed breed dogs. She thinks purebred dogs are hyper, neurotic and all mixed up. She's wrong, of course, and I've told her so. But she isn't the only person to believe that myth.

A dog is the result of its genetics—the genes its parents pass on to it—its early socialization, training and living environment. All of these factors figure into its adult personality.

A purebred dog is a known entity; you know what the breed was designed to do (such as herding or hunting), and certain behaviors can be predicted because of this. With a purebred dog you will also have a good idea about the dog's adult size, height, weight and coat type.

A mixed breed dog, especially one that is a mixture of several different breeds, is very much an unknown. It may be big or small, have long hair or short, straight hair or curly, and may be friendly and social or incredibly protective. A mixed breed dog is a surprise!

Now, that does not mean you shouldn't own a mixed breed dog. Many are absolutely wonderful pets and companions. However, if you decide you want a mixed breed puppy, make sure you know as much about its roots as possible, and make sure you are willing to live with any surprises that might show up along the way.

The Least You Need to Know

➤ Before you choose a breed, decide what canine characteristics are important to you.

➤ There are more than 140 breeds of dogs recognized by the American Kennel Club and over 400 breeds are known worldwide, each with different characteristics.

➤ Make sure you choose a breed that you will be comfortable with for coat care and type, trainability, exercise requirements and ability to be a companion.

➤ A mixed breed dog can be a wonderful companion, but will probably also produce some surprises because of its unknown genetic history.

Where Puppies come from!

Chapter 3

Creating a Puppy

In This Chapter

➤ What is genetics?

➤ What do the parents contribute to a puppy?

➤ Breeding, conception and gestation

➤ Birth—new life

➤ Breeding a dog should be a well-thought-out decision

Recently my husband and I were searching for a new puppy. We knew what breed we wanted, knew that we wanted a female and that she should be between eight and ten weeks of age. We also wanted the puppy to have a personality and temperament that make her want to do things, because we like to participate in dog sports. We wanted her to be curious, trainable and intelligent, but not so active that she was hyperactive. So we were researching breeders, asking questions and looking for just the right puppy. A friend of ours didn't understand why we were doing all this work. "A puppy is just a puppy!" she said. "Just go to the pound and get a puppy."

I'm still not sure she understood when I tried to explain that a puppy is more than just a puppy, so I will try to make my explanation a little better here. Yes, a puppy is just a puppy, just like a horse is just a horse and a car is just a car. However, there are big differences between a Thoroughbred race horse and a wild Arabian; just as there are differences between my big Ford Econoline van and my husband's Nissan 300-ZX sports car. Many factors come together to make each puppy a unique individual, and each of those factors makes that puppy different from all other puppies—even his littermates.

What Is Genetics?

The study of genetics began with studies not on people, horses or dogs, but on green peas. In the late 1800s a Czechoslovakian monk named Gregor Mendel grew green peas with different color flowers in the garden behind his church. He began writing down the results of his experiments, noting the apparent hereditary traits that showed up in each generation. He sent his findings to a scientific magazine in 1866, but his work went unnoticed for many years. It wasn't until the 1900s that some scientists rediscovered Mendel's studies and realized their importance. In his honor, the principles of inheritance he discovered were named Mendel's Law.

Mendel's Law of Inheritance affects nearly all life on earth. Simply put, Mendel discovered that characteristics could be passed from parents to offspring through the combination of genes. He found that some traits are more dominant than others, and called this the Law of Dominance. He also found that the way genes combine in offspring can be affected by chance, and called this the Law of Independent Assortment.

Mendel also found that certain paired characteristics of parents do not necessarily blend with or alter each other in the offspring. Instead, either one or the other characteristic manifests itself, thus resulting in contrasting or differing traits in successive generations. In other words, a pea with a red flower and one with a white flower will not produce offspring with pink flowers. Rather, some offspring will have white flowers and some will have red flowers. This is called the Law of Segregation.

By using these laws and experimenting with them, dog breeders (as well as horse breeders, cat breeders and agricultural experts) can breed animals or plants better suited for their purpose.

Puppy Tails

Care Bear and Ursa, two of my Australian Shepherds, are brother and sister. They are a good demonstration of Mendel's Laws. They are very much alike in many ways, especially in breed traits. However, personality-wise, they are very different. Care Bear is affectionate, loving and knows no strangers. Ursa is protective and aloof with strangers. Care Bear is easy to train and loves to work. Ursa is difficult to train and needs to be motivated to work. They are alike but different.

The reproductive cells (sperm) of the male dog have 78 chromosomes, as do the reproductive cells (eggs) of the female. The inherited genes are found within these chromosomes. Upon breeding, one half of the male chromosomes unite with one half of the female chromosomes to create a unique, individual puppy.

What characteristics those genes create is not really known until the puppy matures. We do know that Mendel's Law says chance plays a big part in it; those genes can arrange themselves just about any way they want! However, his law also says some genes are more dominant than others, so the dominant genes will probably prevail. Dominant genes can encompass many different characteristics, and these may differ from breed to breed. Eye color, coat color, ear set, tail position, physical characteristics, tendency towards ailments or diseases, even coat length can all be inherited.

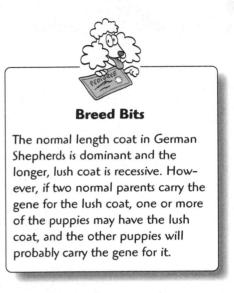

Breed Bits

The normal length coat in German Shepherds is dominant and the longer, lush coat is recessive. However, if two normal parents carry the gene for the lush coat, one or more of the puppies may have the lush coat, and the other puppies will probably carry the gene for it.

What Do the Parents Actually Contribute?

Experienced breeders use Mendel's Law to their advantage by studying the parents, grandparents, great-grandparents and even distant ancestors of their potential breeding stock. By knowing what those dogs were like and what kinds of puppies they produced, some of the risks and unknowns can be eliminated from the breeding process.

Breed Heritage

The parents' breed contributes many characteristics to the puppy. Purebred puppies have many genes in common with their ancestors. Those genes control how big the puppy will grow up to be; what type of coat he will have; how long, short, silky or coarse the coat will be; and what color. Other genes will decide the shape of his head, the length of his body, the shape of his tail and much, much more.

Paws for Thought

Purebred dogs are those whose parents, grandparents and ancestors for several generations back all were of the same breed.

A puppy that is a mixture of two or more breeds is a good example of Mendel's Law of Independent Assortment. If a male dog of mixed breed heritage (for example, his mother was a Cocker Spaniel-Springer Spaniel mix and his father was a Poodle) breeds with a female dog of a different mixture (German Shepherd and

The ancestors of this Australian Shepherd were working sheep dogs, and Lucy has inherited those instincts, as well as a strong desire to please her owner.

Labrador Retriever), the puppies would each receive their own assortment of genes. That means each puppy could be totally different from its brothers and sisters. One puppy might look more like a Cocker Spaniel but with German Shepherd coloring, while another might be all black like a black Lab, but with a Springer Spaniel's coat. Each puppy got 50 percent of its genes from each parent, but exactly which genes each puppy got were different.

The puppy's breed heritage also affects behavior. As we mentioned in Chapter 2, many breeds (and types of breeds) have characteristics that make them unique. Herding breeds like to herd, and this can cause them to nip heels or pants legs. The breeds designed to be protective will be protective naturally, without training. All of these characteristics, and the many other traits associated with different breeds, are inherited from the puppy's parents, grandparents and his more distant ancestors.

Temperament

It is always a good idea to see the mother of a litter of puppies before you get a puppy from that particular litter. If you can, see the father of the litter, too. Not only will you see what they look like, how big they are and how healthy, but you will also see what their personalities and temperaments are like.

Most experts believe probably 10 to 20 percent of a puppy's personality is inherited. The other 80 to 90 percent comes from the puppy's own unique personality, the environment in which the puppy is raised, his training and socialization, and his life experiences. All of these factors come together to make the puppy who he is. However, 10 to 20 percent is still a significant portion, and if the parents are shy, fearful, overly aggressive or have other personality flaws, this could have a major impact on the puppy.

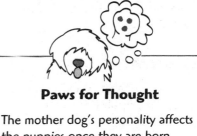

Paws for Thought

The mother dog's personality affects the puppies once they are born, too. If she is fearful, shy, anxious or overly aggressive, her puppies will feel those emotions and learn them, even when they're very young. This could have a lasting impression on their personalities.

If you meet the mother dog while she has puppies, don't be surprised if she is protective when you come to the door. However, if her owners let you in, she should calm down and come over to meet you. If she continues to show uncontrollable aggressive behavior or extreme fear, she could have a personality flaw that might have been passed to her puppies.

Conformation

A dog's physical conformation is the combination of how he is put together (ear set, tail set, the angles of his joints and so on), as well as his size and body shape. All of the physical things that make a particular breed unique contribute to that breed's conformation. These attributes are hereditary and are passed to the puppy from his parents.

Breed Bits

The supreme athlete is the Border Collie. This breed is strong, lean and wiry, with a deep chest that has lots of room for an athlete's big heart and lungs. This is a breed designed to work quickly and hard all day long.

Serious breeders will study their breed's standard. This written description describes the perfect specimen of that breed. Breeders can compare their potential breeding stock against the standard and see how their dogs measure up. At dog shows, the judge will also use the standard to evaluate the dogs that are competing, and the winners will be those that best embody the standard. When trying to produce the best possible dog, breeders use the standard, the judges' opinions and their own evaluation to decide which dogs should be bred—and which should not.

But good conformation means more than just a pretty show dog. The dog that is conformationally correct is usually also a physically sound dog, able to do the work the breed was developed to do. A Greyhound that is not built correctly—perhaps is short-legged and heavy bodied— will not be able to run as well as a Greyhound should run. A German Shepherd that is too heavy or doesn't have the chest capacity for strong lungs and heart will not be able to herd all day long, as a German Shepherd should be able to do.

Health

The parents' health affects puppies in a couple of different ways. Genes passed on to the puppies from their parents could cause health problems, physical deformities or weaknesses, or could make the puppy susceptible to problems or diseases. Certain breeds are known to have a problem with certain health threats, and although the threat itself may or may not be hereditary, the propensity to have this problem certainly is.

Paws for Thought

The hip joint is a ball that fits into the hip socket, held in by ligaments. In a dog with hip dysplasia, loose ligaments and a shallow hip socket create excessive wear and tear on the joint, sometimes resulting in debilitating lameness.

There is still an awful lot we don't know about hereditary diseases and physical problems. For example, for many years it was thought that hip dysplasia was 100 percent inherited. Now many experts think the deformity itself may not be inherited. Instead, there might be an inherited weakness that makes the dog susceptible to it. Other experts are arguing with this theory. Basically, we really don't know yet, but research is continuing.

The parent's health also affects the puppies from the moment of conception. Ideally, both parents of a litter should be physically healthy. A healthy male will be more apt to have strong, healthy sperm with no defects. The female's health is of utmost importance, since she not only passes on genes that could affect the puppies' health, but also nourishes the puppies during the pregnancy and while she is nursing them. If she is not as healthy as she could be, the puppies could be stillborn, born with deformities, born underweight or not thrive once they are born.

A Little Romance

By now it's clear that breeding is an activity best left to the experts. There are so many variables involved, and so many things to learn before you can even contemplate a breeding. However, just as we all want to know where we came from, it's fun to know where our puppies came from, too.

Most female dogs (bitches—it's okay to say it!) come into their first season at about six months old. When we say a bitch is in season or in heat, it means she is fertile and receptive to mating. However, even if she is in season, a six-month-old puppy should never be allowed to breed. Most bitches are not physically and mentally mature enough to breed until they are two years old. In addition, many of the health threats that every breeding animal should be checked for (including hip dysplasia and eye defects), cannot be determined for sure until a dog is two years old.

Male dogs become sexually mature at seven to twelve months of age. Many will start to show mounting behavior before that, but at a young age mounting is dominance behavior rather than sexual. A young male may start lifting his leg to urinate to mark territory at about the same time as he becomes sexually mature.

Males remain sexually fertile all the time after they have reached maturity. However, the bitch is only fertile during her heat season. She will come into season two to three times a year.

The Right Time

The first signs of the heat season are usually behavioral. Some females get very loving and affectionate, while others get nasty. (There is a reason why bitches are called bitches!) Next, the vulva starts to swell slightly and you may see some blood spots. Some females spot just a little, while others bleed quite a bit. The spotting lasts about a week to 10 days. After the spotting stops, the vulva gets very swollen and the female will start acting more receptive to male dogs, although she may not be quite ready for a few more days.

Paws for Thought

Estrus, the heat season, usually lasts about three weeks. If the bitch is not pregnant, the signs of her season will gradually subside. The swelling in the vulva decreases, although it will never return to the size it was before the bitch's first season.

Experienced breeders usually breed bitches between the 10th and 14th day after the beginning of the heat cycle. However, many bitches are not ready until much later in their cycle, and since this can vary so much, a trip to the veterinarian might be in order. A veterinarian can do a hormone test to determine exactly when the bitch should be bred.

The Right Partner

Most dogs don't need any help in the romance department. When a bitch is in season, any unneutered male in the neighborhood will be willing to help her! However, responsible breeders do not want the neighborhood Romeo to come visiting. Instead, the appropriate stud dog will have already been chosen. This dog may be owned by the breeder, or he may be owned by another breeder. In any case, arrangements must be made for the breeding significantly ahead of time, so that there will be no frantic phone calls to arrange for the romantic visit.

Paws for Thought

Both the male and the female should be excellent representatives of their breed in their conformation, their working abilities and their emotional and physical health.

Depending upon the breeders and the dogs involved, a male can go visit the female or the female can be sent to the male. Usually, this is determined according to the personal preferences of the breeders. However, some males are shy and will not perform anywhere other than at home. Other female dogs are quite protective and will not allow another dog in their home, especially when they are in season. These details need to be worked out before the female comes into season.

Artificial insemination (AI), where sperm is collected from the male and then artificially inserted into the female, is also available through many veterinarians. In fact, the American Kennel Club will register dogs from AI breedings and litters. This is particularly useful when the male and female to be bred live a long distance from each other. The sperm can be collected from the male and shipped to the female. New technologies have made this a relatively easy procedure, and much safer than shipping dogs all over the country.

If two dogs are going to make puppies the old-fashioned way, when a female is ready to be bred she will stand as the male approaches and twitch her tail to one side, allowing him access. He mounts her, clasping her around the body with his front legs. He thrusts a few times, penetrates, and then relaxes while still on her back. He then comes off her back while his penis is still within her. This is called a *tie*, and is the result of the swelling of a gland in the penis, which is held inside the bitch by her vaginal muscles. A tie can last anywhere from 10 minutes to an hour. While tied, the dogs should be held so that they do not struggle and, in the process, hurt each other. Never try to separate dogs while tied, as this could cause injury to both dogs.

She's Pregnant!

Gestation lasts about nine weeks, or 63 days, give or take a day here or there. For the first few weeks it will be difficult to tell whether or not any puppies have been conceived, as most bitches do not get morning sickness or show any other outward signs of pregnancy in the beginning. The more obvious signs, such as enlarged mammary glands and a bigger belly, will show up later.

A healthy bitch will not require any special care for most of her pregnancy. Good nutritious food, normal exercise and plenty of rest will allow her to maintain her health and nourish her growing babies.

Later in the pregnancy, toward the fifth and sixth week, she should be restricted from strenuous exercise and should be encouraged not to jump, as she could hurt herself or her babies. As her body gets heavier from the weight of the growing puppies, she will get clumsier and may not realize how much her body has changed. That's why she needs to be reminded not to do things that could hurt her.

At this point, too, she needs more food. Many breeders feed their pregnant bitch puppy food, since it is high in calories, protein and fat. It is also advisable to feed the bitch several small meals throughout the day, rather than one or two large meals. Her stomach capacity may be decreasing as the puppies grow, and she may be unable to eat a large meal.

G-r-r-r!

Once she has been bred, most bitches are still fertile. Several males can father different puppies in the same litter—with each puppy the result of an individual sperm and egg. Bred bitches must be protected from other males.

What's Happening Inside?

In dogs, the uterus has two long horns (think of branches) so that it can accommodate a large litter of puppies. After conception, the fertilized eggs move into these horns, where they implant themselves into the uterine walls. This is also where the placental connection develops. During the 63 days of gestation, the puppies grow from these fertilized eggs into recognizable puppies, complete with hair and tiny little toenails.

Before the date the puppies are due to arrive, the breeder must build a nest, called a whelping box, for the bitch and her babies. It must be big enough for the bitch to comfortably lie down and move around. The walls should be high enough so that puppies cannot wander away, yet low enough so the bitch can comfortably get in and out. Newspaper or other bedding is spread in the bottom.

The box is placed in a quiet spot where the bitch is comfortable. She is introduced to the box by placing her blanket in it, getting encouragement to sleep there for a few nights. Often her nesting instinct will kick in, and she'll scratch up and tear the newspapers.

One of the first signs of imminent birth is restlessness. The bitch may have a hard time getting comfortable and may move around a lot, shift positions, ask to go outside and then ask to come back in. She may not eat and she may drink quite a bit of water. As her time grows closer, her vulva will swell and it may change colors slightly. Abdominal contractions will begin before the first puppy's birth, and many first-time mothers get quite distressed. Breeders soothe their bitches with gentle touches and quiet words. They stay calm, so their bitch will also feel calm.

The Puppies Arrive!

Most puppies are born head first and are often still in their sack. The bitch should instinctively break this sack, ripping it quickly. If she doesn't, the breeder must do this. The breeder must also cut the umbilical cord that attaches the puppy to the placenta, if

Breed Bits

Bulldogs have trouble giving birth, as the puppies have very large heads. Often these puppies must be delivered by cesarean section.

the mother doesn't chew through it. Many times a bitch will eat the placentas of her puppies. It's disgusting to us, but perfectly natural to her!

Once the birth process has started, the puppies are usually born one right after another at about 30-minute intervals. Most puppies are born without any problems, but trouble can arise. If a puppy is born tail first, it may get stuck in the birth canal and will die unless freed quickly. Sometimes contractions will stop before all of the puppies have been born—again, a problem with tragic results. If anything seems wrong—even slightly wrong—during the birth process, a call to the veterinarian is in order.

Puppy Tails

Why do bitches eat their placentas? Nobody knows for sure, but there are several theories. One is that the bitch instinctively knows she needs the iron and other minerals and nutrients it contains. Another is that it is a leftover from wild dog behavior. Blood products left lying around in the wild attract predators, so it's best to dispose of them.

Think Long and Hard Before You Breed

As I mentioned before, the purpose of this chapter is not to encourage you to breed your dog (male or female). That is best left to the experts. Instead, my purpose is to show you where puppies come from and how unique each puppy is. There are, unfortunately, far too many puppies being born each day, and thousands of dogs are killed each year in shelters and humane societies all over the country simply because they are homeless.

A male and female dog used for breeding should each be excellent representatives of their breed. That means the potential breeder should read the breed standard. Ask other experienced breeders who have been successful in your breed what they think of your dog. What are your dog's strong points or weak points? Talk to more than one

Amber, a Golden Retriever, is the result of a planned breeding of two healthy, well-cared-for parents with all the right qualities of their breed.

person who is an expert in the breed (not your neighbor or best friend), so you get more than one opinion.

You should also attend a dog show where your breed will be judged. Does your dog compare favorably with the dogs being shown? Enter a few dog shows and see how your dog fares. Do the judges like him or her? Most experienced breeders will not breed a dog until it earns its breed championship, as well as a working title appropriate to the breed (such as obedience, hunting, herding or another activity).

The dogs used for breeding must also be healthy. They should be vaccinated, de-wormed and free of internal and external parasites. They should be screened for any potential inherited defects. The veterinarian should be consulted; he can screen for defects as well as check the dog's health. He can also test for any sexually transmitted diseases before the breeding.

Paws for Thought

Yes, dogs have sexually transmitted diseases too! Some can make a dog sterile. That's why a health check is a must before every breeding.

A Lifetime Responsibility

Last, but certainly not least, before the breeding there should be several serious puppy buyers waiting for future puppies from this breeding. Not someone who says, "Oh, I'd love a puppy from your Sweetie-Pie!" but a serious buyer ready to put down his name and a non-refundable deposit.

Responsible breeders look out for the welfare of every single puppy they bring into the world, *for the life of the dog.* That means carefully screening potential buyers, and taking back an adult dog that you sold as a puppy if the owners can no longer keep him. That means watching out for inherited health problems. It's a big responsibility.

Bringing a litter of puppies into the world is not a decision to be made lightly. It should be a well-thought-out, well-researched decision, undertaken with the understanding that you are responsible for all these canine lives.

The Least You Need to Know

➤ Because of the genes passed to him from his parents, each puppy is a unique individual, different even from his brothers and sisters.

➤ The parents' genes affect many aspects of the new puppy, including breed heritage, temperament, conformation and physical health.

➤ Breeding a dog and allowing the dog to give birth is very natural, but it requires a great deal of care, energy and thought. The process should not be taken lightly.

➤ The dogs used for breeding should be the best representatives of their breed.

Chapter 4

Off to a Good Start

In This Chapter

➤ How do the puppies develop and change in the first three months of life?

➤ The mother dog is a caring mother and a puppy's first teacher

➤ Why are littermates so important?

➤ The breeder's responsibilities

Puppies are born helpless. About all they can do is find their mother and latch on to a nipple. They eat and sleep, eat and sleep for days. However, their growth and development is rapid, and what happens in the first two months has a tremendous effect on what your puppy will grow up to be. The love the mother dog shows, her confidence in herself and the discipline she teaches her puppies are vitally important. What the breeder does is important, too, especially the early handling and socialization.

Most Momma Dogs are Good Mothers

Instinct is a wonderful thing, and it controls most of a mother dog's behavior. Unlike primates (including humans), she didn't learn how to be a good mother from her mom; her instincts tell her what she needs to do. She knows to let the puppies have access to her nipples so that they can eat. She knows to wash their bottoms so they can urinate and defecate. She knows to keep them cuddled together so they stay warm. She may not know why she needs to do these things, but she does them.

Some mother dogs need help in small ways, though. Some don't roll over far enough on their sides to let the puppies reach the nipples. Then the breeder must gently encourage her to roll over more. Some momma dogs get up before the puppies have finished eating, and again, the breeder can help by having her stay down until the pups are full. A little bit of help is usually all most moms need. The breeder, however, needs to be aware of the normal behavior of the puppies so that if one is anxious, crying too much or whining, he or she can step in and figure out what is wrong.

Early Puppy Development

A well-fed, happy puppy will eat and sleep for most of the first two weeks. If a puppy seems to be unhappy, something is wrong. Perhaps the mother doesn't have enough milk or the puppy is not able to nurse enough. A variety of things could go wrong, which is why close communication with a veterinarian who has a good working knowledge of breeding and puppy raising is vitally important. A responsible breeder will watch the mom and puppies closely, assist the mother when she needs help and call the veterinarian at the first sign of a problem.

A responsible breeder will also gently and briefly handle every puppy every day, right from the start. This early handling will ensure the puppies feel safe and comfortable around humans.

Day 1 Through Day 14

During this period, about 90 percent of a puppy's time is spent sleeping. In the first week, the puppies' eyes and ears are not open yet. Their most active senses are those of smell and touch, and the puppies use these to find their mom and her nipples. They are able to move by performing a swimming type crawl, usually without lifting their tummies off the ground. As their legs get stronger from day to day, they will be crawling more than swimming.

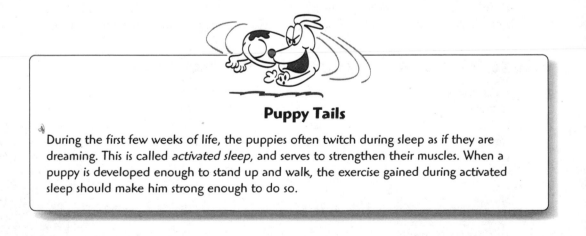

Puppy Tails

During the first few weeks of life, the puppies often twitch during sleep as if they are dreaming. This is called *activated sleep*, and serves to strengthen their muscles. When a puppy is developed enough to stand up and walk, the exercise gained during activated sleep should make him strong enough to do so.

The puppies huddle together for warmth, as they cannot yet control their own body temperature. If chilled slightly, the puppies will seek each other or their mom for heat. If allowed to chill too much, a puppy will stop moving and will very quickly die. However, too much heat is also a bad thing, because puppies can't cool themselves down, either. It's a delicate balance.

At this point in life the puppy cannot defecate or urinate on his own, and mom will stimulate him to do so by licking his tummy and genitals.

If mom is overly anxious during this period in the puppies' lives, her anxious behavior can imprint onto the puppies and they, too, will be nervous, anxious dogs—even if they do not originally receive the genes to be that way. It is important that mom remain calm, relaxed and quiet as much as possible.

Day 15 Through Day 21

The puppies are more awake now and do not need quite as much sleep as they did the last two weeks. They are still nursing quite strongly and should not yet be weaned. Some formula can be offered toward the end of this period to introduce the puppies to the idea of food.

Their eyes are opening now, although their eyesight is still quite dim. Light and dark can be perceived, as well as movement. The ears also open early in this period, although they do not focus well on sounds yet. The puppies will startle at unexpected sharp sounds at about 21 days.

The puppies are developing better motor skills now, and can crawl. Their muscles are also getting stronger through additional movement, as well as the activated sleep. The puppies' tails start to wag between 18 and 21 days. Towards the end of this period the puppies will also start urinating and defecating without their mother's help.

During this period, early social skills are being established. The puppies begin to recognize their littermates and their mother. They begin interacting with one another, too, chewing and pawing each other.

Stages of Puppy Development

Week 1: Neonatal—the puppy eats and sleeps.

Week 2: Development—the puppy eats, sleeps and grows.

Weeks 3 and 4: Senses—the puppy becomes aware of his senses.

Weeks 5 and 6: Discovery—the puppy discovers the world close around him.

Weeks 7 and 8: Social awareness—the puppy learns social rules from his littermates and his mother.

Day 22 Through Day 35

This is a period of big changes. The puppies are sleeping less and are more active. Their senses are developing rapidly, with vision and hearing becoming more clear. Each puppy is also much more aware of his environment. As the puppy learns to move his head, he can better use his senses of vision, hearing and smell.

Puppies can be introduced to soft foods now. Most mother dogs will start weaning their puppies toward the end of this period, especially because the first teeth begin to appear now. The mother dog may regurgitate semi-digested foods for her puppies, and the breeder should allow her to do so.

Physically, the puppies are stronger and are no longer crawling. They can walk, run, stand and will even start to jump and pounce. Their vocal cords are also mature, and they can now bark.

The puppies are also leaving the nest now to eliminate, and if it's possible, mom should be allowed to start taking them outside to go potty. In this way, the puppies will learn housetraining skills very quickly.

Social skills continue to develop. Play becomes more important, and the puppies will play vigorously with each other. As they bite, chew and wrestle, the puppies become aware of their own strengths and learn how easy or hard to bite by the reactions of their littermates.

G-r-r-r!

Orphan puppies that do not receive early canine socialization can grow up not understanding discipline and not realizing that they are dogs—both of which can lead to a host of behavior problems.

The puppies also start showing instinctive hunting behaviors now. A puppy will grab a toy or a piece of newspaper (or a littermate) and shake his head as if to tear off a piece of meat or to break the neck of his prey. The instinct to chase kicks in now, too. A toy pulled slowly across the floor is enough to cause the puppy to chase, pounce and grab it.

The mother dog will interfere with the puppies' playtime if things get too rough. She will also correct a puppy that bites her too hard or shows disrespect. This initial discipline helps teach the puppies to accept other discipline later in life.

The breeder should start handling the puppies a little bit more during this period. However, puppies should not be handled by many other people, as it is important to keep stress levels low, especially if the mother dog is protective of her babies. But the breeder and the breeder's family can gently massage and cuddle the puppies to accustom them to human handling.

Day 36 Through Day 49

The puppy begins to respond to his environment in emotional ways now. He may whine or cry when afraid, cry when he's hurt and show excitement while playing. He is also beginning to remember things and is capable of learning.

At this point a puppy becomes very interested in his environment and will try to explore. He will try new things, such as investigating toys. Because of this, a variety of different toys is very important now. Other things—including some very simple objects—can enrich his environment. A large, round, empty oatmeal container smells interesting and rolls very nicely. An empty plastic milk jug with a few small stones in it makes a nice sound. A cardboard box is a fun den. It doesn't take much to get puppies interested, and it is a very important stage in their development.

Many adult behavior problems (or personality flaws) have roots in young puppyhood. Adult dogs that have difficulty coping with anything out of the ordinary, including unfamiliar objects, may not have had the opportunity to explore new things as a puppy. That oatmeal box, cardboard box or milk jug can all teach puppies to investigate new things and to be brave (instead of afraid) when discovering the strange and unusual.

The puppy can be weaned now, as he has teeth and is capable of eating more solid foods. Physically, he is growing rapidly and looking a little bit more like he will as an adult. His muzzle is lengthening and his ears may start to stand up (if they are supposed to).

The puppy's mother is acting very much like a pack leader. She will be very affectionate, patient and will even play with the puppies. However, if a puppy is disrespectful in any way, or is too rough, or tries to steal food, she will correct him firmly and sharply.

Puppy Tails

Most breeders do not allow the father of the puppies to be involved with the pups. Sometimes males can be dangerous to the puppies, and often the mother gets worried when the male is around. However, some males are excellent fathers and need to be involved. Chocho, a Papillon I know, was an excellent father and was just as involved with his puppies as their mother was—playing with the pups, disciplining them when needed and washing their faces.

The breeder needs to be very involved with the puppies now. They need careful, gentle handling to teach them to trust people. Playtime with people is also important, although again, the play needs to be gentle—no scary, rough stuff right now; this is the time to build trust in people. Individual attention from people—away from mom and littermates—is also important now. Just a few minutes each day alone with a person will help each pup bond with people later.

Week 8 Through Week 12

Most puppies go to their new homes during this period. However, care should be taken during the eighth week of life to make sure the puppy is not frightened. The eighth week is what is commonly called a "fear period," and anything that scares the puppy now could become a lifelong fear. If the puppy is frightened during his first car ride to his new home, he may retain that fear of cars. If he is hurt during his trip to the veterinarian's office for his vaccinations, he may always be afraid of that office. Luckily, it is believed this particular fear period lasts for only a week.

The brain is fully mature at this age and the puppy is very capable of learning. He may have a short attention span, but he can learn and remember what he's learned. Gentle, positive training should be started now, to take advantage of this. He can also start learning some household rules, including housetraining.

Social activities with people are very important. This is when the puppy is capable of bonding with people in general and his new owner in particular. Time must be spent caring for the puppy, teaching him to accept grooming and, of course, feeding him. It is important that he learns where his food comes from. He will also be very eager to play, and he needs to learn how to play with people. He needs to learn that he cannot bite and chew on people as he did with his littermates.

Paws for Thought

When possible, puppies should leave for their new home when they are nine weeks old, to avoid the critical fear period.

Breed Bits

Some breeds are more prone to using their teeth than others. As hard-working herders, Australian Cattle Dog puppies do nip. The puppy should be told, "Acck! No bite!" each and every time teeth touch skin or clothes.

Mom Is the Puppy's First Teacher

The mother dog is caring and affectionate to her puppies, and this is important to their survival. However, her position as the puppies' first teacher is also critical to their survival with people.

She teaches her puppies how to play together and how to play with her. She will encourage them to play with toys, sometimes even holding a toy right in front of a puppy, dangling it there until the puppy chases it. She may hold the toy as the puppy grabs it in his jaws and struggles with it, growling and tugging. She may walk away slowly, holding on to the toy, dragging the puppy behind. The variations in play are endless, and the mother dog will encourage the puppies to play with her or allow them to play by themselves.

During playtime, the puppies learn to give and take. They learn to be submissive when it's necessary and how to be dominant without being a bully. If a puppy turns into a bully, mother dog will correct him quickly. By playing, the puppies also learn what it is to be a dog—something we know is important to them but cannot really understand. We do know that puppies who do not spend this time with their mother and littermates are never really comfortable around other dogs. Momma dog's puppies learn many of life's lessons through play, and by helping her puppies play, she is giving them a chance to learn.

Paws for Thought

Dogs use their body language very effectively to communicate. A dog that wants to say "Let's play!" will do a play bow, lowering his front end to the ground while keeping his hips elevated.

Your puppy's mother is his first teacher, and she makes it easier for you later on.

Momma dog also teaches the puppies to accept discipline and this, too, has an important effect on her puppies' future. When a puppy makes a mistake, the mother dog will correct the puppy quickly and firmly, using just enough force to do the job, and she will never, ever hold a grudge. Her correction may be a growl, body language or she may pin the puppy to the ground. No matter what she does, the puppy understands and must accept it. She doesn't give him any choice. By teaching him to accept this discipline, she makes it possible for his future owners to correct him, too.

The Importance of Littermates

In the first few weeks of life, littermates are simply fuzzy little heating pads; they help each other stay warm. Since their bodies cannot yet control their own temperature, these puppy piles hold in heat. However, very quickly littermates become much more than that: They become friends, playmates, buddies in exploration and more. Littermates teach each other, give each other courage and egg each other on into otherwise scary escapades.

Dog trainers have known for years that puppies who were singletons (born without siblings) are much more difficult to train and socialize. Behavior problems are more common in singleton puppies, and even more common in singleton puppies that were hand-raised by people. Mother nature designed the canine species to have more than one puppy for a reason—they thrive much better with littermates!

Puppies begin interacting with each other during the third and fourth weeks by chewing and pawing at one another. As their coordination increases, their senses develop, and they are more aware of their surroundings; play also increases. By the fifth week of life the puppies are wrestling, chasing and chewing on each other. Toys are chewed on and stolen from one another. Puppies trade places being at the top and bottom of the puppy piles.

G-r-r-r!

Puppies that are taken away from their mother and littermates too early—before the end of the seventh week of life—show behavior problems later, especially a lack of socialization to other dogs and an inability to accept discipline.

All of this fun yet serious play teaches the puppies how to interact with each other. They learn how hard to bite and when it's too hard. If one puppy bites too hard, the one that's bitten will yelp and then retaliate, letting the biter know he was too rough. Puppies learn to be dominant and submissive when one is on top during a wrestling match but is on the bottom during another match. They teach each other to share toys. There is so much for them to learn, but they teach each other quite well.

The Breeder's Job Is an Important One

So many litters of puppies are produced that seem doomed from the start. Perhaps the mother or father of the litter was not really good enough quality to have been bred, or was not as healthy as he or she could have been. Sometimes the breeder gets overwhelmed by everything involved with a litter and doesn't do the best job he or she could have done. In any case, it is ultimately the puppies that suffer needlessly.

A responsible breeder will make sure his puppies are well socialized. Here a litter of puppies is introduced to some friendly people.

Remember in Chapter 3 I said breeding was best left to the experts? The fact that a breeder's role in the development of a litter is so important is yet another reason why this is so. Responsible breeders must:

➤ Make sure both the mother and father of the litter are absolutely the best they can be concerning their breed standard, temperament, conformation and working instincts.

➤ Make sure both parents are healthy, well vaccinated and free from any inherited genetic diseases.

➤ Do any medical tests necessary to determine that both are healthy.

➤ Assist the mother dog in any way needed during birth and while the pups are growing.

➤ Make sure each puppy is carefully handled each day to ensure his good health and to familiarize him with people.

➤ When the puppies turn five weeks old, provide a stimulating environment. Supply toys, interesting objects and let the puppy hear a variety of household noises.

➤ Make sure potential puppy buyers understand the characteristics of the breed, know what to expect from a puppy and are fully aware of what they need to do to raise this puppy correctly.

➤ Never sell puppies before seven and a half weeks of age, and, if possible, keep them until they are nine weeks old.

➤ Be available to puppy buyers so they feel comfortable calling back to ask questions.

➤ Take responsibility for every puppy they bred, for the life of the dog.

The breeder's job is time-consuming. A litter should never be planned unless you have the time and energy to do all the things on this list.

Puppy Tails

By keeping track of puppies after they have gone to their new homes, the breeder can follow the puppies' growth and development. Did the puppies grow up to be nice, healthy dogs? If there are problems, where did those problems come from? Good follow-up can help the breeder evaluate her breeding program.

The Least You Need to Know

➤ Most mother dogs are instinctively good mothers and take very good care of their puppies.

➤ Puppies are born helpless, but their physical, emotional and intellectual development occurs rapidly.

➤ The mother dog is a very good teacher and gives the puppies some of the social skills necessary for them to survive with people.

➤ Littermates teach each other, too, and help each other learn many of life's lessons, including dominance, submission, and other social skills necessary for survival.

➤ The breeder's responsibilities are heavy. Make sure you can do all that is necessary before planning a litter.

Chapter 5

Where Oh Where Can He Be?

In This Chapter

➤ Finding a reputable breeder

➤ What about puppies in pet stores, humane societies and breed rescue?

➤ Comparing puppies in a litter

➤ How to do puppy tests, what they mean and how to use the results

➤ Making the right decision for you, your family and your prospective new puppy

---

As we've learned in the previous chapters, you have certain requirements as far as puppy ownership goes. You have particular likes and dislikes regarding coat types and how much grooming is or is not required for those coat types. Some dogs have higher energy levels than others, and you've decided what you can handle comfortably. We've talked about breed characteristics, activity levels and trainability. We've even talked about the creation of a puppy—what makes her unique and how she develops. Where do you go from here? How do you find that special puppy?

Finding a Reputable Breeder

The best place to find a puppy—if you are looking for a purebred dog—is from a reputable breeder. What is a reputable breeder? It's someone who loves her breed, is trying to better the breed by breeding only the best dogs and is always working to increase her knowledge about the breed. This person probably belongs to the local and national clubs devoted to her breed, and probably shows her dogs in dog shows. She is probably also active in the dog activities that suit her breed, such as herding and stock dog work for the herding breeds, agility or flyball for the high-energy dogs, and earthdog trials for the terriers.

Puppy Tails

In earthdog trials, a series of tunnels are set up with a caged (for its protection) rodent at the end. Terriers run through the tunnels to find the varmint, and are judged on how quickly they are able to negotiate the maze and how well they respond to their handler's commands.

In addition, a reputable breeder is concerned about her puppies and will ask you as many questions as you will ask her! A good breeder will also willingly give you references of other people who have bought her puppies, so you can talk to them.

How do you find these breeders? There are lots of ways. If you see a nice dog of the breed you are interested in, ask her owner where he got her. That might lead you to a local breeder. Your veterinarian might also know. Call the American Kennel Club and ask for a referral to a breeders' list, or to a regional branch of the national club. You might also find an ad in the newspaper or in a dog magazine.

Once you have a few names and numbers, it's time to ask questions. Call each breeder on your list and ask the following questions:

➤ **How long have you been breeding?** Some experience is usually better, and you should be cautious about buying from a breeder's first litter. However, many years is not always better. Sometimes the "old-timers" never allow themselves to learn anything new. Nor is a newcomer necessarily bad; sometimes the newcomers try harder.

➤ **What health problems do you screen your dogs for?** If she says her breed has no problems, beware! There is no such thing as a totally problem-free breed. Ask your veterinarian (and several other veterinarians, too) what health problems he sees in this breed and ask the breeder about them.

➤ **Can I see the paperwork regarding health screenings?** The breeder should at least be able to show certifications that the hips have been x-rayed for hip dysplasia and the eyes have been certified clear of hereditary defects.

Finding the right puppy for you and your family may take some work, but it is well worth the effort.

➤ **What kind of guarantee do you offer with your puppies?** Is the puppy guaranteed free of hereditary health defects? This should be very important to you. Make sure you understand the terms of the guarantee. Is the puppy guaranteed to have working instinct? You can decide whether this one is important to you or not.

➤ **Can I stop by to see some of your dogs?** The answer should be yes, of course. You should be able to see the mother of the litter, possibly the father and several of the other dogs.

When you go meet the breeder and see her dogs, there are some basic things you should look for:

➤ **Is the area where the dogs are kept clean?** Feces should be picked up and urine washed down. A kennel doesn't have to smell like one. A dirty kennel is a poorly run one, and probably an unhealthy one.

➤ **Are the dogs active, alert and happy?** If the dogs do not settle down after your arrival and appear fearful, shy or overly aggressive, leave without a puppy.

Puppy Tails

A backyard breeder is someone who is breeding her pet dog, and doesn't have the knowledge that a reputable breeder has. The backyard breeder probably has no sales contract, no paperwork regarding health concerns or hereditary defects, and may not even have registration papers. She might produce a nice litter of puppies, but it would be a gamble.

➤ **Does the breeder know each dog, his name, his background and his health?** She should. If she has too many dogs to immediately identify each one, leave without a puppy. She may not even have her paperwork in order.

➤ **Can the breeder show you the vaccination and health records for the mother of the litter as well as the puppies?** She should have these on file. If she makes odd excuses for why they are not handy, suspect that she may not have them at all and leave without a puppy.

➤ **Can she show you the registration papers for the mother and the litter registration papers for the puppies?** Her paperwork must be in order or you will not be able to register your puppy. Don't accept a promise that "the papers will be along later."

➤ **Does she have a sales contract that she uses for puppy purchasers?** She should. Make sure you read it, understand it and agree with *all* of it before deciding on a puppy.

Paws for Thought

Some breeders want to co-own certain puppies. The breeder may ask you to show the puppy or use the puppy in a breeding program. Make sure you are 100 percent comfortable with all the terms *before* agreeing to co-own a puppy.

You should also ask the breeder for references. Realize that she will probably only give you the numbers of people who will give her a good reference, but you can still ask them some pointed questions: Were you happy with the process of buying a puppy from this breeder? Did she deliver everything she said she would (contract, registration papers, health information, etc.)? Would you buy another dog from her? You can find out a lot from some simple questions.

When you are through with your questions, the breeder will ask you some, too. She is going to be concerned about your ability to give her puppy a good home. She will ask what you know about the breed, its temperament and its needs. She will ask about your fence and your yard, your plans for training the dog and who your veterinarian is. Don't take offense at her questions. Instead, be happy that she is asking them. I am always concerned if a breeder *doesn't* ask me any questions. Perhaps she doesn't care enough!

What About Puppies in a Shelter?

Often humane societies, animal control and other shelters have puppies available for adoption. Usually these are mixed breed puppies, but often there are purebred puppies, too. These are usually the result of unplanned breedings or are the puppies produced by a backyard breeder that she was unable to sell. These puppies are usually available for a very reasonable fee, plus a refundable deposit that you can get back once the puppy has been spayed or neutered.

Many people like to get a puppy from a shelter because they feel good about saving a puppy's life. After all, in most shelters there is a time limit, and if the puppy isn't adopted within that time limit, it will be destroyed. There is a real sense of pleasure involved in saving a life; it makes you feel good inside.

However, there is a down side to shelter adoption. This puppy will be a total unknown. While a breeder will be able to show you the mother, the father and possibly the grandparents of a particular puppy, even the breed of a shelter puppy could be unknown. Many puppies look alike when they're very young, and identifying a breed or a mixture of breeds can be a challenge.

G-r-r-r!

Because of privacy laws, many shelters are not allowed to show you any paperwork from the puppy's previous owner. However, you can explain that you only want to know about the puppy, and ask them *if* they could read you any pertinent information.

If you are looking for a specific breed, mixture of breeds or type of dog (such as a herding breed), you may have a difficult time finding the right shelter puppy for you. The genetic health of this puppy will be unknown, too, as will her actual health before going to the shelter. There will be many unanswered questions, some of which could lead to problems.

If you do wish to adopt a puppy from a shelter, stack the odds in your favor as much as possible. Ask to see any paperwork that came with the puppy. Did the person turning the puppy in leave any information, and if so, what was it? Ask the shelter workers about the puppy. What did they notice about the puppy's actions, behavior and health? Even with a shelter puppy, the more you know the better.

Many great pets have come from shelters, so don't let my words of caution dissuade you. Just be careful and learn as much as you can before you set your heart on a particular shelter puppy.

Pet Store Puppies

The song says, "How much is that doggy in the window? I do hope that dog is for sale." Unfortunately, buying a pet store puppy is not always a good idea. Reputable breeders do not sell their puppies to pet stores. Reputable breeders want to know where their puppies are going and want to control the sale themselves. Therefore, the puppies found in pet stores are from unplanned breedings, from breeders wanting only to make a profit from a popular (or rare) breed without concern for the puppies' welfare, and from puppy mills.

G-r-r-r!

Puppy mills are breeding farms where dogs are raised as livestock. Do not imagine dogs running free over grassy fields; these dogs are raised in cages, no care is taken as to their emotional well-being, they are not screened for inherited defects nor is emotional stability or working ability taken into account.

The puppies sold at pet stores are as much of an unknown in terms of quality as are the puppies in the shelter. You have no idea about the health of the puppy's parents or grandparents, and of course, there is no way you can see the puppy's parents. A pet store puppy is an unknown entity.

In addition, pet store puppies are often very difficult to housetrain. These puppies are in a display cage most of the day and have to relieve themselves in their cage. When they do so day after day, they lose their natural instinct to keep their bed clean. Trying to retrain this behavior can be very difficult, and sometimes it is impossible.

These puppies can also have behavioral and training problems resulting from being taken from their mother and littermates very early. Many times the puppies are taken away at five to six weeks of age, so that they can be in the pet store by eight weeks of age. These puppies never have the littermate socialization that is so important, nor does the mother dog ever get a chance to teach the puppies to accept love, affection and discipline. All of these factors make it very difficult for these puppies to live a normal canine life.

Puppy Tails

Don't let anyone tell you a dog's quality is determined by whether or not it has registration papers. Registration papers are only a guarantee that a dog is a particular breed. They are no guarantee of quality. In fact, this what the AKC itself says about registration papers: "AKC registration means a dog, its parents, and its ancestors are purebred, but it does not indicate health or quality."

Finding a Puppy Through Purebred Dog Rescue

If you're sure you want a purebred dog, breed rescue is another option for you. Most national breed clubs, such as the Australian Shepherd Club of America and the German Shepherd Dog Club of America, sponsor breed rescue groups. These volunteer groups help place dogs of their breed into new homes. In the process, the dogs are screened as to personality, temperament, training and social skills, and are often fostered by volunteers while awaiting their new homes. This rescue process has saved thousands of dogs each year that might have otherwise been destroyed in animal shelters all over the country.

Most of the dogs taken in by rescue groups are adults. However, some puppies find their way into the system. A mother dog and her litter might be turned in, or a family may have decided that their four-month-old puppy is too much for them. For whatever the reason, puppies do turn up in rescue every once in awhile.

You can find a rescue group in your area by calling your local humane society or animal shelter. Most maintain a list of local breed rescue groups. The AKC also maintains a list of national breed rescue coordinators. You can find the list on the AKC's Web site at www.akc.org.

When you call the rescue group, tell the person who answers the phone that you are looking for a puppy of their breed and ask if any are available. If not, put your name on the waiting list.

When a puppy becomes available, ask as many questions about this puppy as you would any other. What has the previous owner told the rescue group? Where did this puppy come from? Is anything known about the breeder? The puppy's parents? Again, the more you know, the better.

Puppy Tails

Mary Fillerup is a foster parent for Australian Shepherd rescue. She takes one dog at a time into her home and keeps him until he is adopted into his new home. She makes sure the dogs are housetrained, have some basic obedience skills and are good with other dogs. Most important, she loves the dogs at a time where they often feel lost and abandoned.

Finding the Right Puppy for You

Choosing a puppy can be a very emotional decision. Unfortunately, an emotional, impulsive decision is often the wrong one. Taking home a tiny, scared puppy from the shelter just because it was small and afraid doesn't mean that puppy is the right one for you. It could be a very fearful, malnourished puppy that will have health and behavioral problems all its life. If you are aware of the problems and are willing to deal with them, that's fine—take home that puppy. But if you want a dog that will grow up to be a friend and companion, one that will go places and do things with you, you will need to make a more careful decision.

Paws for Thought

Male or a female? The two sexes are often more alike than different in temperament once they're spayed or neutered, although many people feel a neutered male is more affectionate. It really all comes down to personal preference.

Puppy Testing

When you hear the phrase "puppy testing," do you have a vision of puppies sitting at a school desk taking an exam? Clear that from your mind—it's not the kind of test I'm talking about. Puppy testing is a way of seeing how puppies react to certain things. By watching their reactions, you can decide which puppy will be better for you.

These tests are best done when the puppies are six to seven weeks old. Many breeders do them, so if you are talking to a breeder about her puppies, ask if she tests them. If she does, ask if you can come watch the process. If she doesn't, ask her if she'll let you perform the test. Most knowledgeable breeders will want to supervise or participate, of course, to protect their puppies, but will not object to you doing the test.

Looking at the Littermates Together

By six weeks of age, the puppies are interacting with each other—playing and mock fighting. By interacting, they are learning social rules. And by watching the puppies together while they are interacting (not while they're sleeping!), you can gain some clues to each puppy's personality.

The boldest puppy—which is often the biggest, but not always—is usually the first to do anything. He is the first to the food, the first to grab a toy and the first to climb out of the whelping box. This puppy is usually a good law enforcement dog, search and rescue dog or herding dog because he is bold. However, this could be a bad choice for someone who lives alone and works long hours, or for a senior citizen who needs a calmer dog.

G-r-r-r!

It's easy to fall in love with more than one puppy in a litter, but don't bring home two littermates. The sibling bond is strong, and those puppies will live for each other—not you.

The puppy who sits in the corner by himself and watches the world go by may seem like a calm, knowledgeable puppy, but in reality this puppy may be a little fearful. Further testing will reveal whether this is simply a calm personality that can cope with life, or a fearful puppy that is sitting back watching for fear of getting involved.

The puppies in between these two extremes will bounce back and forth. In one situation one puppy will be bolder or more dominant, while in another situation one of the other puppies will take over. It's important to watch and see who is roughest during play, who accepts a correction from a littermate when he bites too hard and who always ends up on top of the puppy pile. Watch, too, and see who has a temper and who is the crybaby.

While you're watching the puppies, don't get involved. Don't interact at all—just watch them and take notes. The more you know about them while they are acting naturally, the better.

Starting the Test

Ask one person to sit on the side to watch and take notes about each puppy's responses. Tell the person to take as many notes as possible, because once you have tested two or three puppies, the results start to get all mixed up and you won't remember which puppy did what!

Test one puppy at a time, and have the puppy do all of the exercises before you go on to the next puppy. Take the first puppy to a room or part of the yard away from his mom, his littermates and other distractions.

Step 1: Set the puppy on the ground and walk away from him, without calling him or even making eye contact. What does he do?

Possible Results: a) He follows you. b) He is underfoot, climbing on your feet. c) He crawls after you, doing a belly crawl. d) He goes off in the other direction.

Step 2: Move away from him, then bend over and call him, clapping your hands to encourage him.

Possible Results: a) He comes to you with tail wagging. b) He chases you so fast that you don't have a chance to call him. c) He comes slowly or belly crawls to you. d) He ignores you.

Step 3: Roll the puppy over on his back and place a hand on his chest, gently restraining him for 30 seconds—no longer.

Paws for Thought

It is much easier to observe and test the puppies if each pup is identified. If the breeder has not already done so, loosely tie different colored ribbons around their necks or put different collars on the puppies.

Possible Results: a) He struggles for a few seconds but then gives in and lies quietly. b) He struggles the entire 30 seconds. c) He cries, tucks his tail up to his tummy and perhaps urinates. d) He struggles for more than 15 seconds, then stares at you or obviously looks away.

Step 4: Placing both hands under the puppy's rib cage, lift the puppy up in the air (without cradling him to you) for 30 seconds.

Possible Results: a) He quietly accepts it without much wiggling. b) He struggles for up to 15 seconds. c) He accepts it with a tucked tail, some crying and perhaps some urinating. d) He struggles for more than 15 seconds and tries to turn around and nip your hands.

Step 5: With the puppy close to you, toss a tennis ball or a crumpled piece of paper away from you.

Possible Results: a) The puppy dashes after it, picks it up and brings it back to you. b) The puppy dashes after it, brings it back, but doesn't let you have it. c) The puppy goes after it but doesn't pick it up. d) The puppy picks it up but then takes it away.

Looking at the Results

There are no right or wrong answers with this test. Instead, you want to use the results to choose the right puppy for you. When I was choosing my latest addition, Kes, I wanted a puppy that was middle of the road when it came to dominance. I wanted an outgoing puppy that wasn't fearful, that liked to retrieve and that would accept handling. By using these tests, and by watching her with her littermates, I chose Kes and she has turned out to be exactly what I wanted.

Get to know each puppy as you go through the exercises. Each one is different and unique.

A puppy whose responses were mostly A's is a middle-of-the-pack dog in terms of dominance. This is not the most dominant puppy nor the most submissive. If this puppy also scored A in the retrieving test, he will suit most families with children or active people. This puppy will accept training, and although he may challenge your dominance as an adolescent, he will accept your leadership.

The puppy that scored A's and B's will be a little more dominant and will probably challenge you more during adolescence. If he scored A on retrieving, he will accept training. If he scored B, C or D on the retrieve, training could be a challenge.

The puppy that scored all B's is a more dominant personality. This could be a good working dog, or a good dog for someone who is also a strong personality— particularly someone who wants to do a lot of things with the dog. A dog like this is not good for someone with a soft personality or someone who doesn't enjoy dog training, because this dog will need the structure of regular training.

The puppy that scored primarily C's is a more fearful or reserved personality. This dog must be handled carefully. If the dog had B's and C's, he could potentially become a fear biter. This dog will need positive training, a calmer environment and careful handling that does not emphasize the dog's fears. This dog would do well with a single adult or in a quiet adult home. This is not the dog for an active, rowdy home environment, and is not the best mix with children.

61

Paws for Thought

These tests are a tool to help you choose the best puppy for you. However, to choose the right puppy, you also need to be honest about yourself.

The puppy that scored C's and D's will have trouble bonding to people, and when he does bond, he could become a one-person dog. A slightly fearful, cautious yet independent personality such as this is a challenge that should only be taken on by someone who doesn't want a clinging dog, but is willing to be quiet and patient. This dog will need calm, positive training.

The puppy that scored mostly D's is an independent soul that isn't convinced he needs people. He will need to spend time with his person so that he can bond. He will also need training, probably using a combination technique with lots of positive reinforcement and calm, non-threatening corrections. (These dogs usually do need corrections in their training; the positives are not enough to convince them to change their ways.) This type of personality is usually better with a family who is gone for hours each day, and rarely suffers from separation anxiety (as do the puppies who score A or B).

Listen to Your Heart

Choosing the right puppy can be hard. An emotional decision is rarely the right one, yet the decision cannot be made totally without emotion either. Use the information in this chapter and in Chapter 2, but listen to your heart as well. A puppy that performed just right for you in all the puppy tests still isn't right for you if there isn't a good feeling there, too. After all, the puppy could be all A's (if A's are right for you), but could still be the wrong puppy if you don't like each other!

The Least You Need to Know

➤ Find a reputable breeder, ask her lots of questions and expect her to ask you questions, too.

➤ Adopting a puppy from a shelter or from breed rescue could save a puppy's life, but you won't know much at all about where the puppy came from.

➤ Watching the puppies in a litter interact can tell you a lot about the puppies' personalities.

➤ Puppy tests can give you more information about the puppies' personalities, temperament and pack orientation.

➤ Use all this information, and your heart too, when choosing a puppy.

Part 2
Bringing Home Your New Best Friend

A new puppy is a unique individual with an unlimited future. There is so much you two can do together! But you need to make some preparations first. What will you need before you bring home your new puppy? How about food, bowls, leashes, collars, toys and things for the puppy to chew on? You will also need to puppy-proof your house and yard, put away breakable knickknacks and tuck away electrical cords.

Once your puppy is home, what happens next? What should you expect the first night? When should you start housetraining? What is socialization and why is it important? There is so much you need to know, so let's get started!

Chapter 6

Before You Bring Your Puppy Home

In This Chapter

➤ What do you need to buy for your puppy?

➤ Puppy-proofing your house and yard

➤ How to find pet professionals you can trust

➤ Is there anything else?

Bringing home a puppy is an exciting experience. This new family member will be with you for the next 12 to 15 years, but your relationship starts on her first day at home. Are you ready? You want to make sure you're prepared, so what should you have on hand? What will you need to buy? You don't want to have to run out to the store on her first day because you forgot something important.

There is more to do than shopping, too. Do you know what veterinarian you would like to use to care for your puppy? If you already have a dog or a cat you probably already use a local veterinarian's services, but if this is your first puppy you may need to do some research. Do you know where you will take your puppy for training? What about grooming? These pet professionals can help you, and will make life much easier.

You'll need to make sure your house and yard are ready for your new puppy, too. So before you bring home your new puppy, read through this chapter and make sure you are really ready. The preparation will make things go just a little bit smoother.

Let's Go Shopping!

Your puppy will need some basic supplies. If you already have a dog, you may have some of these things on hand. However, if this is your first puppy, a shopping trip is definitely in order. Where you go shopping is up to you. The larger pet supply stores will have everything you need, but their prices may be a little higher than a big discount store. Still, the discount store won't have everything you need. If you don't mind shopping around, you can compare prices and get what you can at the discount store and everything else at the pet supply store.

Puppy Food

Find out from the breeder what the puppy has been eating. A sudden change in food can cause gastrointestinal upset, including diarrhea, so you will initially want to keep the puppy on her normal diet. If you would prefer to feed another food, change the diet very gradually over a two- to three-week period so that she can get used to it. Make sure you have a two- to three-week supply of food on hand the day you bring your puppy home.

Food and Water Bowls

It may seem odd to list these, since everybody knows their dog will need bowls. However, bowls from the cupboard won't work well. Why? Because puppies play with their bowls, dump them over and use them as toys. Plastic bowls will be chewed, and breakable bowls will be broken.

A metal food bowl is a good idea, and the water bowl should be unspillable. An unspillable bowl will be just as wide on the bottom as it is on top, and the bottom will be heavy.

Collar and Leash

Get a nice, soft buckle collar for the puppy. A nylon collar that you can make larger as the puppy grows is great. A four- to six-foot leash is fine. You may need some other collars and leashes during training, but we'll talk about that later.

Identification

You will want to put some identification on your puppy right away. A collar tag is good to start, and temporary ones are available at most pet supply stores. Later a permanent engraved tag can be ordered. When it comes in, put it on the collar and toss the temporary one.

Puppy Tails

There are two permanent means of identifying dogs: tattoos and microchips. A microchip is a tiny chip encased in glass that is implanted under the skin between the shoulder blades. A tattoo is an identifying number put on your dog's inner thigh. For either to work, the identifying number must be registered with one (or all) of the national recovery organizations (they're listed on the Reference Card).

Crate

A kennel crate is a wonderful puppy training tool. In Chapter 7 you will learn how to introduce your puppy to the crate, and in Chapter 9 you will learn how to use it for housetraining. For now, just remember that the crate you buy should be big enough for the puppy to stand up, turn around and stretch out in when she's full grown.

When you go to buy the crate, you will find there are two types: plastic ones that are solid with barred windows, and heavy metal wire crates that look more like cages. I prefer the plastic crates because my dogs seem to be more comfortable and secure in them. However, the wire crates are sturdy and do provide more ventilation in hot climates. Look at both types of crates, and choose the one you think will suit you and your puppy best.

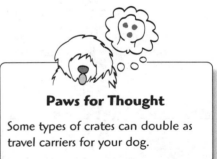

Paws for Thought

Some types of crates can double as travel carriers for your dog.

Baby Gates

Baby gates were, as the name suggests, made to keep human babies safe. Put across the head or foot of the stairs, a baby can be kept away from that danger. Baby gates are also a wonderful training tool for puppies. Use baby gates to restrict the puppy's access to other rooms where she might get into trouble.

Grooming Supplies

Your puppy's breeder should be able to show you what grooming supplies you will need. You may need a comb, a slicker brush or a soft bristled brush. You will also need shampoo and maybe even a dematting conditioner. A professional groomer can also help you decide what supplies are needed.

Cleaning Supplies

When housetraining a puppy, I always keep a gallon of white vinegar on hand. If the puppy has a housetraining accident, after cleaning the spot I generously dab on some vinegar. That keeps the puppy from coming back to that spot.

You will need other household cleaners for the dirt the puppy tracks in and for other puppy disasters. Read the labels to make sure all cleaners are safe; many are poisonous to people and animals. Never use a poisonous cleaner on something the puppy might chew.

Pooper Scooper

A pooper scooper is, as the name suggests, something to help you clean up after your puppy in the backyard. A pooper scooper is usually a two-tool combination—a flat shovel and a rake or a scraper. Using this is much easier than a garden shovel. Look at the various types available at the pet store and choose one you think will be comfortable and easy for you to use.

Of course, you can always just pick up after your pup with plastic bags or sheets of newspaper. But a good pooper scooper will make a nasty job much easier!

G-r-r-r!

Too many toys is not better. If the puppy has too many toys to chew on, she will think everything is hers and everything can be destroyed. Give her a few toys and teach her that those are hers.

Toys

Looking at the selection of dog toys available in a pet supply store can be very exciting as well as very confusing. There are so many toys! One of my dogs' favorites is a Kong toy. A Kong is made of hard rubber, looks like three balls smashed together, and is hollow. The inside of it can be filled with treats or peanut butter to occupy a puppy. When thrown it bounces weirdly, adding excitement to the game.

I also like (and so do my dogs!) the Buster cube. This is a hard plastic hollow cube. You can fill it with dog kibble and set an adjustable opening to let the food out piece by piece. As the puppy bounces the cube, food falls out. This will keep a pup occupied for a long time. If you get any other toys, make sure they are safe. Your puppy should not be able to chew off and swallow pieces.

Is Your House Safe for Your Puppy?

Before bringing your puppy home, you will want to make sure your house is safe. The easiest way to do this is to get down on your hands and knees and look at your house from a puppy's point of view. You may want to do this when no one else is home because you'll feel silly, but it works. Look at that telephone cord dangling off the end table—it's inviting a puppy to chew it. Tuck it away. Tuck away all electrical cords, too.

Are there magazines on the floor? Those will be torn up unless they are put away. How about the slippers under the couch or the knickknacks on the bottom shelf of the bookcase? Put away everything that looks inviting and everything that is of value to you. Pick up anything that is dangerous to the puppy.

Paws for Thought

Puppies (just like human babies) will put everything in their mouth, so they must be protected from danger. If your puppy does eat something potentially dangerous, call (900) 680-0000 for a 24-hour poison control hot line.

Make sure everyone in the family knows about the cleanup program, too. If someone leaves something within the puppy's reach and it is destroyed, it is not the puppy's fault! She needs to learn what to chew on and what not to chew on, and that takes time and training. Meanwhile, prevention is the key. Put everything away!

Your kitchen can be a source of many dangers. Use latches on the cupboard doors to keep your puppy safe.

Make sure cupboards containing dangerous substances (cleaners, insecticides and so on) have latching doors. Puppies can get into trouble just the way small children can. Cupboard safety latches work very well.

Some Dangerous Substances Around the House

In the bathroom

Medicines

Vitamins

Bathroom cleaners

Some shampoos, conditioners and hair care products

Toilet bowl cleaners

Makeup items, including nail polish and remover

In the kitchen

Oven cleaners

Cleansers

Floor cleaners and waxes

Bug spray and insect traps

In the rest of the house

Cigarettes

Many houseplants, including English ivy, dumb cane and poinsettia

Many pens, including felt tip pens

Laundry products

In the garage

Car maintenance products, including oils, gas and antifreeze

Fertilizers

Insecticides and sprays

Rose care products, including systemics and fungicides

Snail and slug bait

Paints and paint removers

Use baby gates to block off certain areas of the house and to restrict the puppy to a specific area. She doesn't need full run of the house until she's grown up. Keep her close to you so that she doesn't get into trouble. In addition, if someone in the family isn't good about remembering to keep things off the floor, don't let the puppy into their room.

Your bathroom can also be dangerous to an inquisitive puppy.

Is Your Yard Safe for Your Puppy?

Your yard can have just as many dangers as your house. Things left out can be chewed on, plants can be dug up and eaten and inappropriate items can be used as toys. Just as in the house, try to look at your yard through the eyes of a puppy.

What is in the yard that a puppy can chew on? Have the kids left their toys outside? Does the lawn chair have a stuffed cushion that a puppy can reach? Are the pool supplies stored outside? Do you leave your leather gardening gloves and hand tools outside? Your puppy will use all of these things as play toys, so if you want to keep them intact, put them away.

Do you have a special garden? Your puppy will enjoy it, too, so fence it off. Many dogs will help themselves to the vegetables and fruit in the garden before their owner gets a chance to pick them. Or, the puppy may think the soft ground of the garden is a good place to bury a special toy.

Many common landscaping plants are poisonous, some dangerously so. If your yard contains any of the plants listed in the following chart, take precautions so that your puppy doesn't chew on them or ingest them.

Some Common Poisonous Plants

Amaryllis	Jimson weed
Anemone	Larkspur
Avocado (leaves, not fruit)	Lily of the valley
Azalea	Locoweed
Belladonna	Marijuana
Bird of paradise	Milk weed
Bottlebrush	Mistletoe
Boxwood	Morning glory
Buttercup	Mushrooms
Calla lily	Oleander
Cherry (seeds)	Peach (seeds)
Christmas cactus	Pennyroyal
Common privet	Poinsettia
Crocus	Poison ivy
Croton	Poison oak
Cyclamen	Poison sumac
Daffodil	Pokeweed
Diefenbachia	Potato (foliage)
Dogwood	Privet
Eggplant	Rhododendron
English ivy	Rhubarb
Foxglove	Sage
Hemlock	Snapdragon
Holly	Sweet pea
Horse chestnut	Tomato (foliage)
Hyacinth	Tulip
Impatiens	Verbena
Iris	Wisteria
Jasmine	Yew

Puppy Tails

Ebony is a black Labrador Retriever. One day she watched her owner plant 100 gladiola bulbs in the garden. When her owner finished, she went inside. Later she looked out the kitchen door and saw Ebony happily guarding a pile of bulbs. Ebony apparently thought her owner was hiding toys, and had found, dug up and brought to the door all 100!

Puppies don't realize that a fence keeps them safe. If there is something happening outside the fence, they just want to join the fun. So you must make sure the fence is secure and strong enough to prevent escapes. Even a small hole in the fence can be chewed on and clawed at until it is big enough for a puppy to wriggle through. Make sure all the boards or wire fencing are tight and secure. Look at the bottom of the fence. Are there any gaps the puppy can dig under? Is the fence tall enough to keep the puppy in when she's bigger?

If the fence has some weaknesses and you cannot replace the weak sections (or the entire fence), think about building your puppy a dog run. A dog run is a much better solution than chaining up a dog (which often results in problem behavior) and is safer than an inadequate fence. A dog run doesn't have to be huge. In fact, 20 feet long by six feet wide is more than adequate for even a large dog, as long as it has a spot that is always shady and a place where the dog can lie down off the ground. A dog run can also prevent problems. If you have exotic plants or fancy landscaping that you would like to keep the puppy out of, a dog run is perfect.

Finding Pet Professionals to Help You

A pet professional can make your life much easier. If you have a rapport with a veterinarian, a groomer or a trainer, you can call for advice when you have a question and you will have someone you trust in an emergency. However, don't wait until there's an emergency to find that pet professional. Be sure to do it now, before you need their help.

Most dog owners find pet professionals through referrals from other people. Ask your neighbor, friend or co-worker where they take their dog or cat. When you see a

A puppy could have easily escaped through the widely spaced bars in this fence, so the owner installed an additional barrier to protect the puppy.

If your puppy will have access to the garage, section it off with a barrier to keep the pup from danger. And make sure the space is comfortable.

well-behaved dog walking down the street with her owner, ask the owner where they went for training. Ask the owner of the well-groomed Bichon Frise where they go for grooming. If the same names keep popping up, that will give you a place to start.

I recently surveyed the people enrolling in my dog training classes, and more than two-thirds of them said they were there because of referrals from a former client. A few saw my Yellow Pages ads, a few saw my newspaper ad and a few were simply driving by, but the vast majority were there because a former client said nice things. However, as much as I appreciate a good referral, it is also important to ask questions of any pet professional.

Breed Bits

The Bichon Frise has a very soft, fluffy coat that needs regular combing, brushing and grooming. Many pet owners keep the coat trimmed quite short for ease of maintenance.

The Right Veterinarian

A veterinarian is one of the most important professionals you will find for your dog. I'll talk more about that in Chapter 11, but here let's look at how you find one. Ask each prospective candidate about your breed. Is the vet familiar with it? If you have a more common breed, such as a Labrador Retriever or a German Shepherd, he will be, but if you have a rare breed like an Anatolian Shepherd, he might not be. Does he know anything about the health problems of the breed? If he's not familiar with the breed, ask if you can give him some reading material so that he will be more knowledgeable.

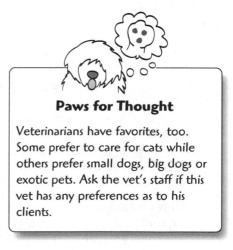

Paws for Thought

Veterinarians have favorites, too. Some prefer to care for cats while others prefer small dogs, big dogs or exotic pets. Ask the vet's staff if this vet has any preferences as to his clients.

Does this veterinarian have any specialties? What are they? Ask the veterinarian what his policies are regarding emergencies. Does he refer to an emergency clinic or will he take calls after hours? What are his payment policies? Does he take the credit card you prefer using? That may seem like a trivial question now, but it won't be when you get your first vet bill! Ask to see the clinic, too. Is it clean? Does it smell clean? Are the cages clean? Are the cages in an area where they can be easily supervised?

The Right Groomer

When you're shopping for a groomer, you can ask similar questions. Is she familiar with the grooming requirements of your breed? What products does she use? Does she use chemical flea and tick control products, or does she use natural preparations? Are you comfortable with the products she uses? How are the dogs caged while they are there? Are the cages clean? Are they easily supervised? Does she handle the animals with care and skill? What is her policy regarding payments? How far ahead must you call for an appointment?

Paws for Thought

There are two professional organizations for dog trainers: The National Association of Dog Obedience Instructors, Inc. and the Association of Pet Dog Trainers. Ask if the dog trainer belongs to either one.

The Right Trainer

You can also ask a dog trainer several questions. What type of training does she do? Some trainers are focused on competitive obedience training, which is unnecessary if you simply want a well-mannered pet. What techniques does she use? What training tools does she use? Every dog trainer has his or her own method of training, but make sure you will be comfortable with the techniques she uses. Does she offer private training or group classes? Private classes are good for a person with a very busy schedule or a dog with problem behavior, but they can be more expensive. A group class is best for a puppy that needs socialization. Ask if you can watch one of her classes so you can see what happens.

What Else Do You Need?

Okay, so you have puppy food, food and water bowls, a leash and collar, and a crate. You have some toys for the puppy. You have grooming and cleaning supplies, and you have a pooper scooper. You've got a couple of baby gates. You've puppy-proofed the house and yard, and you have the phone numbers on hand of a veterinarian, groomer and trainer. What else do you need?

How about a couple of old towels for the puppy's bed inside the crate? Don't buy an expensive stuffed dog bed; the puppy will just chew it up. A couple of old towels will work just fine, and are easy to throw in the wash.

How about a long leash for taking the puppy out to play? If you take her to the park (after she's had her vaccinations), don't let her off leash. Instead, use a length of clothesline rope or a long leash. We'll talk about that more in upcoming training chapters, but for right now, a long leash will give the puppy more freedom to play.

That should do it. You may want to get the puppy some more toys or some rawhides for her to chew on, but you can get those later. *Now* you're ready to bring home your new puppy!

The Least You Need to Know

➤ You need to go shopping before bringing home your puppy. Get puppy food, bowls, leash and collar, toys and the other necessary stuff.

➤ Puppy-proof your house, making sure all valuables are picked up. Make sure your puppy will be protected from dangers, including electrical cords and poisonous substances.

➤ Double-check to make sure your yard is escape-proof and the fence is secure. Pick up anything in the yard you don't want the puppy to chew on and fence off the garden.

➤ *Before* bringing home the puppy, find a veterinarian you can trust, as well as a groomer and a dog trainer.

Chapter 7

The First 24 Hours

In This Chapter

➤ When should the new puppy come home?

➤ Bringing the puppy home is not always easy

➤ What will you name your puppy?

➤ What should you do once the puppy is home?

➤ Bonding with your new puppy

Okay, you've chosen your new puppy. Now what? When should you bring him home and what happens when you do? What should you expect? First of all, expect the first 24 hours to be the most difficult. You and your puppy will be getting to know one another, and he will be missing his mom and his littermates. You will have to make some adjustments to having a puppy in the house, and at the same time your puppy will be exploring his new home. The first 24 hours will be nerve wracking, anxious, scary. At the same time they will also be full of joy, as you get to know this cuddly new being.

When Should Your Puppy Come Home?

As we learned in Chapters 4 and 5, the best time for a puppy to leave his mom is between seven and eight weeks of age. During the eighth week he will go through a fear period, and if he is frightened at that time (of the car ride, for example) those fears could remain for a long time. If you can't bring the puppy home during the seventh week, then wait until he's nine weeks old and bypass that scary eighth week.

If you work a Monday through Friday work week, try to bring your puppy home on a Friday evening. This will give you the entire weekend to get the puppy used to his new home, his new family and the new routine. If your work week varies, try to schedule the homecoming when you will have at least one full day at home after picking up the puppy.

If at all possible, do not pick up the new puppy if you will have to leave him alone the next day. That is a recipe for disaster. A lonely puppy will cry, scream and try to escape. A puppy that is too lonely and afraid may fail to thrive, become sick and, in the worst case, even die.

The Trip Home

The car ride home from the breeder can be very scary for young puppies, but there are a few things you can do to make it easier. First of all, let the breeder know when you will be stopping by so she doesn't feed the puppy for three or four hours before you come. The pup will be less apt to get carsick if his tummy is not full.

Many puppies also do better on car rides when they're in a crate. In Chapter 6 I suggested you purchase a kennel crate for the puppy. This will primarily be used as the puppy's bed and to help prevent problem behaviors, but crates were originally designed to keep dogs safe while traveling. What better time to protect your puppy than on his first car ride home?

Paws for Thought

What kind of music do you normally play in the car? On the way home, don't play anything that is loud, rough, vibrating or angry. This is the time for elevator music.

Again, the breeder can help you by introducing the puppy to a kennel crate before you come to pick him up. If the breeder can put a kennel crate in with the puppies (with the door tied open), the puppies can investigate the crate by themselves. A toy or treat hidden in the crate will encourage the puppies to go inside.

For the trip home, you can use a seat belt to strap the kennel crate down to keep it from moving. Your puppy can then ride home in safety. If he gets anxious, stick a finger into the crate and let him sniff it. A toy or two in the crate will keep him occupied. Most puppies, however, go to sleep as soon as the car starts moving.

The trip should ideally be from the breeder's place directly home. Don't stop to pick up a few things (you bought all your puppy supplies in advance, right?). Don't stop at a friend's place to show off the new puppy, either. Leaving his mom and littermates is a big step for the puppy, and too much too soon can be frightening. Just go straight home. People can meet the puppy later.

A Sample Schedule

Okay, you and the puppy are home. What now? What should you do? What should you expect? Well, don't expect a whole lot. This first weekend should be pretty quiet. It might go something like this:

Friday, 5:30 p.m. You walk in the door from work. Change clothes, look around the house to make sure everything's ready for the puppy, grab the puppy's crate and leave to go pick him up.

7:30 p.m. You sign the paperwork for the puppy, pay for him, get his papers, load him in the crate and use the seat belt to secure the crate in the back seat of your car. You head for home.

Paws for Thought

If you have to leave your new puppy alone for any period of time, ask a neighbor to help you or hire a professional dog walker. While you're at work, have someone come visit the puppy, play ball and give him a tummy rub. They'll probably both enjoy it!

8:00 p.m. At home, you immediately take the puppy outside to relieve himself. When he's done, you bring him inside to meet the rest of the family. Everyone is told to be calm and quiet, letting the puppy come to them.

9:00 p.m. According to your instructions, the breeder hadn't fed the puppy before your arrival, so you offer the pup a small meal. Afterward, you take him outside again to relieve himself.

9:30 p.m. You sit on the floor and cuddle the puppy, rubbing his tummy and playing with him. You start to see more of his personality.

9:45 p.m. The puppy falls asleep on your lap, so you stay in that uncomfortable position on the floor while watching your favorite sitcom. You'd rather move to the more comfortable couch, but you don't want to wake the puppy.

10:30 p.m. You take the puppy out for one more chance to relieve himself before you both go to bed. When the puppy has finished, you put him in his crate, give him a treat and get ready for bed yourself.

Saturday, 6:30 a.m. The puppy wakes you, asking to go outside. You stumble out, praise him for relieving himself in the right place, and leave him outside in the fenced yard while you go to your bathroom. When you are more awake, you let him in the house, keeping him close to you so you can watch him.

7:30 a.m. You feed the puppy breakfast and then take him back outside. You leave him outside for a little while.

9:00 a.m. The neighborhood kids show up and want to see the puppy. You tell them they'll have to wait a few days, because you don't want to overwhelm the pup with lots of new people.

9:30 a.m. You bring the puppy inside while you clean up the kitchen and wash the dishes. It's good for him to hear normal household sounds. Every once in awhile you reach down to pet him, scratch his ears and tickle his tummy.

10:00 a.m. You call the veterinarian and make an appointment for the vet to meet the new puppy and look over his vaccination records. The receptionist tells you to bring in a stool sample to check for worms. Oh, joy!

Noon. The puppy has fallen asleep in the middle of the living room floor where everyone will trip over him, so you carry him back to his crate and put him to bed.

1:30 p.m. The puppy is awake, so you take him outside and stay out there with him for awhile. When he's finished relieving himself, you walk him around the yard and watch him explore his new territory.

2:00 p.m. Your daughters want to teach him to play ball, so you watch from the porch, laughing at them. Kids and puppies are made for each other.

4:30 p.m. Your mother comes over and wants to meet the new family member. You bring the puppy in from the yard, but tell your mom to watch the puppy in case he needs to relieve himself. She does, and gets him outside in time.

6:00 p.m. It's time for dinner, so you feed the puppy and then take him outside to relieve himself.

7:30 p.m. You introduce the puppy to a brush and comb. He wants to chew on them and your hands, but you correct him gently when he does. Eventually you get him brushed.

9:30 p.m. You take him back outside for a chance to relieve himself, and then it's time for bed.

Sunday is very much like Saturday, except the puppy is left alone in his crate while the family attends church services or runs errands. Otherwise, this first weekend home is just a matter of letting the puppy get to know the new people in his life, and his new home and yard.

Where Will He Sleep?

Before bringing home the puppy, you should decide where he will sleep, which areas he will be allowed in and which areas will be out of bounds.

I like to have my puppy sleep in the bedroom with me. Not in the bed, of course—he needs his own place. But if his crate is in the bedroom with me I can hear him when he needs to go outside. Young puppies usually need to go outside once or twice during the night for a week or two, and if you hear the puppy get restless, you can take him out before there is an accident.

I also feel that by being in the room with me, the puppy will feel less alone and more secure. Even though he is in his crate, he can still hear me snore, hear me turn over and can smell me. He isn't alone; he is with his new family.

Don't be surprised if the puppy is anxious and restless the first night at home. He isn't sure where he is and why he's no longer with his mom and littermates. A stuffed toy to cuddle up against will soothe many puppies. For a particularly worried or anxious pup, put a clock that ticks inside a stuffed toy, or wrap the clock in a towel. The ticking seems to soothe many puppies.

When you put him in his crate to go to bed (after he's relieved himself outside), offer him a treat and shut the crate door. Turn off the bedroom lights. If the puppy is restless, just leave him alone. If he cries, do *not* let him out of the crate. That simply teaches him that crying works (and it means he knows how to train you better than you know how to train him!). If you know that he's relieved himself and doesn't have to go outside, there is no reason to let him out. Instead, talk to him, let him know you're close by and let him get used to his crate.

Paws for Thought

Teach your puppy a command that means "go to your crate." I use "go to bed." When I say it, the dogs run down the hall to their respective crates and wait for me to open the door. They pop in, turn around and wait for the treat they know is coming.

Where Will He Eat?

Deciding where your new puppy will eat is not nearly as important as what he will eat, but it is a decision that requires some thought. The location should be quiet, away from the family traffic. If the puppy is fed in the kitchen in the evening while dinner is being prepared, he may feel that he will be stepped on while he's eating. He may become nervous, which can affect his eating habits or his digestion. He may try to defend his food and show aggression when someone comes too close. He may be distracted by the activity around him and simply not eat.

G-r-r-r!

Don't let people disturb the puppy while he's eating. He should never feel rushed or threatened. Let him eat in comfort and peace.

It is better to find a quiet spot where the puppy can eat in peace. You may want to feed him in his crate in the bedroom, in his outside run or in the garage if he has access to a safe, puppy-proofed area there.

Where Will He Hang Out?

When you can watch him, keep the puppy restricted to the room you're in. Don't let him wander off to another room where he can get into trash cans, chew on shoes or have a housetraining accident. Freedom is not a right for puppies—it's something they earn as they grow up and mature. Your puppy may be close to two years old before he's mature enough to have free run of the house when you can't supervise him.

*Your puppy needs a safe
place to hang out and just
be a dog.*

Paws for Thought

If the puppy is in the room with you
demanding attention, but you have
things to do, distract him with a
chew toy. He can then still be with
you but won't be annoying you.

To keep the puppy close, set up baby gates to block off
hallways or close the doors. Make sure other family
members close doors, too, and understand the importance of restricting the puppy's access.

If you can't watch the puppy, put him in his crate or
put him outside in a safe place. Preventing problems in
the first place is the best way to make sure your puppy
doesn't get into trouble.

Where Will He Relieve Himself?

Chapter 9 goes into much greater detail regarding
housetraining, but you must decide right away where
you want the puppy to relieve himself. What you teach him in these first 24 hours at
home is very important.

Where do you want your puppy to go to relieve himself? Would you prefer he use a
corner of the yard, or do you mind if he goes anywhere in the yard? Will he have to go
on the concrete patio, or do you have to walk him down the street to relieve himself?

If you want him to go in a particular spot or area, start taking him to that spot right now, in his first hours at home, so that he can learn where to go. If you try to change things a few weeks from now your puppy will be very confused and you could set back his housetraining—so decide now.

Supervising the Puppy

The puppy will require almost constant supervision during the first 24 hours. No matter how carefully you puppy-proof your house, there is still too much trouble he can get into if he's unsupervised. He could chew on the furniture, the carpet or flooring. Some puppies even chew on the plaster wall board! The puppy should be in the room with you.

Paws for Thought

Dog urine can burn grass, producing yellow spots of dead grass on the lawn. To prevent this, teach your puppy to relieve himself in a spot where you have sand, dirt or gravel. This can then be soaked with the hose after feces have been picked up.

The idea of supervising the puppy is to protect him from dangers, to protect your house from canine destruction and to prevent problems from occurring. If your puppy never learns that the kitchen trash can has food in it, he will be less likely to raid it. During these supervised times, you can also teach him. You can tell him to leave the trash can alone and you can give him one of his toys to chew on when he picks up your leather shoe.

If you can't watch him, he should be in his crate or in a safe place outside. He can stay in his crate for short periods of time during the day. Fifteen minutes here, a half an hour there is okay, especially when he gets plenty of attention in between. If he has a safe place out in your yard, he can go back and forth between being in the house with you, to his crate, to the yard.

G-r-r-r!

Puppies can get into trouble in places you would never think of. To see if your yard is safe, go outside with your puppy, don't interact with him and watch to see what he does and where he goes.

However, double-check to make sure the yard is safe (Chapter 6 has more information about puppy-proofing a yard). Now that your puppy is home, you may feel that he is awfully small and your yard looks very big and dangerous. If you're concerned about the safeness of your yard, set up a dog run. It can be temporary, maybe six feet wide by 12 feet long, made up of fence sections securely fastened together. A tarp over part of the top can provide shade and shelter. If you set up a run like this, teach your puppy to relieve himself here.

How Much Can He Be Handled?

Everyone loves a puppy! Puppies just seem to be made to hug, cuddle and squish. However, too much handling can be very stressful, and stress is just as bad for puppies as it is for people. On the other side of the coin, you don't want to isolate the puppy. You need to find a balance so that the puppy feels loved and welcome but is not overwhelmed by too much handling.

G-r-r-r!

Never lift a puppy by putting your hands around his tummy. That hurts!

During the first 24 hours, try to limit the puppy's exposure to close family members. Invite them to sit on the floor with the puppy and let the pup come to them. If the puppy climbs up on their lap, great! They can hug, pet and cuddle him. However, if the puppy wants down, they should let the puppy move away.

People can lift the puppy to hug him or to move him from one place to another, but this should be kept to a minimum. Instead, encourage the puppy to follow you when you want him to go somewhere. Pat your leg, call him and walk slowly so he can follow. Praise him when he follows you.

It's very important to teach children the proper way to hold a puppy. Place one hand behind his forelegs and the other hand under his rump, and lift slowly, gently. Make sure you support his front and back as you hold him. Holding him against your chest will make this easier.

Children must also understand that they should not pick the puppy up often. It's better for them to get down on the floor and let the puppy come to them.

When Can Your Friends Meet Him?

After the first 24 hours the puppy can be introduced to new people, but limit the exposure to one or two people at a time. Socialization is important, and we'll talk about that more in Chapter 10, but too much too soon is not good. When he meets new people, ask them to kneel, crouch to his level or sit on the floor and greet him calmly and softly. This is not the time for screaming and shouting! Again, if he wants to move away from the people he's meeting, let him walk away. At this point in his life, don't force him to meet anyone.

Why Is He Crying?

Much like a human infant, a crying puppy is usually crying for a reason. A healthy, well-fed puppy is not going to cry unless something is bothering him. Some common reasons include:

➤ He's hungry. If it isn't time for a meal, offer him a treat or a chew toy.

➤ He's lonely. Remember, he just left his mother and littermates. This is probably the first time he's been all alone in his short lifetime. However, he does need to learn to be alone. Keep his times alone short, letting him get used to it gradually. Distract him with a toy, a chew toy or a ticking clock.

➤ He's hurt. Maybe he bit his tongue, stepped on a rock or got his nose stuck somewhere. He's a baby and doesn't tolerate hurts very well.

➤ He needs to relieve himself. He doesn't know how to tell you yet that he needs to go outside.

Breed Bits

Some breeds, including German Shepherd Dogs, are supposed to be reserved and aloof with strangers. Some dogs will begin showing this trait even in early puppyhood. These dogs need socialization, but should also be allowed to get to know new people gradually.

➤ He wants attention from you. You will very quickly become the center of his life and he needs your attention. Give him the attention he needs, but do not let him rule your life. He still needs to learn to be alone. Find a balance.

Fido, Rover, or Spot?

What are you going to name your puppy? I see more than a thousand dogs per year in my dog training classes, and am constantly fascinated by the names people give their dogs. A few years ago I went through all of my class enrollment sheets and made a list of the most popular names. They included Max, Bear, Sandy, Brandy, Amber, Kody (or Cody), Maggie, Ruby, and Charlie. Some other favorites include Bandit, Nicky (or Nikki, Nickie or Niki), Caesar and Sugar.

Some people like to give their dog a name usually associated with people. In the last few years I have had in my classes a Beagle named Fred, a Rhodesian Ridgeback named Alice and a mixed breed named George. A Basset Hound named Duncan was just as classy as his name. A Scottish Terrier named Angus and his friend, another Scottie named Bonnie, were perfectly named.

Many dogs are named after characters on television or in the movies. A Portuguese Water Dog named Kramer was just as crazy as his *Seinfield* namesake. My dogs, Kes and Dax, are named after strong women characters in *Star Trek*, of which my husband and I are fans.

Before you decide on the puppy's final name, take a little while to get to know him. My husband and I usually have two or three names picked out. Then, when the puppy comes home, we watch him for a day or two. It won't hurt to call him "Puppy" for a few days. Then, as his personality appears, we decide on the right name.

Names can complement a puppy's unique characteristics. Blue was named for his startling blue eyes.

For example, with Kes we had picked out Kes, Kira and Troy. All are female *Star Trek* characters. All are strong women with different characteristics. As the puppy started to show her own personality, we decided that Kes suited her better, both from the television character viewpoint and from the sound of the name.

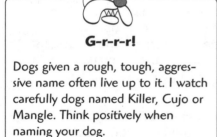

G-r-r-r!

Dogs given a rough, tough, aggressive name often live up to it. I watch carefully dogs named Killer, Cujo or Mangle. Think positively when naming your dog.

Make sure, too, that the name has a good, strong vowel sound that will carry. Can you call the dog from a football field away with that name? A friend of mine named his Scottish Terrier Magillicudy—a cute name but impossible to use in many situations. He ended up shortening it to Cudy—an ugly name but one that was much more usable.

As you think about the puppy's name, remember this name will be his identity for 12 to 14 years. Maybe the name Baby suits him now, but will it suit him 10 years from now? Will you be comfortable in public calling the dog with this name? Can you say the name happily? Does it suit the dog's breed, looks and personality?

Teaching Him His Name

Once you have decided on a name, teach the puppy that this sound refers to him. Call him by offering a treat, patting your legs and encouraging him to come to you as you say his name. Use a happy, higher-pitched tone of voice, much the way a child says "ice-cream!" when the ice cream truck comes by.

Say your puppy's name in a high-pitched tone of voice, and when he looks at you, praise him. If he doesn't look, make another noise, like knocking on the wall with your knuckles. When he looks
to see what the sound is, say his name again and praise him for paying attention.

A Registered Name

If your dog is purebred and the breeder gave you an application for registration, you will need a more formal name for registration. Often the breeder will ask you to use his kennel name as a prefix. For example, Dax's registered name is Apache Trails Jadzia Dax. Apache Trails is her breeder's kennel name. All of his dogs have Apache Trails in their registered name.

Dax's name happens to be a part of her registered name, but that doesn't always apply. The registered name doesn't have to correspond with the dog's common name at all (breeders refer to the dog's common name as the *call name*). My old Aussie, Ursa, is named for the constellation Ursa Major. However, her registered name is Little Bear of Starcross. Ursa isn't in the registered name at all, but it is her call name.

Registered names must be unique. If another dog already has a particular name, the registration

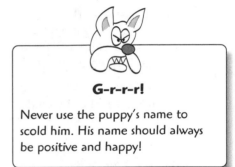

G-r-r-r!

Never use the puppy's name to scold him. His name should always be positive and happy!

form will be sent back to you and you'll have to come up with a different name. Or the registry will add a number to the name. So your dog might be Robby XXXIV, instead of just Robby. This need to be unique is why many dogs have such bizarre registered names—much like Thoroughbred horses, which have to have unique names, too.

Establishing the Bond

Dogs and people have a special relationship, unlike any other relationship between people and domesticated animals. Even cats and horses—both of which have been with humans for thousands of years—do not share the same closeness with us as dogs do.

The emotional bond dogs form with their owners is special and unique. Dogs bonded with their owners will do anything, including giving up their life. Law enforcement dogs and military dogs are often in the news because of their heroism.

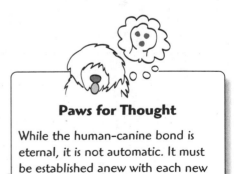

Paws for Thought

While the human-canine bond is eternal, it is not automatic. It must be established anew with each new puppy.

Paws for Thought

You will know the bond has formed when you look at your puppy and smile at him, even when he's gotten himself into trouble!

Just recently a police dog in my area gave his life protecting his partner. The German Shepherd Dog jumped in front of his partner, taking the six bullets a drug smuggler meant for the human police officer.

Pet dogs are just as heroic, though. Golden Retrievers are not noted for their protective instincts, but one named Jupiter was bound and determined to protect his owner from a burglar and did, scaring the burglar out of the house. Cassie, an Australian Shepherd, fought a thousand-pound bull, turning it away from her owner, who was on the ground after having been gored. Many dogs have protected their owners from burglars, trespassers and other dangers, including house fires. Why? Because they are bonded with us.

But the bond works both ways. Dog owners will do anything for their dog, too. Many a dog owner has gone back into a burning house to find his dog, even when firefighters warn of the dangers. Dog owners will spend thousands of dollars for veterinary care to help an injured or ill pet. Why? Because we love them!

The tendency to bond with people can vary in strength from individual to individual and from breed to breed. Some breeds bond strongly to one person or one family, while others are a little more aloof and standoffish. As a general rule, those breeds

You bond with your puppy by spending time with him and caring for him.

developed to work for humans, taking directions and following orders, bond more strongly than those breeds that worked alone, following their instincts. However, there are always exceptions.

The best time for a puppy to bond with people is between 8 and 12 weeks of age. If a puppy stays with his mother in a kennel situation without much human contact until after he's 12 weeks old, he may never be able to form a strong, trusting bond with people. This type of puppy is often more like a wild animal, trusting only other dogs. However, if the puppy has good positive contacts with people, the bond can still be formed.

When you bring your puppy home, the bond will form as you spend time with him. Your kind, gentle, firm but fair behavior will allow the puppy to learn to trust you, to respect you and to bond with you. You will become the most important person in the puppy's life, and at the same time, you will also be bonding with the puppy.

The key ingredient for building the bond is time with your puppy. If your puppy spends more time with your older dog, he will bond more strongly with that dog than with you. If the puppy spends long hours outside alone, without contact, the bond may never form. However, if you spend time with him before and after work, if you play with him, cuddle him and feed him, a wonderful human-canine bond will tie you both together for life.

The Least You Need to Know

➤ Bring home the puppy when you will have at least one or two days to spend with him before you need to go back to work.

➤ Decide where the puppy is to sleep, eat, relieve himself and spend time.

➤ Supervising the puppy is time-consuming, but is necessary right now. When you can't supervise him, make sure he has a safe place to spend time alone.

➤ Handling the puppy should be limited to family members right now, and should be carefully monitored so that stress is kept to a minimum.

➤ What are you going to name the puppy? Make sure the name suits the puppy, and that you'll be comfortable using it in public for the next 14 years!

➤ The bond between dogs and their owners is what makes this relationship so special. But you have to work at it.

Chapter 8

Setting Some Household Rules

In This Chapter

➤ You can and should set rules for your puppy

➤ Plan ahead for your puppy's adulthood

➤ How to prevent problems from occurring

➤ You need to be your puppy's leader, not her buddy

It's never too early to start teaching your puppy some household rules. By teaching her when she's young, she will never learn the unacceptable behavior that so many puppies do learn—the behavior that often results in the dog being exiled to the backyard. Teach her as a puppy what is expected of her, and she'll grow up meeting your expectations.

It's Your House—You Can Set Some Rules

Since your puppy is joining you in *your* house, you have every right to set some rules of acceptable behavior. After all, you're paying the bills, buying the dog food and cleaning up all the messes. You have the right to expect a certain level of behavior.

When you establish the house rules very early—as soon as the puppy joins your family—she never learns the wrong behavior. For example, if you want the puppy to stay off the furniture, never allow her up on the furniture. Some dog owners will allow their dog up as a small pup, and when the dog is 80 pounds they want to change the

Paws for Thought

By eight to 10 weeks of age, a puppy's brain is fully functional and capable of incredible learning. Although she may appear to be a baby physically, she is ready and willing to learn.

rules and keep her on the floor. That's not fair! First you teach your dog to join you on the couch, then suddenly you get mad when she does. How confusing is that?

Instead, start teaching the puppy now, as a youngster, exactly what you expect of her. She's capable of learning—you just need to teach her.

When you establish the household rules, make sure everyone in the household will accept and enforce them. If your teenage son likes to cuddle with the puppy on the sofa and encourages her to get up there whenever no one will see them, the puppy will be confused. Is she supposed to be up on the sofa or not? If your son invites her up, but whenever anyone else catches her up there the puppy is corrected, this is entirely unfair. Everyone must be consistent with the rules.

Posting a list of the rules in a prominent location works for many puppy owners. List each rule with a command, such as "off the sofa!" so that everyone is enforcing the same rules using the same commands. Put the list up on the refrigerator where everyone will see it every day.

What Will the Household Rules Be?

When trying to decide what rules you would like to establish, think about your dog as a puppy, but also as an adult. A toy breed dog is much easier to deal with on the furniture than a giant breed with a heavy coat. It is also much easier to allow a small terrier in the kitchen than a tall dog that can stand flat-footed and still reach the counter. Think about what your dog will be when she's full-grown. Picture that dog in your house, and establish the rules accordingly.

Your rules should also take into account your daily routine. Of course, a dog will change your routine, especially if you haven't had a dog before, but you can work a compromise between your normal routine before dog and after dog.

Here are a few suggestions for some household rules that are relatively easy to teach your puppy:

➤ **Do you want to allow the puppy in the kitchen?** Some dog owners like to keep her there because if she has a housebreaking accident it's easy to clean up. I don't like to keep the puppy in the kitchen because there are too many dangers there for my peace of mind. I don't want her underfoot when I'm cooking or using a sharp knife. There are cleansers and other dangerous substances under the kitchen sink. Plus, when they're grown up, my dogs could easily reach the kitchen counters. So I teach my puppies to stay out of the kitchen. You can

Before you allow your puppy up on the furniture, think about the adult dog she will one day be. Do you still want her up there?

weigh the pros and cons and decide for yourself—is the puppy allowed in the kitchen or not?

➤ **Is the puppy allowed on the furniture?** The owners of small dogs usually do allow their puppies on the furniture; it's easier than reaching down to pet a tiny puppy on the floor. Plus, a small dog isn't going to be as big a mess as a big dog. Personally, I allow my big dogs to get up on the furniture, too. Why? Because I like to cuddle with them! My dogs are not allowed to play on the furniture, but they are allowed up to snuggle with me or my husband. The downfall of allowing the dogs on the furniture is the added wear and tear, the dirt and the dog hair. I compensate for some of that by keeping a blanket or sheet over the sofa to protect it. Before deciding on whether or not you will allow your puppy on the furniture, think about the size your dog will grow to be, her coat and whether or not you will be upset about the wear and tear on your furniture.

➤ **Is the puppy allowed on your bed?** How about the kids' beds? Many dog owners do let their dog sleep on their bed. However, this is one household rule that I feel pretty strongly about: The dog should not be allowed to sleep on your bed! She should sleep in your room, but in her crate or in

Breed Bits

All Poodles are smart, but Toy Poodles seem to top the other sizes in terms of training their owners. They seem to have a way of making their owners do exactly what they want them to do, and most Toy Poodle owners don't seem to mind!

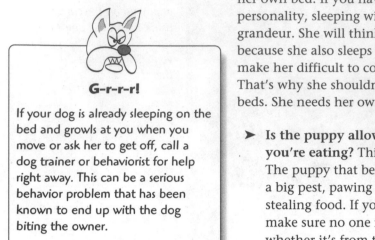

her own bed. If you have a dog with a more dominant personality, sleeping with you will give her delusions of grandeur. She will think she is just as good as you are, because she also sleeps in the big bed. That attitude will make her difficult to control in other circumstances. That's why she shouldn't sleep in your bed or your kids' beds. She needs her own bed.

➤ **Is the puppy allowed to beg for food while you're eating?** This really isn't an acceptable habit. The puppy that begs for food usually ends up being a big pest, pawing legs, licking hands or even stealing food. If you don't want to allow begging, make sure no one feeds the puppy as they eat, whether it's from the table or when you're snacking off the counter. No exceptions!

➤ **Do you want to restrict certain parts of the house?** If you wish to keep the puppy out of the kids' rooms so that she won't get into their stuff, that's fine. If you have a nice formal living room, teach her to stay in the family room and restrict her from the living room. In fact, as I've mentioned before, the puppy does *not* and should *not* have free run of the house. To restrict her access, close doors and use baby gates to keep her in the rooms where she is allowed.

What else is important to you? Think about it. What will make life with a dog easier?

Prevention Is the Best Cure

It is always easier to teach the puppy what you want her to know, instead of breaking or correcting a bad habit later. By preventing problems in the first place, you can teach your puppy acceptable behavior. If your puppy learns bad behavior and thinks it's fun, changing it later can be very difficult.

For example, if your dog never learns the joys of chewing a hole in the couch cushion and throwing the stuffing all over, you will be able to trust her in the house alone much sooner than you will a dog that likes the fun of chewing up stuff. By preventing bad behavior, you can make your training much, much easier.

Part of preventing bad behavior is restricting your puppy's access. Keep her in the room with you and keep an eye on her. Don't allow her to sneak off down the hallway where she can get into trouble without you knowing about it.

You also need to teach your puppy what is acceptable and what is not. When she grabs the sofa cushion, take it away from her and hand her one of her toys instead. When she picks up your good leather shoes, take them away, put them in the closet, close the closet door and hand the puppy one of her toys.

I made a mistake with one of my Australian Shepherds years ago. Ursa was a good puppy, so I gave her more freedom in the house. Obviously I let her have too much freedom too soon, because she got into the kitchen trash can. Ursa was very food motivated, and she found out that the kitchen trash can had food in it. Wow! All those treasures! For years afterward she was not trustworthy around the kitchen trash can. Even as an older dog, she would risk anything to get into that trash can because she learned as a puppy that food was in there.

Paws for Thought

When your dog is doing something right, give her permission to do it and praise her. For example, if she is picking up her toy instead of your shoe, tell her, "Get your toy! Good girl!" Reinforce that good behavior.

I learned something, too. My next dog, Dax, was never given the opportunity to discover the trash cans. I made sure her access was restricted and her freedom curtailed until she was old enough to be trusted. Now Dax, at three years old, can be trusted totally in the house. I can even leave food on the coffee table and it will still be there when I come home. Kes, my one-year-old puppy, is being trained the same way, and although it will be a while before she is trustworthy in the house alone, she is learning good habits and I am preventing her from learning bad ones.

Preventing problems from happening may take some work on your part. You will have to look at your house and yard from your puppy's perspective: What is attractive to your puppy? Can she reach your potted plants? The hose is fun to chew on—can you put it out of her reach? What about the outside trash cans—are they where she can get into them?

Be Your Puppy's Leader

When your puppy was still with her mother, mom started teaching the pups. They followed her out to the yard, watched where she relieved herself and then did as she did. They watched her play with a toy and then tried to play with her. She was teaching her puppies what it is like to be a dog.

Now it's your turn to continue her lessons. Your puppy needs a leader. You, as the leader, are always fair, never asking anything that the puppy is unable to give. Praise, corrections and commands will be given as needed, in a spirit of fairness. The leader is firm when needed but is always affectionate and loving. The leader always demands respect.

If you are not your puppy's leader, you will not be respected. In the dog's terms, a dog that is not respected is considered weak and low in the pecking order. The one that is not respected is dominated, often by mounting behavior. The low dog on the totem pole has her food stolen from her, gets no toys and is often growled at, snapped at and otherwise tormented. That should not be your position in your dog's pack!

Some dog owners want to be their dog's buddy and best friend. That is usually possible—after all, that's why we have dogs. However, it is usually possible later, *after* the dog is grown up and mature. During puppyhood you must be your dog's leader, not her equal or best buddy. She must learn to respect you as well as love you.

Puppy Tails

Max was a 100-pound unneutered male Rottweiler. His owner recently went through a divorce and bought the dog as a companion. She wanted the dog to be her buddy, and treated him like that. Max slept in his owner's bed, went everywhere with her and ate when his owner ate. Because his owner wouldn't set any rules and didn't provide any leadership, Max began thinking his owner was weak and began growling at her. Max's owner called for help but wasn't willing to make any changes. "I don't want to be his leader, I want him to be my friend," she kept saying. After Max bit her severely on three occasions, he was put to sleep. Things didn't have to happen that way.

Here are a few things you can do to help your puppy understand the fact that you're the leader. They are not necessarily the things her mother would do—after all, we aren't dogs. But they are things you can do that will help your puppy understand your respective places in the family pack.

➤ **Always eat first, then feed your puppy.** In a wild dog pack—which we know is not the same as our family, but serves as a good example—the leaders of the pack always eat first and best. Then the subordinate pack members eat. To your dog, you should be the giver of food. This makes you very important. To maximize this importance, you should eat breakfast or dinner first, then give your puppy her meal.

➤ **Go through doors first, then give permission for your puppy to either stay behind or follow you.** The puppy who dashes through doorways is going to get into trouble. One day she may dash out the front door ahead of you and end up in the street in front of a car. Or she may trip you, causing you to fall. You have the right to tell her to wait for your permission.

➤ **Each and every day, have your puppy lie down and roll over for a tummy rub.** This is a submissive position, and even though she probably loves the tummy rub, it is still a position that teachers her to be submissive to you. This is good! As the leader, you have to be more dominant than your dog.

➤ **At least once every day, as you stand up, bend over and gently hug your puppy to your knees.** Don't kneel down to her level. Instead, stand over her, hugging her close as you pet her and praise her. Standing over her like this is a dominant position. Again, that's good.

G-r-r-r!

If you have an adult dog with a more dominant personality, do not try these exercises without consulting a dog trainer or behaviorist first. These exercises are for puppies. An adult dog could take offense, especially if the dog does not view you as her leader.

➤ **Give her permission to do things.** If she's picking up her ball, tell her to get her ball and then praise her for doing it. This is what some trainers call "free" training. The puppy was going to do it anyway, so take advantage of it.

➤ **Set some household rules and stick to them.** As I said before, it's your house. Make sure the puppy understands that you will enforce those rules every day in every situation. No exceptions!

➤ **Don't pet your puppy every time she asks for petting.** This is hard for many puppy owners, but it's important. You can actually pet your pup too much, and she will then feel that she is the center of the universe and incredibly important. Even if your puppy *has* become the center of your universe, she doesn't need to know it! Pet her when you want to pet her, or after you have had her do something for you, such as sitting or lying down.

The Least You Need to Know

➤ It's your house, so set some rules of behavior that will make life with the dog easier.

➤ In making the house rules, consider what your dog will be like as an adult. Do you want a 90-pound dog in the kitchen or on the furniture?

➤ Preventing problems from happening is a huge part of teaching your dog household rules.

➤ You must be your puppy's leader. After all, you are taking her mom's place.

Chapter 9

The Perils and Pitfalls of Housetraining

In This Chapter

➤ What do you want your puppy to do?

➤ Where do you want him to do it?

➤ You need to set a routine and stick to it

➤ A crate is your (and your puppy's) best friend

➤ What to do when an accident occurs

When you're housetraining this puppy, what do you want the puppy to understand? Most puppy owners want to teach their puppy to relieve himself outside, sometimes in a particular area, and they want the puppy to be able to tell them when he needs to go outside.

You should also teach your puppy a command that means "try to go now," so that when you're taking him for a walk, or letting him out in bad weather, or when you're traveling, the puppy will at least try to relieve himself when you ask him to.

How Can a Crate Help?

Adding a puppy to the household can be a wonderful experience, but that wonder will disappear quickly if the carpets and floors are being ruined by housetraining accidents. However, there is a training tool that will enable you to train your new companion and avoid disaster. It's a crate. A crate (often called a kennel or a kennel crate), is a carrier for dogs. Originally developed for dogs being transported on airplanes, it now has a variety of training uses, including helping dogs learn housetraining skills.

All dogs are born with the instinct to keep their bed clean. When your puppy was old enough and strong enough to toddle away from his brothers and sisters, he would do so to relieve himself. Before that, his mother stimulated him to relieve himself and she cleaned up after him. Using a crate as a training tool takes advantage of your puppy's instinct to keep his bed clean and helps him develop more bladder and bowel control. It also helps him learn that there are right and wrong places to relieve himself.

G-r-r-r!

Often pet store puppies are difficult to housetrain. Because they had to relieve themselves in their cage, they have lost their inhibition about soiling their bed. A crate does not work for many of them.

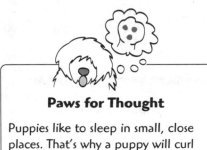

Paws for Thought

Puppies like to sleep in small, close places. That's why a puppy will curl up under the coffee table or under the foot of your recliner. A crate allows you to use this preference as a training tool.

There are two types of crates available. The first type is made of plastic or fiberglass. It has a metal barred door and barred windows for ventilation on each side. The top separates from the bottom in this type of crate, so it is easily cleaned. The second type is made of heavy gauge wire, and is more like a cage. It usually has a metal tray in the bottom that can be pulled out to be cleaned.

Which kind of crate to use is a personal preference. I think the plastic crates provide the puppy with more security, but the metal ones provide more ventilation. The metal ones fold up into a relatively flat, compact (if heavy) bundle, whereas the plastic ones are quite bulky. Look at the different types in the local pet supply store and choose the one that will best suit your needs.

It's important that you, as the new puppy owner, understand the crate is not a jail. A crate is your puppy's own personal space. It is his den or cave. It is a place where he can hide his favorite toys or bones. He can retreat to his crate when he's tired or doesn't feel well. He will sleep in his crate at night and will spend some time there during the day when you are unable to supervise him. But he will not be left in the crate for long periods, and it will not be a place of punishment.

Choose a crate that is big enough for your puppy to stand up, turn around and stretch out. But too much room is not better. Don't get a crate that will be big enough for a St. Bernard if you have a Shih Tzu! If the crate is too big, the puppy can relieve himself in a back corner and still have enough space to get away from it. The purpose of using a crate to housetrain your puppy is to capitalize on his instinct to keep his bed clean.

If you want to buy a crate that's big enough for your dog as an adult, it may be too big for your puppy. Some wire mesh crates come with a divider, so you can block off part of the crate. You can also block off an area using a sturdy box such as a plastic milk crate. Just remember that your puppy must be able to stand up and turn around comfortably in whatever space is left.

Introducing the Crate

Hopefully, your puppy's breeder has introduced your puppy to a crate. However, if she didn't, or if you got your puppy from somewhere else, you will need to introduce him to the crate. Take your time doing this, because you want the puppy to be comfortable with his crate.

Open the door to the crate and toss a treat inside. Tell him, "Sweetie, go to bed!" as you urge the puppy toward the crate. Let the puppy go in, grab the treat and come back out. Repeat this a few times until the puppy seems comfortable with the crate.

G-r-r-r!

Urge your pup into the crate with your voice and treats, *not* with your hands. Remember, the crate should be a positive place.

Now start feeding the puppy in his crate, again with the door wide open. Set the food in the back of the crate. Feed the next couple of meals this way, with the door open. When the puppy is going all the way inside to eat with no signs of stress, close the door behind him.

Do *not* let him out if he throws a fit! You don't want him to learn that barking, crying and screaming will get you to let him out. Instead, let him out when he's finished his meal and is calm.

Put the crate in your bedroom at night so the puppy can hear you, smell you and be close to you all night. This is eight hours of closeness that you couldn't find the time for any other way. With the puppy close to you, you can hear him if he gets restless and needs to go outside. If he doesn't have to go outside and is just restless, you can reach over, tap the top of the crate and tell him, "No! Quiet!"

During the day, put the puppy in his crate for a few minutes here and there, whenever you are too busy to supervise him. Since he has to spend many hours in his crate at night, try to limit his time in it during the day. Twenty minutes here and 30 minutes there are okay, as long as he gets plenty of attention, exercise and time with you in between his times in the crate.

Preventing Problems with a Crate

The kennel crate can help you prevent problems. As I mentioned in Chapter 8, if you can prevent the puppy from learning bad habits, training will be much easier. In addition, the damage caused by the puppy will be much less, and stress will be reduced (yours and the puppy's!).

When you can't supervise the puppy, put him outside in a safe place in the yard or put him in his crate. By ensuring he doesn't get into trouble, you are preventing him from learning problem behavior. For example, he will never learn that it's convenient to eliminate on the kitchen floor or behind the sofa.

There's No Place Like Home!

Once the puppy is comfortable with the crate, it becomes a place of security. You can then bring the crate with you in the car, strapped down with seat belts, so that the dog is secure and safe. You can also take the crate when you travel, and the dog will always have his own bed no matter where you go. And you'll know your dog is safe, protected from danger and out of trouble.

As your dog grows up (in two or more years) you can give him more freedom, but you will find he will still want his crate. The crate is his bed and place of refuge, and although he may choose to sleep elsewhere once in a while, he will always want his crate available.

Ursa was introduced to a crate as a puppy. Today, 13 years later, it is still her bed and her place of refuge.

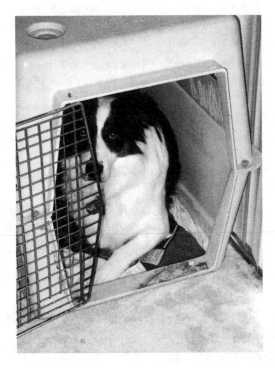

Housetraining (or Housebreaking) Your Puppy

Neither housetraining nor housebreaking seem to be the right words for what we're talking about. We want to teach the puppy to relieve himself outside—not in the house—and to try to go when we tell him to.

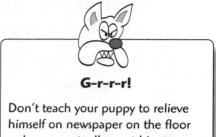

With all the conflicting advice and misinformation about housetraining that bombards new puppy owners, it's amazing that most dogs do eventually become well housetrained. However, housetraining doesn't have to be mysterious or confusing. If you understand your puppy's need to keep his bed clean, and if you limit your puppy's freedom, teach him what you want and where you want it and set a reasonable schedule, your puppy will cooperate.

G-r-r-r!

Don't teach your puppy to relieve himself on newspaper on the floor unless you actually want him to go potty in the house, on newspaper. Instead, start taking him outside right away.

Good Teaching!

Take your puppy outside where you want him to relieve himself. Stand outside but don't interact with him. When the puppy starts to sniff and circle, just watch. After he has started to relieve himself, tell him softly, "Go potty. Good boy to go potty." (You can use whatever vocabulary you wish, as long as you say the same thing every time.) When he has completed his business, praise him even more.

You will need to go out with him to this particular spot every time he needs to relieve himself, for several weeks. Yes, weeks! You cannot simply send the puppy outside. If you do, how will you know he has done what he needs to do? How can you teach him the command if you aren't there? And how can you praise him for doing what needs to be done if you aren't there?

G-r-r-r!

If you walk your puppy, always, *always* pick up after him. It's very easy to carry a plastic bag in your pocket for this. Invert a plastic bag over your hand, scoop up the feces and then fold the bag over it. Dispose of it in the nearest trash can.

Housetraining is one of the most important skills you will ever teach your dog. Many dogs end up at animal control shelters all over the country because they haven't been well housetrained. Take the time now to properly teach your dog. This is too important to take lightly.

Establishing a Schedule

All babies need a schedule, and puppies are no exception. Housetraining is much easier if the puppy eats, sleeps and goes outside on a fairly regular schedule. Variations are allowed, of course, but not too many.

I'm not going to give you a schedule here, although many books do. That's because each puppy is different, and will need a different schedule. Start by keeping in mind that a very young puppy will need to eat two or three times a day, and will need to go outside to relieve himself after each meal. Watch your pup and you will soon learn exactly how long after eating he needs to relieve himself. He will also need to go outside after playing, when waking up from a nap, and about every two hours in between.

Paws for Thought

Some people have trained their toy dogs to use a litter box, like a cat. It can work, but I still recommend taking your dog outside to eliminate, no matter what his size.

You need to set up a schedule that takes all this into account. As your pup becomes familiar with his schedule, he will learn to wait for his regular potty times.

As he gets older and develops more bladder and bowel control, he will be able to wait longer between trips outside, but this is a gradual process. Many puppies can be considered housetrained and reliable by five to six months of age, as long as they are not required to hold it too long. However, it is not unusual for some puppies to need a strict schedule and many trips outside until seven, eight and even nine months of age. Just as children potty train at different ages and rates, so do puppies. It has nothing to do with stubbornness and everything to do with physical control. A puppy will be housetrained when he is ready and able to be.

Many of the tiny breeds seem to have more difficulty with housetraining. Some experts believe the size of the world around them is a problem—when they get outside, everything seems so overwhelming that they just don't feel comfortable. Others believe it's the size of their bladder. In any case, the toy breeds often need more help. Make sure they get outside regularly.

"I Need to Go!"

In the early stages of housetraining, you will be taking the puppy outside on schedule and teaching him the command "Go potty" (more on that in a moment). However, as he learns the command, you can start teaching him to notify you when he needs to go outside.

I start by asking my dogs as we head towards the door, "Do you have to go potty?" I use a high-pitched tone of voice—my happy voice. This usually gets the puppy excited.

Then, as we go outside to the dog's potty place, I tell him in a more normal tone of voice, "Go potty." Of course, I praise him when he does.

As the dog gets more control and can remain inside longer, I check with him, "Do you have to go potty?" If he needs to go, he starts wiggling and dancing. I praise him and take him outside. If he just stares at me and doesn't move, that means he doesn't need to go outside right now, thank you!

Later, my dogs come to me and stare at me when they want my attention. When I turn to look at them, the dogs may bark, nose my hand or get my attention in some other way. (Dax brings me a toy.) I'll then ask if they need to go outside. When the answer is yes, I take the dog outside.

This training technique requires that when my dog comes to me to get my attention, I do pay attention. I cannot ignore the dog and then get angry if there is a puddle on the floor later.

G-r-r-r!

I don't teach my dogs to bark to go outside because as a dog trainer, the most common problem behavior dogs seem to have is barking. I don't want to teach any dog to bark even more.

Be careful with this training. It takes time and maturity for the dog to learn to let you know he has to go out. Don't rely totally on the dog's reactions for many months. Some dogs don't want to go outside and leave the happenings in the house, and will not ask to go outside even when they have to relieve themselves. You still have to remember the dog's schedule and make sure he gets outside when it's time.

Doggy Doors

Doggy doors are devices that allow the dog to go from inside the house to the outside and back again without any assistance from you. They can be bought or built. Doggy doors can be very useful for an adult dog, especially one that is alone for many hours. However, I do not recommend them for puppies.

Right now, in puppyhood, you need to go outside with your puppy so you can teach him exactly where you want him to relieve himself. You need to be outside with him to teach him the command to relieve himself, and so you can praise him when he does. If he goes in and out of a doggy door, you aren't part of the picture at all.

In addition, if he can go in and out freely, how do you know whether he's relieved himself? If you're getting ready to go to bed and want to put him in his crate, do you know whether he's relieved himself? If you go out with him you do know, but if he goes out by himself you have no idea.

A doggy door also gives a puppy entirely too much freedom. He ends up with free access to the house, and to a puppy home alone, that is a bonanza of stuff to get into and chew up.

The only doggy door I would consider for a puppy is one that allows him access from the yard to a section of the garage fenced off from the rest of the garage. That way, if you are at work all day, the puppy can get inside and have shelter from the weather. Don't allow him free run of the garage, either, though. Garages are usually full of dangers. Make sure you fence off a section of the garage that is safe for the puppy, and make sure you make it comfortable for him.

When Accidents Happen

Accidents *will* happen. You might as well know that now. Usually it's because you didn't stick to the housetraining schedule, or weren't watching the puppy closely enough. That makes it your fault—and it's important to remember this.

When an accident does happen, you must handle it very carefully. It is important that the puppy learns urinating and defecating are not wrong, but that the place where he did it was wrong. If the puppy believes relieving himself is wrong, he will become sneaky about it, and you will find puddles in hidden places behind the furniture or in the back bedroom.

If you come upon the puppy as he is having an accident, use a verbal correction: "Acck! What are you doing? No!" Scoop him up and take him outside. Then clean up the mess but do not let him watch you clean it up. (In dog and wolf packs, only subordinate pack members would clean up this way.) If you find an accident after the fact, *do not correct the puppy*—it's too late.

Don't rub the puppy's nose in his mess. This is disgusting, and it teaches him that the urine or feces caused the problem, which is not what you want him to learn. Remember, the act of relieving himself is not wrong; it is the act of relieving himself *in the house* that is wrong. Make sure your message is very clear.

Don't drag him to his mess and shake him or yell at him, either, because he will have absolutely no idea what you are yelling about. Puppies remember what they've done for about five seconds (I'm not exaggerating!), and after that they're on to the next adventure. Scolding a puppy for *anything* after the fact is totally useless. It will hurt the bond you are trying to form with him, and it will not teach him anything.

Paws for Thought

Your puppy may leak a few drops of urine when you greet him or scold him. This is called submissive urination. Keep the greetings low-key and take him outside. If you don't make a big deal out of it, he will grow out of it quickly.

Paws for Thought

If your puppy has been housetraining well and then regresses, there may be a reason. Frequent urination may indicate a bladder infection, while frequent defecation or soft stools could be caused by internal parasites. Tell your veterinarian.

If your puppy is having a few accidents in the house, you need to make sure you are going outside with him so that you can praise him when he relieves himself outside. Make sure he knows when and where is correct. You will also need to pay more attention to the puppy's schedule. Are you getting him outside enough and at the right times?

Successful housetraining is based on setting the puppy up for success by allowing few accidents to happen, and then praising the puppy whenever he does the right thing. That means every single time be goes outside in the correct spot. *Every* time.

Using the "Go Potty" Command

It is important your puppy understand his command to relieve himself. If you take the puppy (or later, the dog) to visit someone, it is very nice to be able to tell the dog to relieve himself before going inside the house. The same thing works when you're traveling. If you stop to get gas, you can take the dog out and tell him to try and relieve himself. Even if his bladder isn't full, he can try.

Begin using a command when you first start housetraining the puppy. Tell him "Go potty," and praise him when he relieves himself: "Good boy to go potty!"

As his housetraining gets better and more reliable, use the commands when you are out on walks, so he learns to go potty in different places. Some puppies learn that they should relieve themselves only in their backyard, and their owners have a difficult time teaching them that it is okay to do it elsewhere. So teach the puppy that when you give him this command, he is to try, even if he can only squeeze out a drop!

Paws for Thought

Male dogs usually have no trouble relieving themselves in different places, since they urinate to mark territory. With some male dogs you will have to curtail the marking, letting him know that you want him to relieve himself entirely in one spot.

Practicing Patience

New puppy owners seem to invite advice. Everyone who has ever owned a dog has a method of housetraining that works better or faster and is more reliable than anyone else's method. Ignore your well-meaning friends. All puppies need time to grow and develop bladder and bowel control. Just establish a schedule that seems to work for you and your puppy, and stick to it. If you keep changing schedules or training techniques, you and your puppy will both be confused and frustrated.

If you follow the right schedule, your puppy will do fine. However, a lack of accidents doesn't mean you can back off on your supervision. Instead, a lack of accidents means your schedule is good! If you back off too soon, your puppy will have some accidents and you'll have to start all over again.

A schedule that works for you and your puppy, along with careful supervision and lots of patience, will pay off. Puppies do grow up, and all your efforts will be rewarded when you find that you have a well-housetrained, reliable dog.

The Least You Need to Know

➤ Teach your puppy to relieve himself outside in a particular spot, and teach him a command to do so.

➤ A crate is a wonderful training tool for housetraining, as well as for helping your puppy develop bowel and bladder control.

➤ Don't rub your puppy's nose in his accidents. Instead, supervise him better.

➤ Be patient. This too shall pass.

Chapter 10

Meeting New People and Seeing New Things

In This Chapter

➤ What is socialization?

➤ Why is it so important for puppies?

➤ What should you do and what shouldn't you do?

➤ Socialization is an ongoing process

Dogs are social creatures. We've already learned that, so what else is there to know about socialization? A lot! Socializing your puppy is one of your most important responsibilities as a puppy owner. The world we live in is busy, chaotic and full of challenges for people and for dogs. The dog that is lucky enough to learn to deal with these challenges as a puppy will be better equipped to handle everything that comes her way. When properly socialized, a puppy learns to deal with the world around her—the sights, sounds and smells of the modern world, as well as all of the different people.

What Is Socialization?

Socialization, simply defined, is the process of introducing the puppy to life among humans. When a puppy meets people of all sizes, shapes, ages and ethnic backgrounds, she will be less apt to shy away from people who are different. For example, many dogs that grow up in a household of only adults are rarely exposed to children. As a result, they often show shyness, fear or aggression toward children. Having never really met children, they seem to view children as creatures from another planet. Although at times we may agree with that assessment, dogs showing poor behavior towards kids are potentially dangerous. It is important, then, that puppies meet people in all their infinite varieties.

Dogs that were isolated from people as puppies, especially during the critical eight- to twelve-week age span, will never be able to form a good, strong attachment to people later. Even when they are born to dogs who were attached to people, these isolated pups will act more like wild animals than domesticated dogs.

Socialization encompasses more than just exposure to people, though. It also includes introducing the puppy to other animals. She needs to learn to tolerate the other animals in your family and your neighborhood, including cats, rabbits, ferrets and any other pets.

Socialization also includes the sights, sounds and smells of the world. A sheet flapping on the clothesline might look like a really frightening thing initially, but if you show the puppy it's nothing serious, she will learn to investigate things that look different. A jackhammer on the street, a motorcycle roaring by and the clang of the garbage truck are all potentially scary sounds, but when introduced properly, the puppy can learn to deal with them.

The more the puppy sees, hears and smells—without getting frightened—the better she will cope when faced with challenges as an adult.

Puppy Tails

Cujo was a female Rottweiler puppy. Her owner had a car lot that he wanted her to guard at night. When, in puppy class, I emphasized socialization, he said he didn't want to do that because Cujo would then like people and not be as aggressive as he wanted her to be. I told him a properly socialized Cujo would instinctively know the difference between customers and intruders, and would still be able to protect his property. But he dropped out of class, and ignored my advice about socialization. Cujo was later euthanized when she severely bit a customer's child. The moral of the story is that socialization is important for all dogs, even working guard dogs.

Why Is Socialization So Important?

In the wolf pack, a pup is raised in her own pack and she learns to identify those wolves. She doesn't have to get along with anyone else in the wider world; the pack is both her family and her support group. However, in our world the puppy must also be able to tolerate other people, including neighbors, meter readers, the paperboy and more.

To make matters even more complicated, in the wolf pack, as the puppy begins to grow up and hunt, she learns her home range and rarely ventures out of that range. However, we routinely go for walks with our puppy, and in doing so, we walk her across other dogs' scent markings—into other dogs' territories. We take our dogs with us camping, traveling and to family get-togethers—all of which are outside of her home range.

Socialization can also affect many breeds' working instincts. During our history together, humans have developed many breeds of dogs to guard our property or livestock against other people or predators. These breeds—which include many of the herding and working breeds—are, by design, more suspicious. Again, in our busy world a dog with these instincts could not cope unless she is well socialized as a puppy.

Because we ask so much of our dogs that is contrary to their ancient behaviors and working instincts, socialization is important. It gives the dog the skills to cope with our world.

At What Age Is Socialization Most Important?

Basic social skills begin as early as the third week of life. At that age the puppy discovers her brothers and sisters and learns to recognize them. They start interacting with one another, chewing and pawing each other. At this age the puppy also learns to recognize her mother as more than simply a source of food.

By the fourth and fifth week of life, the puppy is more aware of the world around her and interacts more and more with her mother and her littermates. The mother dog will start correcting the

G-r-r-r!

You *must* take time to do all of the socialization necessary to prepare your puppy for life with humans. You cannot be too busy right now. If you don't socialize her now, you will never be able to make up for it later!

puppies, and this social behavior teaches the puppy that life has rules that must be followed. She also learns that there are consequences to her actions—an important social lesson!

The breeder should be handling each puppy individually at this age to introduce them to human interaction. By massaging and cuddling the puppies, the breeder can teach them that human touch is safe, comfortable and pleasurable.

During the sixth and seventh weeks, the breeder must be very involved with the puppies, spending as much time as possible with them. The pups can learn a lot about people now, and gentle handling is very important. Play time with people is also good, although the play must be gentle to help build trust in people. There should be no rough, tough, scary play.

After you bring your puppy home, socialization continues to be very important. During weeks eight through twelve, she needs to meet lots of different people and other animals, and see and hear all the new (to her) things in this world. Socialization continues throughout puppyhood, but the period between eight and twelve weeks of age is the most important.

Fear Periods

During the puppy's eighth week of life, she will go through what is called a fear period. At this age, she has become very aware of the world around her, and sometimes that world is very scary. It is important at this age that you try to prevent frightening things from happening, but if they do, do not reinforce your pup's fear. If you do, the puppy will remain afraid and that fear will stay with her.

Breed Bits

Five to seven-week-old Golden Retriever pups love the water and will splash happily in their bowl. However, eight-week-old puppies will approach the water with caution. At nine weeks, these same puppies will again enjoy splashing.

For example, if, on the car ride home, she is frightened by a fire engine's siren, you should be matter-of-fact about it and try to distract her. If you cuddle her and soothe her with "Don't be afraid, baby," she will take that as praise for being afraid, and will think being afraid was the correct response. Since you don't want her to be afraid of sirens and other loud, shrill noises, distract her with a toy or a pat and don't make a fuss.

Puppies show they are in this fear period in many different ways. Some will become cautious about everything, approaching objects (even familiar things) tentatively. Other puppies will be more selective, acting bold about some things and cautious about others.

You can do several different things to handle your puppy's fear. First of all, talk to your puppy. Use either your calmest, most businesslike voice, or you can use a higher pitched, fun tone of voice. Just don't use that soothing, "it's all okay" tone. You can distract your puppy by turning her away from whatever scared her. When you turn her away, offer her a toy or a treat: "Here! What's this? Here's your ball!" Make her think about something else.

If the object of her fear is accessible, you might want to walk up to it, touch it and show her it isn't as scary as she thought. Walk up to the motorcycle and pat it (as if you were petting it) and tell your puppy, "Come see!" If she walks close to it, praise her enthusiastically and tell her how brave she is. If she is really afraid, however, and plants her feet, don't force her to go up to the object of her fear. You can touch it, but let her sit back and look at it. When she's ready, let her go up to it. If you force her, you may just make the fear worse.

Paws for Thought

During fear periods, you will need to plan your outings carefully to avoid fearful situations. Take some treats with you, too, and use them as a distraction when something happens that could be frightening.

The puppy will go through other fear periods as she grows up. Some puppies have a short fear period at about four months of age and others go through one at about 14 months. You might think a dog 14 months old is grown-up, but that's not true. A 14-month-old dog is an adolescent—a teenager—and is still mentally immature. This is usually the last fear period most dogs go through, but it should still be treated the same way you handle fear periods in puppies.

Puppy Tails

A friend's 14-month-old Newfoundland was very obvious about her fear period. She walked out their back door and started barking at the picnic table. That table had been in the same spot since she was a puppy, but apparently she just noticed it, was in a fear period and barked at it. My friend had to walk the dog up to the table and coax her to sniff it before she would stop barking at it.

How to Socialize Your Puppy

Much of your puppy's socialization can be as simple as allowing her to meet new people. Take her outside and introduce her to your neighbors. Let her meet the neighborhood kids, the retirees down the street and the teenagers across the way. Let her meet people of all ages, sizes, shapes and ethnic backgrounds.

This Labrador Retriever puppy is being petted by someone he doesn't know. He is worried right now, but is learning that other people can be friendly and fun.

You can also plan a few outings so that your puppy can go to different places and meet other people with you. Take her to the pet supply store with you. Let her meet the sales clerks and the other customers, and then reward her by letting her pick out a new toy. In the pet supply store, your puppy can also learn how to walk on slippery floors and see things she wouldn't see at home (such as display shelves and stacks of aquariums). She can also learn to walk next to a shopping cart—something that is very different!

Take your puppy to the veterinarian's office even when she doesn't have an appointment. Just walk her in, have the receptionist give her a treat and then leave again. Such a visit makes the veterinarian's office someplace special to go to instead of someplace scary.

Pack up a picnic lunch, go to the local park and have a nice quiet outing. You can sit on your blanket and read while your puppy chews on a toy. She can meet people who walk by and can watch and listen to the kids playing basketball.

Go for a walk by the local elementary school while the kids are at recess. Let the puppy hear all the children laughing, screaming and shouting. Let her watch them run and play. If you stop by after school, let one or two kids (*not* a whole crowd!) pet her very gently and give her a treat.

Go for a walk by the local nursing or retirement home. If some of the residents are outside, introduce your puppy and ask if they would like to pet her.

Ask your neighbor if your puppy can meet their pet rabbit. Hold her carefully and encourage her to gently sniff the rabbit. Don't let her chase the bunny; remember, you want to teach your puppy good manners! If you can, introduce her to other pets, including cats, ferrets, birds and tortoises.

G-r-r-r!

Do not introduce your puppy to every dog in town. Socialize only with healthy, vaccinated, well-behaved dogs that are safe with puppies. Don't be afraid to ask questions to protect your puppy!

If one of your neighbors has a healthy, vaccinated adult dog that is good with puppies, introduce the two. Let them play, if you can.

Enroll your puppy in a puppy kindergarten training class. Not only will this help you train her, but it is wonderful socialization to other puppies and other people.

Sometimes socialization takes planning, but it is very important to your puppy's future. So make the time for it now, when it's most effective!

Puppy Tails

My Australian Shepherd Dax came from a working dog breeder who lives in a very rural area. I brought Dax home at seven weeks of age and started her socialization then. At three years old, she is a well-adjusted, calm, socialized dog that is trustworthy in any situation, with all people and other pets. Her litter brother, who grew up on the ranch and rarely leaves it, is fearful, shy and uncomfortable when he's off the ranch.

What Should Your Puppy See, Smell and Hear?

Introduce your puppy to as much as you can. Not all at once, of course, but throughout puppyhood. Let her become familiar, comfortable and confident about the world around her.

While protecting her from harm (without reinforcing her fear), let her see, hear, smell or experience:

➤ The vacuum cleaner

➤ The dishwasher, garbage disposal and trash compactor

➤ A plastic garbage bag being shook open

➤ A plastic bag being popped

➤ A crumpled paper bag

➤ A broom and mop being used

➤ A metal cookie sheet being dropped to the floor

➤ A car engine being revved

➤ The trash truck out front

➤ A motorcycle zooming down the street

➤ The lawn mower

➤ A weed whacker and leaf blower

➤ Cats

➤ Rabbits

➤ Ferrets

➤ Turtles and tortoises

➤ Horses, goats, cows and sheep

➤ Children's toys, including some that make noise

➤ Balloons

➤ Balls of various sizes, shapes and colors

➤ Walking up and down stairs

➤ Walking over a wooden footbridge

➤ Walking over a metal manhole cover

➤ Taking an elevator

➤ Walking on carpet, artificial turf, slippery floors and rubber matting

What else is a part of your life that will be part of your puppy's life? What else does she need to be comfortable with? Think about it, and expose your puppy to as much as possible while she's still young.

What NOT to Do

Don't try to introduce your puppy to everything all at once. Overwhelming her is just as bad as not socializing her at all. This should be a process that takes place gradually over the first few months of her life.

Paws for Thought

The puppy's adult personality is shaped by several things: her breed and genetic heritage, her mother's care, the socialization and training she receives, and you.

In her first week at home, especially if she comes home during the eighth week of life (during that first fear period), introduce her to things around the house. You can make sure she isn't frightened, or if she is, that you don't reinforce those fears. Keep things upbeat, happy and matter-of-fact.

During her second week at home, take her outside a little more, introduce her to a few things around the neighborhood and let her meet some new people. There are some things you must control, however, to protect your puppy:

G-r-r-r!

When your puppy meets new people, you *must* control the situation. Never let people get rough for any reason, even in play. If you think something is wrong, stop it. If you have to, pick up your pup and walk away.

➤ Don't let people—kids or adults—run around the puppy. This could be frightening or overstimulating.

➤ Don't let kids scream and yell while playing with the puppy. Again, this is overstimulating or scary.

➤ Don't let people grab your puppy and hug her.

➤ Don't let kids throw themselves on the puppy or grab at her.

➤ Don't allow people to blow in her face or stare at her.

Remember, the whole idea is to make these outings fun and to build social skills, not to scare the puppy.

Each week, you can do more and introduce her to different things. Just take it slow, and if the puppy seems overwhelmed, stop and relax for a little while.

For example, when she meets new people, let her meet two or three people at a time, no more. If five or six kids swoop down on her, make several stand back and wait. They can pet her when the first group is through.

*Your puppy should meet
all kinds of friendly people,
but it's your job to keep
the experience positive and
protect her from harm.*

When Your Veterinarian Says,
"Keep Her at Home!"

Your veterinarian will probably tell you to keep your puppy at home until she has
received all her vaccinations. Until then, she may be at risk of picking up a contagious
disease from unvaccinated, unhealthy dogs. However, I have just finished telling you
to take your puppy out into the world, to introduce her to people and other animals
and worse yet, to enroll her in a kindergarten puppy class. Obviously, there is a con-
flict here!

Your veterinarian is concerned about your puppy's health. As a dog trainer, I am
concerned about the serious consequences of a lack of socialization. Thousands of dogs
are given up by their owners every year because of behavior problems. Not all of those
are the result of a lack of socialization, but a great many of them are. You can socialize
your dog and keep her safe, too.

First of all, don't take her anywhere there are other dogs, especially dogs that may be
unvaccinated, until your puppy has had at least two full sets of shots. These vaccines

120

should include distemper, hepatitis, leptospirosis, parvovirus and parainfluenza. After their second set of shots, most puppies have good immunity. Most kindergarten puppy classes will not allow puppies to attend until they have had these two sets of shots.

When you take your puppy out in public, ask questions of dog owners *before* you let the dogs sniff each other: "When were your dog's last shots?" If they get upset, too bad! It's your puppy's health, and you have every right to protect her.

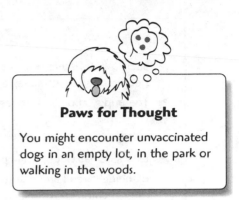

Paws for Thought

You might encounter unvaccinated dogs in an empty lot, in the park or walking in the woods.

Most of the dangers to your puppy's health come from unvaccinated dogs and their wastes. Keep her away from unknown dogs and don't let your puppy sniff other dogs' feces and urine. Keep her away, and pull her away quickly if she tries to sniff.

You can keep your puppy safe by being aware and careful, yet still get her the socialization she needs for good mental health.

Socialization Is an Ongoing Process

Although the most important socialization period is during early puppyhood, socialization is an ongoing process until the puppy's second birthday. Most dogs are not mentally grown up until they are at least two years old, and socialization is a big part of that mental maturity.

I am always exposing my dogs—even my adult dogs—to different things. On any given weekend, we may play at the playground, go to a different park, meet a parade horse or watch a marching band. My dogs have swum in the ocean, sniffed noses with a Budweiser Clydesdale, visited with Alzheimer's patients and ridden on a San Francisco cable car. And they take it all in stride, because we continue to do different things all the time.

My grandmother always said that parents should raise their children to take the path they want them to take. Basically, it's the same with puppies. Raise your puppy to take your path with you. If you like to do different things and go different places, introduce the puppy to those things now, and when she's grown up, she'll be right there by your side.

The Least You Need to Know

➤ Socialization is the process of introducing your puppy to the world around her, including people of all sizes, shapes, ages and ethnic backgrounds.

➤ The puppy also needs to see, hear and smell different things.

➤ Socialization is an ongoing process, but is especially important between eight and twelve weeks of age.

➤ During socialization, it's important to protect your puppy without reinforcing her fears.

➤ By being careful and controlling all interactions, you can socialize your puppy before she has completely finished her immunizations.

Part 3
Your Puppy's Health

A healthy puppy is a happy puppy. You will be much happier if your puppy is healthy, too, because there's nothing sadder than a puppy that doesn't feel good. We'll start this section by talking about your puppy's first visit to the veterinarian. What will the vet be looking for when he examines your puppy? What vaccinations should your puppy receive? What should you do if there is something wrong? What else should you know?

We will also talk about how to maintain your puppy's health. We'll look at puppy food, exercise, grooming, fleas, ticks, internal parasites and everything else you need to know about in order to keep your puppy healthy. We'll also talk about first aid, what to do in an emergency and who to call.

Chapter 11

The First Visit to the Veterinarian

In This Chapter

➤ The veterinarian is your partner in your puppy's good health

➤ Bring the puppy in within 24 hours

➤ What vaccinations should your puppy receive?

➤ Make the vet's office fun for your puppy

I know you read Chapter 6 and have already researched local veterinarians before bringing home your puppy. As I mentioned there, if you have already picked out a veterinarian, you won't need to go through the Yellow Pages in a panic once you have the puppy.

The veterinarian you choose is vital to your puppy's good health. When you choose this professional, make sure you are comfortable with the vet's professional skills, bedside (or tableside) manner, emergency procedures, location, payment policies and staff.

The First Exam Should Be on the First Day

Ideally, the veterinarian should see your puppy within the first 24 hours after you bring him home. Why do you need to rush the puppy in so quickly? Well, there are several very important reasons.

If you have bought this puppy from a breeder, you need to make sure the puppy is healthy. There is a possibility the veterinarian could discover congenital defects you

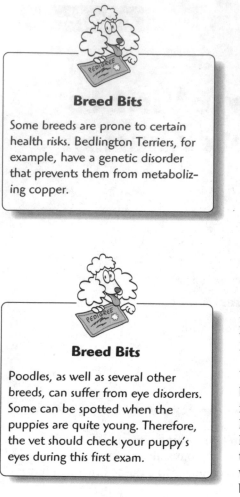

Breed Bits

Some breeds are prone to certain health risks. Bedlington Terriers, for example, have a genetic disorder that prevents them from metabolizing copper.

Breed Bits

Poodles, as well as several other breeds, can suffer from eye disorders. Some can be spotted when the puppies are quite young. Therefore, the vet should check your puppy's eyes during this first exam.

might not be able to see. If the puppy has untreatable or potentially expensive health problems, or is generally unhealthy, you have the right (if you so desire) to return the puppy to the breeder. If the puppy has a problem and you decide to keep him anyway, the breeder should be willing to give you a full or partial refund.

If you adopted the puppy from a shelter or breed rescue group, you should still have the vet see him right away. If you discover potential health concerns that you might not be able or willing to deal with, you can return the puppy before you become so emotionally attached that you cannot return him. If you decide to keep the puppy, knowing about the health concern early may help you deal with it—depending upon the problem, of course.

You will also want to have the vet see the puppy right away if you have another dog at home. Your new puppy can be started on a vaccination schedule and you can make sure the puppy is healthy and not a threat (in terms of disease) to the dog at home.

You can actually call and make your first appointment before bringing home the new puppy. Many veterinarians' offices book several days in advance. So if you have made arrangements to bring the puppy home on Friday evening, call on the Monday or Tuesday before to make an appointment for Saturday morning. This way, you won't have to scramble to find a time to bring the puppy in, and you can be assured the vet will be able to see your puppy right away.

When you call to make the appointment, make sure you tell the receptionist this is your new puppy's first visit. She will ask you some information about the puppy (to start the health record), and she will tell you to bring in some of the puppy's stool. The stool will be checked for signs of internal parasites. Bring in a small piece (half a teaspoon is enough) of that morning's stool. The fresher the stool, the better, because as the stool ages and dries out, signs of parasites are harder to see. To collect a sample, invert a plastic sandwich bag over your hand, pick up the stool and then pull the plastic bag off your hand, over the stool and seal it. Don't forget to bring the sample with you!

The First Exam

The first exam will be quite thorough. The vet will weigh your puppy, so that his growth can be followed on subsequent visits and to determine correct dosages for any medications required. He will look at your puppy's mouth to make sure the puppy teeth look healthy and straight, and to see if the gums are pink and the throat looks healthy. He will check the ears to make sure there is no infection and no mites. The eyes should be clear and bright with no matter or discharge. He will feel the glands in the neck to make sure there is no swelling.

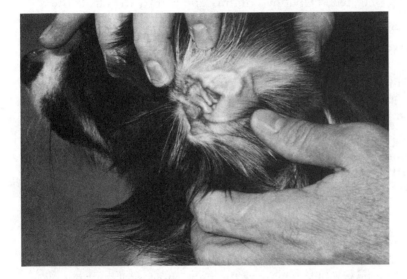

The veterinarian will check your puppy's ears, and may even smell them.

The eyes should be clean, bright and free of matter.

Paws for Thought

Don't be surprised if the veterinarian sniffs in the ears or smells the puppy's breath. A healthy puppy's breath should smell like milk, and ears with a problem will smell musty.

He will continue by feeling down the neck to the shoulders and front legs. He wants to feel the puppy's body and will pay attention to any lumps, bumps or anything out of the ordinary. He will check the puppy's feet, looking at and between the pads. He may even show you how to trim the puppy's toenails.

The vet will continue the exam by feeling the dog's rib cage, down the back and the hips. He may look at the tail to make sure it hasn't been broken or hurt. He will feel the puppy's tummy and will try to palpate the abdomen to see if he feels anything unusual or if there is any tenderness. The vet will make sure male puppies have two descended testicles, and that there is no discharge or infection in female puppies. He will also look at the puppy's skin to see that it looks healthy, and check whether or not the puppy has any fleas or ticks. He will check out the puppy's coat, again, to make sure it is clean and healthy.

He will listen to the puppy's heart and lungs to make sure nothing is wrong. The vet will use a rectal thermometer to take the puppy's temperature. A dog's normal temperature is between 101° and 102°. Many puppies are stressed by the thermometer, but if you help hold your puppy and scratch his ears while his temperature is being taken, you can distract him enough so that he doesn't get too upset.

The veterinarian will want to know as much as possible about your puppy's previous care. The breeder may have dewormed the puppy before you took him, or she may have given the puppy his first vaccination. Make sure you give the vet as much information as you can, so that he can help you make the right choices for your puppy's care.

By the time the vet finishes this first exam, the stool sample will have been processed and he will be able to tell you whether or not the puppy has any internal parasites. These can be treated with either a tablet or an injection, depending upon the parasite in question, the vet's professional opinion and the health of the puppy.

This is the point where you should ask questions. If you have any concerns about your puppy's health, ask them now.

Vaccinations

The puppy's immune system protects him from disease. When he was born, the immunities he received from his mother helped protect him. But by the time he is about 12 weeks old, his own immune system must develop the ability to protect him. The immune system does this by producing antibodies, which are substances that protect the body from invaders. Each invader must be dealt with by an antibody developed specifically to deal with it, so puppies (and people) develop antibodies to every bacteria or virus they encounter. If the body can produce these antibodies fast enough, the body will be protected and the puppy won't get sick.

Vaccinations work by giving the puppy a dose of a disease that has been treated so the puppy can develop the right antibodies without the threat of getting sick. Most vaccinations stimulate the body to produce enough antibodies to protect the body for a specific length of time—usually about 12 months. Booster shots are then given each year for these particular diseases.

Puppy Tails

Vaccines are either modified live (the virus is altered to decrease its virulence but is still a live virus) or killed (the virus is dead, but it still stimulates the body to produce antibodies). Modified live virus is more effective at stimulating the body to produce antibodies, but it can also cause the disease. Killed is considered much safer by most experts.

The most common vaccinations given to puppies include the following:

➤ **Distemper:** Canine distemper is a virus that is similar to the human measles virus. It can affect many of the dog's organs, including the skin, eyes, intestinal and respiratory tracts. The virus can be transmitted through any of the dog's excretions or through the air. The first symptoms are usually nasal and eye discharge. This is a deadly disease, and before vaccinations, entire kennels of dogs would die very rapidly from distemper.

➤ **Hepatitis:** Canine hepatitis is a virus found worldwide. It is spread through nasal discharge or through urine, usually by direct contact. This virus starts with a sore throat; the dog will not want to swallow, drink or eat. But it rapidly progresses to other organs. Hepatitis develops so quickly that dogs can die within two hours of showing the first symptoms.

➤ **Leptospirosis:** This is a bacteria, not a virus, that affects the kidneys. It is passed from the kidneys in the urine, and is transmitted to other dogs when they sniff contaminated urine. Urine-infected water sources can also spread the disease— not just to other dogs but to other animals, including people. Symptoms include a fever, poor appetite, dehydration and vomiting. This bacteria can cause death.

➤ **Coronavirus:** The first symptom of this virus is diarrhea, from mild to extreme, and in severe cases blood may be found in the stool. Puppies are at risk of severe dehydration.

➤ **Parvovirus:** This virus has killed thousands of dogs, and since the virus continues to mutate and change, it is still a deadly threat. This virus is the most deadly, dangerous and fatal disease known to dogs. Vomiting, diarrhea, dehydration and death are all common, especially in puppies and young dogs.

➤ **Adenovirus:** Often mistakenly called kennel cough, this virus is only one of several that can cause coughing. Adenovirus (often referred to as CAV-2) is transmitted through the air by a dog coughing out droplets of the virus. Adenovirus is rarely fatal to healthy adult dogs, but can be dangerous to puppies, dogs with a weakened immune system or old dogs.

➤ **Parainfluenza:** This is one of the viruses that is also called canine cough or kennel cough. It is easily spread through the air by coughing—the first and primary symptom. It may turn into pneumonia, but generally is simply a cough that is gone within a week or two.

➤ **Bordetella Bronchiseptica:** Bordetella is a bacteria that causes coughing and other canine respiratory problems. It is contagious and is spread by contact and through the air by coughing. It can spread rapidly throughout a kennel or household, but is rarely dangerous to healthy dogs, although puppies can be quite sick.

➤ **Lyme Disease:** This is caused by a bacteria spread by infected ticks, flies and fleas. Lyme disease was originally identified in Connecticut, but is now found in all 48 contiguous states. A fever is usually one of the first symptoms, followed by muscle soreness, weakness and joint pain. Severe and permanent joint damage can follow. Neurological damage is also possible.

➤ **Rabies:** This virus is always fatal once the disease is contracted. It is transmitted through contact with an infected animal, usually a bat, skunk, squirrel or fox. The first symptoms are neurological, including staggering, drooling, seizures or changes in behavior.

Most veterinarians recommend a schedule of vaccinations for puppies. Their recommendations will be based on their clinical experience, and on what diseases are prevalent in your part of the country. All recommend vaccines for distemper, leptospirosis, parvo and hepatitis. Some vets suggest corona and bordetella. Several years ago, only a few vets recommended puppies get the Lyme disease vaccine, but now almost all veterinarians recommend it.

It's a good idea to talk to your vet, find out which vaccines he recommends, why and at what age. If you would like your puppy to get a vaccine your vet doesn't recommend (for whatever reason), talk to him about it. Find out why he doesn't recommend it. Perhaps the disease is not found in your area. Or maybe he has another reason. In any event, it's your puppy and your puppy's health, so don't be afraid to ask questions.

Paws for Thought

In most parts of the country, the rabies vaccine *is* the only vaccination required by law.

A Puppy Vaccination Schedule

Just as most veterinarians have their own recommendations concerning vaccines, they also set up their own vaccination schedules for puppies. A sample schedule might look like the one in the box. But remember, your veterinarian may have a similar schedule or may have a totally different one, especially if he recommends a different combination of vaccines.

Sample Vaccination Schedule

8 weeks: distemper, hepatitis, leptospirosis, parainfluenza, parvo (often given as a combination shot called DHLPP) and Lyme disease

10 to 11 weeks: distemper, hepatitis, leptospirosis, parainfluenza, parvo and bordetella

13 to 15 weeks: distemper, hepatitis, leptospirosis, parainfluenza, parvo and Lyme disease

16 to 18 weeks: rabies and bordetella

All boosters are given one year after the previous vaccinations.

Potential Problems With Vaccines

Even though modern vaccinations have saved thousands of dogs' lives, there are still potential problems with vaccines. Some dogs develop a sterile abscess at the site of the injection. This is a hard lump under the skin. It will go away on its own.

A worse problem is the allergic reaction that some dogs have to vaccines. Reactions can be as mild as a lack of energy for a day or two, or as severe as anaphylactic shock. Some dogs will show other symptoms that may take a week or two to develop, and these reactions may be as mild as lethargy or lameness or as severe as seizures or thyroid dysfunction.

Paws for Thought

Many veterinarians and dog owners are concerned that too many vaccines may overwhelm the puppy's immune system. Because of this, a different vaccination schedule may be set up, giving the vaccines over a longer period of time.

Because of the concern about reactions, you should remain at the veterinarian's office for at least half an hour after the puppy receives a vaccination. Severe reactions that are life-threatening, such as anaphylactic shock, will occur relatively quickly, and if you're still in the office, treatment can be started immediately.

Some experts are also concerned about the numbers of vaccines being given. Modern medicine has given us vaccines to prevent many diseases that used to kill vast numbers of dogs, but in return, larger numbers of dogs are suffering from immune system disorders and many more dogs seem to be dying of cancer at younger ages. These problems have not yet been directly linked to vaccinations, but enough people are concerned that questions are being asked.

Some experts are now suggesting that vaccinations be given over a longer period of time and that fewer combination vaccines be given. For example, instead of giving a DHLPP (distemper, hepatitis, leptospirosis, parainfluenza and parvo) combination, the vaccine can be broken down and given as a DHL one week, parainfluenza can be given two weeks later, and two weeks after that parvo can be given.

Unfortunately, this, too, can cause problems. The vaccines are normally given during the period of time when the immunity the puppy received from his mother is wearing off and his immune system is developing its own antibodies. The puppy is in danger of catching diseases during this time, and the vaccinations can help protect him. If the vaccines are spread out over too long a period, he can get sick. And many of these diseases, especially parvo, are common and are often fatal.

G-r-r-r!

Just because there are potential problems from vaccinations doesn't mean you should decide not to vaccinate your puppy. Before these vaccines were available, thousands upon thousands of dogs died from diseases that are now preventable.

So on one hand you have potential dangers from the diseases themselves, and on the other hand you have the potential dangers from the vaccines. What can you do? First of all, talk to your veterinarian. Express your concern. What vaccines does he use? Are they modified live or killed vaccines? What brand does he use and how is their safety record? Is he seeing any vaccination-related problems? Is he seeing any of the common diseases in his practice, especially parvo? What does he recommend you do?

Only vaccinate your puppy once he has received a clean bill of health from your veterinarian. If he has a health problem of any kind, do not vaccinate him until it clears up. There is more of a risk of a vaccination reaction when a pup isn't healthy, because the puppy's immune system will not tolerate the shot as well. In addition, the puppy's body will not produce antibodies as well as it could if the puppy were healthy.

Then, when you do vaccinate your dog, no matter what the schedule, watch him closely. Report any reactions—any at all, even sleepiness—to your vet and asked that they be recorded in your puppy's health record. A minor reaction now may give clues to related health problems later.

Make Each Vet Visit Fun

Because the veterinarian is your partner in your puppy's good health, you will want your puppy to enjoy his visits there. If he is stressed and afraid, examinations and treatments will be much more difficult. In addition, when your puppy is stressed, his body goes into overdrive with heart rate, blood pressure, respiration and everything else increasing dramatically. It is much harder for your veterinarian to see what is normal and what is a problem when your puppy isn't relaxed.

Keep the visits fun by having staff members offer your puppy a treat when he comes in. They can also pet him, rub his tummy and talk to him in a happy tone of voice.

When he is afraid, don't reinforce those fears. If you coddle him, talk to him softly and say, "It's okay honey, don't be afraid," he will assume your soft talk is telling him he was right to be afraid. Instead, distract him from his fears. Offer a treat or rub his tummy. Bring one of his toys to the vet's office and play with that. If he's afraid of something specific, like standing on a scale, make it fun. Stand on it yourself and let him watch you. Then encourage him to walk on it.

Try to stop by the vet's office a few times when your pup doesn't need any care at all. Walk him in, ask the staff to make a fuss over him, offer him a treat and then leave again before anything scary happens. Your puppy will remember those positive visits, too, and they will help overcome any less happy visits.

Paws for Thought

A vitamin B complex supplement started a few days before each vaccination and continued for a few days after will help the puppy's body cope. Give the puppy one quarter to one half (depending upon his size) of an adult human dosage, twice a day.

Paws for Thought

When your puppy is getting his temperature taken, his ears examined or is getting a shot, you can help distract him. Hold him as close as you can, talk to him in a happy tone of voice, and with one finger, rub his head between his eyes. Most puppies will concentrate on this and forget what else is happening.

The Least You Need to Know

➤ Your veterinarian is your partner in your puppy's health care.

➤ Bring your puppy in to see the vet within his first 24 hours at home.

➤ The first exam will be very thorough, so your vet can get to know your puppy and establish exactly how healthy he is.

➤ Vaccinations can be life-savers for your puppy, but they do not come without some risks.

➤ Make each visit to the vet's office fun, so your puppy will like going there and will not be quite as stressed.

Chapter 12

Maintaining Your Puppy's Health

> ### In This Chapter
>
> ➤ The importance of exercise and the fun of playtime
> ➤ Plain talk about spaying and neutering
> ➤ Working with your veterinarian
> ➤ How to give medication to a puppy
> ➤ Preventing accidents

Maintaining your puppy's good health is an on-going project. Good nutrition is a part of it, and I'll talk about that in Chapter 14. But so are exercise and play time. Spaying and neutering are also important for several reasons, including your puppy's long-term health.

As I mentioned in Chapter 11, your veterinarian is your partner in your puppy's good health. This begins with your puppy's first visit to the vet's office and will continue throughout your dog's life. I'll give you some ideas here about how to work with your vet to maintain your puppy's health.

And finally, puppy proofing your house and yard before bringing the pup home eliminated many dangers, but accidents can and do happen. Your goal is to prevent as many accidents from happening as possible, and we'll talk about how you can do that.

Exercise and Playtime

A healthy young puppy will need several exercise periods every day. She will need time to use up energy, burn calories and strengthen her bones and muscles. This exercise will also help her learn to control her body and become more coordinated.

Playtime with an older, well-behaved, healthy dog will teach this puppy how to be a dog.

Exercise for a young puppy must be carefully tailored to the puppy's age, physical abilities and breed. A 10-week old Papillon puppy is very tiny and fragile because of her build, but is more coordinated than the much larger but more rapidly growing St. Bernard puppy. The Papillon puppy will be able to move faster, balance herself better and twist and turn better than the larger puppy. The St. Bernard, because of her greater weight, height and bulk, and because she is growing so rapidly that her body changes daily, will not be nearly as coordinated.

When exercising your puppy, make sure she can perform the exercise without getting sore or overly tired. A nap after exercise is normal, but an exhausted extended sleep is not. For example, if you and the puppy go for a neighborhood walk and the puppy quits in mid-walk and refuses to get back up, you've gone too far. The chart on the next page contains some ideas for activities you can do with your puppy at different ages.

Exercise Ideas for Puppies of Different Ages

8 to 12 Weeks Old	A walk around the neighborhood A walk around the local park, harbor, shopping center or school A short, easy hike in the local woods or meadow Throw the tennis ball (short throws)
12 to 18 Weeks Old	Slightly longer walks Very short jogs on a soft surface such as grass Climbing sessions on playground equipment (carefully assisted and supervised, of course!) Slightly longer hikes in the woods or other wildlands
Older Puppies	For the more athletic breeds, introduce them to your bicycle and *very gradually* and *very slowly* start teaching them to run alongside the bike Very gradually increase the distance and speed of walks Very gradually increase the distance and speed of jogs

Exercise is vital for a healthy body and a healthy mind, but must be tailored to the age of the puppy. Hard exercise, such as running with a bike, is for older puppies only.

G-r-r-r!

Don't wrestle with your puppy. Wrestling teaches her to fight you and to use her strength against you. This is always a bad idea.

G-r-r-r!

Don't play tug of war with your puppy. This teaches her to use her jaws and her strength against you. Play games that require her cooperation instead.

Playtime Should Be Fun

Playtime can be a part of exercise, especially if you play retrieving games with your puppy, but playtime can also be separate from exercise. Playtime is fun, and this fun you and your puppy have together helps create the bond between you. Here are some play ideas for young puppies:

➤ Lie on the floor and roll the puppy over. Rub her tummy and roll her back and forth. Let her squirm and flail her legs.

➤ Play short, quick retrieving games with different toys.

➤ Play easy, short hide-and-seek games.

And for slightly older puppies:

➤ Make the retrieving games a little longer.

➤ Make the hide-and-seek games slightly more difficult, but still easily accomplishable.

➤ Teach the puppy some fun tricks, like shake, roll over, speak or dance (see Chapter 21).

➤ Teach the puppy the names of her toys, such as ball, bone or squeaker.

Let's Talk About Spaying and Neutering

Most dogs should be spayed (females) or neutered (males). The only dogs that should be bred are those that are the best representatives of their breed in physical conformation, temperament, genetic health and working characteristics. A goal such as this one could help make sure that future puppies are healthier, with fewer genetic defects, and with good sound temperaments.

Unfortunately, this hasn't been the case for much of our history, and the end result has been hundreds of thousands of dogs born only to be destroyed. Some are "put to sleep" because there aren't enough homes available for all of them, while others are euthanized because of health or temperament problems.

Each and every dog that is given up as unwanted, or becomes a stray, or is involved in a dog bite situation, ends up costing taxpayers money. Because of this, many cities and counties across the United States are now trying to regulate dog breeding. Many have instituted fines or costly licenses to try to discourage dog breeding.

These measures may inconvenience the reputable, responsible breeder, but unfortunately, they won't do anything to control indiscriminate, accidental breedings. However, a spayed or neutered dog cannot reproduce, even accidentally!

Traditionally, dogs have been spayed or neutered at about six months of age. However, in an effort to discourage breeding, many humane societies have been spaying and neutering very young puppies—some as young as eight weeks of age. Surgery at this age has so far been shown to have no ill effects on the puppy's health, and early spay/neuter programs have been very successful.

Spaying a female dog consists of a surgical ovariohysterectomy. The ovaries and uterus are removed through an incision in the abdomen. Your veterinarian will tell you to keep her quiet for a few days, but most dogs don't show any signs of discomfort and recuperate very quickly. Her stitches will come out in about 10 days.

A male dog is neutered, or castrated. This consists of removing the testicles through an incision just in front of the scrotum. Again, your vet will tell you to keep the puppy quiet for a few days, but that could be difficult because the puppy won't appear to be uncomfortable at all.

While stopping unwanted reproduction is a powerful reason to spay or neuter your dog, there are many other health benefits, as well.

For females:

➤ Decreases incidence of breast or mammary gland cancers.

➤ Protects her against cancers of the reproductive system.

➤ Decreases the incidence of female aggression.

For males:

➤ Decreases male sexual behaviors, including leg-lifting, marking, roaming and fighting.

Paws for Thought

Spaying and neutering your pet does cost money, although it is usually very reasonable and discount programs are available all over the country. But you will get that cost back in reduced dog license fees once your pet is spayed or neutered.

Paws for Thought

A female that has been spayed will no longer go through her "heat season," ending that twice-a-year hassle. She will no longer spot on your floors and carpets, and male dogs will no longer come calling!

Paws for Thought

Have you heard that a spayed or neutered dog will get fat? It's a myth. Too much food and not enough exercise make dogs fat!

➤ Decreases the desire to escape from the yard.

➤ Decreases the incidence of fights.

➤ Protects him from testicular cancer.

If you think your spayed or neutered dog will miss having sex, think again. Dogs don't make love as part of a complex relationship, they copulate as a response to biological urges. Remove the biological urges, and they'll never think about sex again. It's really that simple.

Paws for Thought

Some breeds or types of dogs, especially the working and guard breeds, are more prone to develop male aggressive behavior. Neutering will decrease the tendency towards problem aggressive behavior without affecting the dog's working ability.

Working with Your Veterinarian

In the previous chapter, I described what your puppy's first visit to the veterinarian should be like, but your relationship with the vet should definitely not stop there. You need to continue to work with your veterinarian to keep your pet healthy.

When your vet sets up your puppy's vaccination schedule, make sure you follow it. Your vet has scheduled those vaccinations with a certain number of weeks in between each shot so that your puppy's body can handle the vaccine and build up antibodies. If you have a question about the schedule, please ask him. I'm sure he will be willing to answer your questions and explain the schedule.

Puppy Tails

Some puppy owners seem to begrudge the money spent at the veterinarian's office. They think that every time the veterinarian suggests a regular check-up or an office visit, he's just out to get their money. Certainly the vet needs to earn a living, just as you and I do. However, your vet is also dedicated to maintaining your puppy's good health. Let him help you do it!

Your vet will also want to see your puppy on a regular basis. Throughout the first few months, he will see the puppy as she comes in for each vaccination. If your puppy is healthy, he may then not need to see her again until she is due for booster vaccines a year later. Or he may see your puppy when she comes in to be spayed. If your puppy was treated for internal parasites at the first visit, he will want to check the puppy's stool again later to make sure the treatment was effective.

Recognizing Problems

Many healthy puppies grow up to be healthy adults that see the veterinarian once a year for booster vaccines. For a dog that never shows signs of any health problems, that's fine. However, you may need to bring your puppy in if she develops a problem of some kind. Recognizing those problems is important, because catching something early may save you, your puppy and your veterinarian considerable grief.

Call your veterinarian if you notice any of these problems:

➤ Vomiting that doesn't stop after a couple of hours.

➤ Diarrhea that continues more than one day, or that contains a lot of mucus or any blood.

➤ A temperature lower that 101° or above 102.5°.

➤ Fainting, collapse or a seizure.

➤ Severe coughing, trouble breathing or a suspected obstruction.

➤ The puppy refuses to eat and misses more than two meals.

➤ A leg that is obviously hurt, with no weight put on it, and is still held up after you massage it gently.

➤ A distended abdomen and obvious tenderness.

➤ Any eye injury.

➤ Potential allergic reactions, including swelling, hives or rashes, especially around the face.

➤ Potential poisoning, especially antifreeze, rodent poisons, snail poisons, insecticides or herbicides.

➤ Cuts or wounds that are bleeding and gape open, or do not stop bleeding with direct pressure.

➤ Suspected snake bites of any kind.

Some things might not be quite as noticeable, but could still signal trouble. Call your vet if you see any of these signs:

➤ The puppy is hiding and doesn't want to come out.

➤ Panting other than after exercise or play time.

➤ Heavy breathing for no apparent reason.

➤ No energy.

➤ Restlessness for no apparent reason.

What Your Vet Will Want to Know

When you call your veterinarian, the receptionist will ask you several questions. It is her job to get as much information as possible and pass it on to the vet. Please, don't give her a hard time, argue with her or insist on talking to the vet. Answer her questions with as much detail as you can. She will then talk to the vet and have some answers or advice for you, or the vet will get on the line to talk to you.

Some questions you will be expected to answer include:

➤ What is the specific problem?

➤ What made you notice it? What are the symptoms?

➤ What is the puppy's temperature?

➤ Has the puppy eaten? When? What? How much?

➤ Is there any vomiting? Diarrhea? What does it look like?

➤ Has the puppy been anywhere or done anything that might have caused this problem or affected her in some way?

➤ How long has this problem been going on?

Give your veterinarian more information rather than less. Let him wade through the information and decide what is relevant and what isn't—that's where his expertise comes into play. Your job is to supply him with enough information so that he can help you and your puppy.

Giving Medicine to a Puppy

Imagine trying to get your squirmy little puppy to swallow a pill! Giving your puppy medication isn't always easy, but there are some tricks to make it easier. If at all possible, keep this experience as stress-free as possible. If your puppy learns to hate medication and treatments now, as a puppy, she will retain that hatred throughout her life—and that could be very difficult.

Pills, tablets and capsules are actually the easier medications to administer. Simply hide the medicine in a bit of food and let your puppy eat it. Some good foods for hiding pills include bits of hot dog, peanut butter, sliced cheese and commercial dog treats.

Puppy Tails

To get my dogs to take their pills, I make a peanut butter sandwich. One slice of bread is spread with peanut butter. It is folded in half, sandwiching the pill inside. I then tear it into three pieces and offer the first two pieces without the pill. The dog is then anticipating the treat and is no longer suspicious about a pill. I then offer the last piece with the pill. One swallow and it's gone!

Liquid medication can be more difficult to give, and much messier. Ask your vet for a few large syringes without needles. The medication can be measured into the syringe. Then place the tip of the syringe in the side of the puppy's mouth, between the back teeth. Squirt the medication in a little at a time, giving the puppy time to swallow.

Eye medication takes a sure, swift, gentle touch. If you fool around, your puppy will get nervous. Try this trick. Take a spoonful of peanut butter and scrape it off on the roof of the puppy's mouth behind the front teeth. As your puppy licks this and tries to swallow it, gently hold her head and apply the medication.

The peanut butter trick works well for ear medications, too. While the puppy is working on the peanut butter, gently wipe out her ear with a cotton ball and apply the medication according to the vet's instructions.

If your puppy has a cut or incision that must be washed, treated or medicated, you can use the peanut butter trick here, too. Just be very gentle, sure and quick (not tentative) as you wash and medicate the cut.

G-r-r-r!

When giving liquid medication, don't try to force the puppy's mouth open. The medication will end up all over you and the puppy.

G-r-r-r!

Follow directions for all medications. If it is to be given three times a day for ten days, then give it three times a day for ten days. Anything more or less could endanger your puppy's health.

Taking Reasonable Care

You puppy-proofed your house and yard before bringing home your puppy, didn't you? Then there shouldn't be too many dangers there for your puppy. However, puppies can be inventive, tenacious and downright surprising sometimes, especially for first-time puppy owners. Puppies can get up on counters, work benches in the garage and shelves where they really shouldn't be able to climb. But they do! Puppies also learn to open cupboard doors, chew their way into boxes and pull stuff down off shelves. Puppies can and do get into trouble, and that trouble can endanger their lives.

However, you can prevent much of this trouble if you look at the world through your puppy's eyes. Make sure anything poisonous or dangerous is put away—really away, where your puppy *can not* reach it. Put latches on cupboard doors. Make sure the trash is unreachable. Do car repairs where the puppy cannot get into the oil, grease, gasoline or antifreeze. All of these are deadly, but especially antifreeze—a lick or two is enough to kill your puppy. By being active and eliminating as many dangers as realistically possible, you can keep your puppy safe.

Common sense also plays a big part in keeping your puppy safe. If you take your puppy to the woods, check her thoroughly for ticks when you come home. If she's playing in long grass, look for burrs and foxtails (grass seeds that stick in the coat). If there is broken glass on the playground, take her somewhere else to play. Don't let her play off leash if there are cars nearby or if she doesn't come when you call her. Use your common sense to keep your puppy safe.

The Least You Need to Know

➤ Appropriate exercise and playtimes will use up energy, help your puppy's strength and coordination and give you an additional way to strengthen the bond between you and your puppy.

➤ Spaying or neutering your puppy will help avoid unwanted and unneeded puppies, will decrease the incidences of unwanted sexual behaviors and will also benefit your puppy's long-term health.

➤ Your veterinarian can help you keep your puppy healthy.

➤ Reasonable care and common sense can prevent accidents and dangers that threaten your puppy.

Chapter 13

Routine Care from Tip to Tail

In This Chapter

➤ Your puppy will need regular grooming

➤ Taking care of those terrible toenails

➤ Yes, you can brush your dog's teeth

➤ The full-body exam

Your puppy cannot care for himself, so it's up to you to do it for him. No matter what breed he is or what kind of coat he has, he will need regular grooming. He will also need to have his toenails trimmed and his teeth brushed. (Before you start thinking that only a complete idiot would brush his dog's teeth, read on!) He will also need to be examined all over to make sure he doesn't have any other problems, such as tangled hair or fleas or burrs lodged in his coat. Grooming and body care for your puppy is like regular maintenance on your car—it's vital, and it has to be done on schedule!

There's No Getting Around Regular Grooming

Many dog owners believe grooming only applies to Poodles and other breeds with long or curly hair that go to the grooming salon for hair cuts. However, grooming encompasses all the routine care of your dog's body, including bathing, brushing, combing, de-matting, hair cuts and trimming. All dogs, regardless of breed and coat type, require some grooming. Some breeds, of course, like Poodles and Pekingese, do require more.

Your puppy's breed (or mixture of breeds) and coat type will affect how much grooming he needs and what kind. The Poodles, Spaniels and Schnauzers have hair that continues to grow all the time. Regular hair cuts to keep their coat manageable are a must. In addition, this hair can gather into big clumps (mat) if it is not combed regularly.

German Shepherds, Siberian Huskies and Alaskan Malamutes have a thick double coat that sheds regularly, and sometimes heavily. These dogs don't need a hair cut, but they do need thorough brushing to pull out the dead undercoat and to keep the shedding manageable.

Puppy Tails

One spring many years ago my German Shepherd Dog Watachie was shedding heavily, so I took him outside to brush. I brushed and brushed and brushed and the grass around us became covered with his thick winter coat. When I sat down to relax and rest my arm, I realized that the neighborhood birds were congregating around us, picking up his hair. A whole generation of baby birds was raised in nests lined with Watachie's winter coat!

Shorthaired dogs are not without their grooming needs. They can shed just as much as their longer haired cousins; the hair they shed is just shorter. Shed short hair is not always easier to deal with, either. Longer hair tends to ball up, forming those infamous dog-hair dust bunnies. Short hair is prickly and sticks into things, including sofa cushions, pillows and your clothes.

A Professional Groomer Can Help You

A groomer is a person whose career is caring for the skin and coat of dogs, cats and other pets. A groomer knows how to brush out coats, de-mat them (when possible) and what type of hair cut each breed should have. Groomers also know about hair care products, including shampoos, conditioners and special products such as de-matting conditioners and flea control preparations.

Some breeds need regular haircuts. These include:

➤ Bichons Frises

➤ Lhasa Apsos

➤ Maltese

➤ Shih Tzu

➤ All sizes of Poodles

➤ All sizes of Schnauzers

➤ All the Spaniels, including Cockers and Springers

➤ Many of the Terriers, including Airedales, Scottish, Welsh, Cairn, West Highland and Yorkshire Terriers

Paws for Thought

If you haven't yet chosen a groomer, especially if your puppy will need regular hair cuts, go back to Chapter 6, which explains how to pick one.

In addition, many other breeds are routinely trimmed for ease of care. These include:

➤ Afghan Hounds

➤ Chow Chows

➤ Old English Sheepdogs

➤ Pekingese

➤ Many of the Setters

Some breeds are brought in to the groomer regularly to have their thick coats brushed out, especially in the spring. These include:

➤ Alaskan Malamutes

➤ Collies

➤ German Shepherds

➤ Keeshonds

➤ Norwegian Elkhounds

➤ Samoyeds

➤ Shetland Sheepdogs

➤ Siberian Huskies

Some breeds are prone to more oily and/or more smelly skin than other breeds. These dogs are often brought to the groomer to be bathed more thoroughly than the owner might be able or have time to. Some of these breeds include:

➤ Basset Hounds

➤ Beagles

➤ Dachshunds

➤ Dalmatians

➤ Doberman Pinschers

➤ Fox Terriers

➤ Labrador Retrievers

➤ Rottweilers

G-r-r-r!

Do not leave your pup at the groomer for several hours until you have made at least three visits with him. If your puppy is frightened by being left there, subsequent visits will be traumatic.

You should introduce your puppy to the groomer and her salon when the pup is between 10 and 12 weeks old, as soon as he has had at least two sets of shots. Don't take him before that, because he will be exposed to other dogs at the shop. However, once he has had two sets of shots, his immune system should be able to protect him.

Bring a few treats with you when you go to the shop, and encourage the receptionist, the groomer and other staff members to give him treats, scratch his ears, pet him and make a fuss over him. You want him to like going to the groomer.

On the second or third trip there, let the groomer put him up on the grooming table and comb or brush him. She can offer him a treat at the same time. Again, you want this to be a very positive experience, because your puppy will be going there regularly.

When you leave him for his first hair cut, try to arrange to leave him for just an hour or two and not much longer. Although most adult dogs spend the day at the groomer's salon, that is too much for a puppy—especially for the first hair cut.

Paws for Thought

A groomer will also trim you dog's toenails on request, and some will even express the anal glands. Expect to pay extra for these services.

When your puppy goes to the grooming salon, his routine will probably go like this:

➤ He will be thoroughly brushed.

➤ He will be bathed.

➤ He will be dried, either in a dryer cage or with a handheld drier.

➤ He will be brushed again.

➤ He will get his hair cut or trimmed.

➤ He will get the final brushing and any final trims or touch-ups.

➤ He's done and can go home.

Grooming Tools

Grooming tools come in a variety of sizes, shapes and uses. Some are right for certain hair types and not for others. It's important to know what tools are correct for your puppy's coat.

Combs are used to go through a coat to smooth it, or to help remove small tangles. Most are metal, with closely spaced teeth on one side and wider spaced teeth on the other. Combs don't have much value on shorthaired dogs or dogs with very thick, dense undercoats, but will work on dogs with fine hair or medium-dense coats.

Flea combs have very fine, closely spaced teeth that drag fleas out of the coat. These work well on shorthaired dogs, as well as medium and fine-haired dogs.

A *pin brush* has spaced teeth mounted on a rubber pad. The teeth are either flat on top or are topped with a tiny round head. Pin brushes are good for dogs with heavy, medium and fine coats, as well as dogs with longer coats, and will help drag the dead and shedding hair out of the coat.

A *slicker brush* has teeth that are made of relatively fine wire and are bent at an angle about halfway along their length. These brushes are good for the top coat, but do not reach deep into a long or thick coat.

The grooming tools you need will depend on what breed of dog you have. Some of the tools you may need include (from left to right) a comb, a de-matter, a brush, a good dog shampoo, nail clippers and a flea comb.

149

A *de-matter brush* has three, four or five blades, usually about an inch and a half long, that are sharp on one side. These brushes are for the thick hair around the dog's neck and the back of the legs. They rake through the thick, dense coat, splitting any tangles or mats. They will also drag out any dead or shedding coat.

A *rake* has four to six short metal teeth set in one row. This is good for brushing a dense coat that isn't too long or too dense. It's designed to find tangles and to drag out dead coat.

There are no set rules about which tools should be used on which breeds. But in general, if your dog has a longer coat you will need a tool with teeth that can reach through it. If your dog has a shorter coat, you can use a tool with shorter teeth or teeth spaced closer together. If your dog has a thick undercoat, you will need something that can work through that coat. Sometimes it's a matter of which tools you are most comfortable using. However, here are a few suggestions made by two different professional groomers:

Paws for Thought

If you have any questions about which tools to use or how to use them, make an appointment with your groomer. Ask her to show you the correct way to use the tools on your puppy, and expect to pay her for her time.

➤ **Cocker Spaniels:** a de-matter for longer hair, especially if it's tangled; a slicker brush for areas with shorter hair, especially if the dog has had a hair cut; and a pin brush.

➤ **Rottweilers:** a natural bristle brush, even one made for people.

➤ **German Shepherds:** a pin brush, a slicker brush and a de-matter for the heavy undercoat.

➤ **Poodles:** a pin brush, a slicker brush, a metal comb and a de-matter.

➤ **Silky and Yorkshire Terriers:** a metal comb, a pin brush and a de-matter.

➤ **Golden Retrievers:** a pin brush, a metal comb and a de-matter.

➤ **Labrador Retrievers:** a natural bristle brush and a slicker brush.

➤ **Australian Shepherds:** a pin brush and a de-matter.

➤ **Shih Tzu and Lhasa Apsos:** a metal comb, a pin brush and a de-matter.

The How-To's of Brushing Your Puppy

Since grooming is going to be a regular part of your puppy's routine care, you want him to enjoy it. If he sees the brush and comes to you wagging his tail with joy, half your job is already done. But if he runs away when he sees the brush, grooming is going to be a hated chore all his life, and a struggle for you both.

Regular brushing will keep your dog's skin and coat in good condition.

To teach the puppy to enjoy grooming, have some special treats on hand and keep the sessions very short. For my dogs, peanut butter is the special treat. I give a puppy a fingerful of peanut butter, brush one side or one leg, and then let the puppy go, praising him, "Good puppy! Yeah! Such a special boy!" The grooming session is then tolerable, quick and full of rewards. As the puppy learns to enjoy it, I make the sessions a little bit longer—very gradually—but continue the rewards.

The mechanics of brushing are really not very difficult. Sit on the floor and invite your puppy to lie down on your lap or between your legs. Give him some peanut butter (if he needs it) and start brushing his head. Using a comb, a soft bristle brush or a pin brush, gently brush the hair in the direction in which it grows. Brush *with* the hair, not against it.

Professional groomers brush their clients' dogs on a grooming table, and many dog owners do the same thing. The table puts the dog at a height where your back is not strained by bending over the dog. However, to teach puppies to enjoy grooming, I prefer to have them on my lap or between my legs. Later, when the puppy likes to be groomed, you can move him to a grooming table if you wish.

Puppy Tails

A friend's Golden Retriever hated certain aspects of grooming, which made the job very difficult. She asked for my help, so I watched and made a suggestion. While she groomed him, I fed him cheese crackers—a favorite treat that he normally wasn't allowed to have. During the grooming sessions, he only got the treat when he behaved himself. Within three brushing sessions, he was perfectly still and well-behaved, happily munching on his cheese crackers.

If your puppy has short hair, use your soft bristle brush and after brushing the head very gently, start working down around the ears, to the neck, shoulders and down the back. Gently brush portions of the body and then let your puppy up to praise him. When the entire body has been brushed and the coat is clean, he's done.

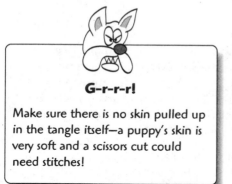

G-r-r-r!

Make sure there is no skin pulled up in the tangle itself—a puppy's skin is very soft and a scissors cut could need stitches!

Medium-coated puppies, puppies with long coats, thick coats or silky coats are a little more difficult. The hair behind the ears in these coated breeds is very soft and fluffy. This hair tangles easily, so comb it out with the metal comb or the de-matter. Be careful you don't comb the puppy's ear by mistake! If there are some tangles that you cannot comb out, you can trim them very carefully. Use round-tipped scissors and put your fingers between the tangle and the puppy's skin so you don't cut him.

The hair around the neck is thick in many breeds, even those with only a medium coat. This hair is called the *ruff*. Comb through the ruff with a metal comb or a pin brush. When you're through with the ruff, work down the shoulders to the back and hips. Comb each leg and the tail. Roll the puppy over on his back and gently comb the chest and tummy. Roll the puppy over on his side and repeat the whole procedure on the other side.

Rub a Dub Dub, a Pup in the Tub

The old wives' tales say a dog should only be bathed once a year, or once in the spring and once in the fall. Obviously those dogs lived outside. They were never allowed in the house because they stank! It doesn't hurt your puppy at all to be bathed more often, as long as you use a good quality shampoo and rinse it out thoroughly.

There are a thousand dog shampoos available commercially and all are good for some dogs. Read the labels and make sure the shampoo is recommended for puppies. Don't get a medicated shampoo unless your veterinarian recommends it. Don't use an insecticide shampoo either unless it is specifically for puppies and your puppy actually has fleas. Instead, get a good quality shampoo that is just made for cleaning the puppy.

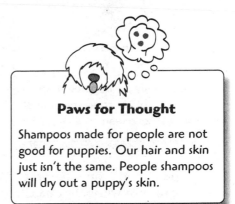

Paws for Thought

Shampoos made for people are not good for puppies. Our hair and skin just isn't the same. People shampoos will dry out a puppy's skin.

I wash my puppies in the bathtub. I have a handheld shower nozzle (a massager type) and non-skid patches on the bottom of the tub. If you have a deep sink in the garage or basement, that might also work. Don't shampoo your baby puppy outside using cold water from the garden hose— that will just teach him to hate baths. Let's make the first few baths pleasant, and later, when he's grown up, you can bathe him under the hose when the weather is warm.

Brush or comb your puppy thoroughly before you bathe him. Make sure all tangles are out of his coat because if they're not, you'll have to cut them out after the bath. Water turns tangles into cement! Before you put the puppy in the tub, grab a few towels, the shampoo and some cotton balls. Put a cotton ball into each of his ears to help keep the ears dry. Set the water to a nice comfortable temperature (it should just feel warm on your hand) and lift the puppy in. If he struggles, calm him with your voice but don't let him fight you.

Use the handheld shower to thoroughly wet him, then turn the water off. Work the shampoo into his coat, from the neck back, and then rinse him off. On his head, run the water away from his eyes and ears. Make sure all of the soap is rinsed out. This takes longer than you think, so keep rinsing!

When he's completely rinsed, towel him off very well and then, if he'll let you, keep him wrapped up in the towel for a few minutes while you cuddle him. Let him warm up a little. If the weather or your house is chilly, use the blow dryer for a few minutes to dry him and warm him up.

Special Cleaning

Sometimes some special care is needed. If your puppy gets into chewing gum, oil or meets a skunk, a regular bath just won't do. Here are some suggestions for special situations.

153

Fleas

A flea comb will catch some of the little pests, especially around the puppy's eyes and ears. Insecticides also work, but many owners are afraid of using too much and it's a very real concern. Talk to your veterinarian about his recommendations for flea control. There are many options available these days (Chapter 15 discusses several of them).

Gum and Other Sticky Stuff

Rub the area with ice to freeze the gum and break it out, or pour on some vegetable oil to ooze it out. (Follow up the oil treatment with a bath.) However, be aware that gum usually needs to be trimmed out.

Paint

Don't use paint solvents on your puppy. They're toxic! Try to wash the paint out with soap and water. If it won't come out, trim away the painted hair.

Motor Oil

Joy dishwashing soap will usually cut the oil. Just make sure you rinse it out well.

Burrs, Foxtails and Other Seeds

Many seeds can simply be combed out. If they're stuck in a tangle, use some vegetable oil (just a little) or some hair conditioner to make the burr a little slippery. You will then have to wash the oil or conditioner out; use Joy dish soap or a good shampoo. If the seed is really worked into the coat, trim it out.

Quills and Spines

Call your veterinarian. Pulling out or working out quills can be very painful, and your vet may want to sedate the dog while he does it.

Skunks

Soak your dog in tomato juice or vinegar, rubbing it deep into the coat. Let it sit for a few minutes, then rinse it out. You may need to repeat the treatment several times. Joy dishwashing soap also helps cut the smell (it cleans out the oil in the skunk's discharge). There are also commercial preparations on the market that work well.

Trimming the Terrible Toenails

Most dog owners absolutely hate trimming their dog's toenails—so much so that many dogs walk around on nails much too long or they take the dog to the groomer or veterinarian to let them do the dirty work. Letting the nails grow too long is more than just a cosmetic problem; it can actually cause the dog pain and, over time, can deform the feet. However, if you learn to trim the toenails while your puppy is young and the nails are soft, it won't become a problem later.

G-r-r-r!

If you cut the quick, scrape the nail along a bar of soap. The soft soap will clog the nail until the blood can clot. Keep the puppy on your lap with his foot up for a few minutes, until the bleeding stops.

Buy a pair of canine nail clippers at the grooming salon or at a pet supply store. The best kind look like a pair of scissors with short, weird, curved blades. These are called guillotine cutters. You will use them just like scissors, too.

Have your puppy lie down in your lap and roll him over so you can see his feet. Give him some peanut butter to keep him occupied while you check out his feet. Taking one toe in your hand, look at the nail. Push the hair away from the nail and hold it with your fingers. If the nail is clear or white, you will be able to see the pink quick inside. The quick is a bundle of nerves and blood vessels. The nail beyond it has no feeling at all—just like your nails. Trim the nail slightly beyond the quick, so there is some leeway. If you cut the quick it will hurt, bleed and your puppy will be very upset!

If your puppy has black nails, check all of his toes. If he has one white nail, that will give you some guidelines for where the quick is, and you can cut the black nails slightly longer than the white one.

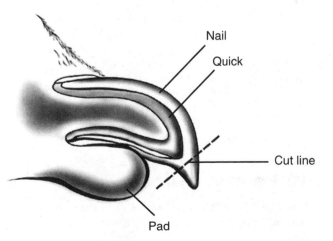

Nail

Quick

Cut line

Pad

If there are no white nails, you will just have to practice and guess a little. When you look at a toenail from the side, you will see it curves out and down. The last third of the nail is much narrower and comes to a point. It is always safe to trim off that last third of the nail. The quick doesn't extend into that narrower part.

Paws for Thought

You may want to trim your puppy's nails weekly. Not only will this ensure that he's used to the procedure, but it will keep those razor-sharp little weapons trimmed.

How often should you trim the nails? When your puppy is standing still, upright on all four paws, his nails should not touch the floor. You may hear them clicking when he's running, but if they touch the floor when he's standing still, they need trimming.

Some puppies are very sensitive about their feet. If your puppy is, try trimming one or two nails at a time, then take a break. Come back to a few more nails later. If your puppy has a problem with his nails, don't force the issue and try to do them all at once. You will simply compound the problem and make him absolutely detest nail trimming. He will hold that dislike forever and it will remain a problem.

Cleaning Your Puppy's Ears

Cleaning your puppy's ears is nowhere near as difficult as trimming toenails. For one thing, there's no chance of making him bleed. You'll need a few cotton balls and either a bottle of witch hazel, alcohol or a commercial canine ear cleaning solution. Any one is acceptable.

Breed Bits

Basset Hounds are famous for their long, heavy ears that are prone to being dirty, getting stepped on, hurt and infected. Pay close attention to their ears and keep them clean and healthy.

Wet a cotton ball with the witch hazel, alcohol or solution and wring out most of the moisture. With your puppy on your lap and distracted by a lick of peanut butter, lift the ear flap and gently wipe the inside of the ear, careful to get in all the folds and creases. Do not try to go deep within the ear canal—just clean what is easily reachable. If the ear is dirty, you may need two or three cotton balls.

How often you clean your puppy's ears depends on the puppy and how dirty he gets. But in general, once a week is about right. Make sure your dog's ears are completely dry after you clean them. Be especially careful with dogs with ears that hang down, because they can be prone to infections.

Brushing Those Pearly Whites

Some dog owners look at me like I'm crazy when I ask them how they brush their dog's teeth. "Why should I do that?" they ask in horror. I usually reply, "Well, don't you brush your own teeth? Isn't it healthy for you? Shouldn't your dog have the same consideration?" The reply is usually a very hesitant yes!

Dogs do need their teeth brushed regularly for the same reasons we need to brush ours. A clean mouth and clean teeth are less likely to be diseased and cause diseases. Particularly in older dogs, dirty teeth and gums can lead to bacterial infections in other parts of the body, especially the heart. If you teach your puppy to tolerate having his teeth brushed now when he's young, you can continue as he grows older.

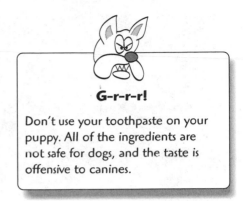

G-r-r-r!

Don't use your toothpaste on your puppy. All of the ingredients are not safe for dogs, and the taste is offensive to canines.

Get a very small child's toothbrush for your dog, or buy one specially designed for dogs. Your veterinarian may have some canine toothpaste, or you can check at your local pet supply store. Or you can use baking soda. Your dog will not need to rinse his mouth when you use a canine toothpaste.

Invite your puppy to lie down in your lap, and open his lips with your fingers. Start by gently rubbing the toothbrush up against the outside of his side teeth. He will probably try to chew on the brush. If he does, take the brush away as you gently discourage him. Then try it again.

This is going to take a lot of patience on your part. Obviously, you can't distract him with peanut butter the way you did for many of the other grooming exercises. Instead, you need to be patient, do a few teeth at a time, and get him used to the procedure.

The Daily Massage

It's important to know your puppy's body very well. You need to know what is normal and what isn't. Your puppy often cannot tell you when there's a problem. Sure, he can cry or limp when he hurts his paw, but how can he tell you when he has an unusual lump on his side? He can't.

However, if you make a habit of examining him each and every day, you can find anything out of the ordinary. Often, noticing a problem a day or two sooner can mean the difference between a minor problem and a major one.

The easiest and most enjoyable way to examine your puppy is to give him a massage. I like to do it in the evening when the television is on. I sit on the floor and invite my dog to lie in front of me between my legs. With him lying on his side, I start at his head and gently feel his muzzle. I peek in at his teeth, look at his nose and eyes, and rub the base of his ears as I look inside each ear. I massage his neck all around, feeling for lumps, bumps, burrs, foxtails, or anything else that might be a problem or out of the ordinary. I work down to the shoulders, the chest, down each front leg to the paws and check each paw. I continue this thorough massage and examination until I have gone over his entire body.

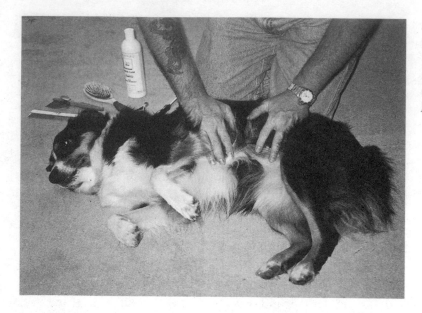

A daily massage will help you find lumps, bumps, cuts, burrs, ticks and any other small problems before they turn into big problems.

My dogs like this so much that by the time I'm done, they are as limp as dishrags, totally relaxed. Of course, I usually am, too!

The Least You Need to Know

➤ A groomer can be of great help to you, both in grooming your puppy and assisting you with grooming questions or problems.

➤ Brushing, combing and bathing your puppy doesn't have to be traumatic or stressful. Introduce your puppy to these routines easily and gently.

➤ Trimming toenails, cleaning ears and brushing teeth are a vital part of the grooming routine.

➤ A daily massage helps you keep aware of your puppy's body and health.

Chapter 14

Let's Eat!

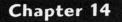

In This Chapter

➤ What is nutrition?

➤ Vitamins and minerals explained

➤ All about puppy foods

➤ What about supplements and preservatives?

➤ How much should you feed, and when?

Every body, be it human, canine or even reptilian, needs good nutrition. What constitutes good nutrition depends upon the body being nourished. What is good nutrition now will not be the same when your puppy is an adult, or later when she is an old dog. Right now your puppy needs a diet that fulfills all of her nutritional needs so that she can grow and remain healthy, while having enough energy left for exercise and playtime.

What Makes Food Good?

Good nutrition is made up of many components. Vitamins, minerals, proteins, amino acids, enzymes, fats and carbohydrates are all necessary for good nutrition. We've all heard those words before, but what are they really?

Vitamins

Vitamins are organic compounds that are necessary for life. Without these compounds, there could be no metabolism of food, no growth, no reproduction and there would be a total cessation of thousands of other bodily functions. Several vitamins, including A, D, E and K, are fat soluble, which means the body can store them in body fat. Other vitamins, including all of the B complex vitamins and C, are water soluble. These are flushed out of the system daily in the urine, and must be replenished through the foods consumed.

Minerals

These inorganic compounds are also necessary for life, although much smaller amounts are needed than vitamins and the other nutrients. Necessary minerals include calcium, phosphorus, copper, iron and potassium, as well as several others. Minerals require a delicate balance for good health—some minerals work only in the presence of other minerals, and more is not necessarily better.

Paws for Thought

Other parts of an animal's body are also protein, including skin, nails, claws or hooves and blood, but these are not as good quality (nutritionally speaking) as is meat.

Protein

An animal's body may be made up of over 30,000 different types of protein. Meat is good quality protein—beef, chicken, lamb, fish or any other meat. Proteins are found in other sources, too, including eggs, dairy products and some plants. Each gram of protein provides four calories of energy.

Complete proteins are those that contain all of the necessary amino acids for good health. Incomplete proteins are those that contain some but not all of the necessary amino acids. Good sources of complete proteins include eggs, red meats, fish, milk and dairy products. Incomplete proteins that are still good nutrition when combined with other proteins include beans, peas, soybeans, peanuts, grains and potatoes.

Amino Acids

Amino acids are necessary for many body functions, including growth and healing. They are also needed to produce hormones, antibodies and enzymes. Amino acids are found in proteins, and in fact, proteins are broken down to form amino acids.

Enzymes

Every cell in the body contains enzymes. These are protein-based chemicals that cause biochemical reactions in the body and affect every stage of metabolism. Some enzymes must work with a partner, a co-enzyme that is often a vitamin, to cause the needed reaction or metabolism.

Fats

Fats have gotten a lot of bad press recently. Low-fat and non-fat diets are being sold as the best foods available. However, fats are necessary, especially for growing puppies. Fats are needed to metabolize the fat-soluble vitamins and to supply energy for activity. Each gram of dietary fat provides nine calories of energy.

Paws for Thought

While it may be a good idea for inactive adult dogs (and humans!) to cut down on their fat intake, puppies need fat to grow and thrive.

Carbohydrates

These are sugars and starches, and are used primarily as fuel for the body. Your puppy's body runs on carbohydrates much the way your car runs on gasoline. Complex carbohydrates (grains, rice, potatoes, pasta and peas) are intricate conglomerations of glucose (sugar) molecules. Each gram of carbohydrates provides four calories of energy.

Commercial Puppy Foods

Commercial puppy foods are designed to supply all of your puppy's needs, including proteins, amino acids, enzymes, fats, carbohydrates, vitamins and minerals. Many of the companies producing dog foods use feeding trials to test their foods. They have fed, literally, generations upon generations of dogs. However, all dog (and puppy) foods are not created equal.

Dog food is one item where you usually get what you pay for. The more expensive puppy foods are—as a general rule—better quality foods. The less expensive foods—especially the generic or plain label foods—are lesser quality foods.

Quality can be based on many things, including testing. Feeding trials are not required for a company to market pet food. Instead of trials, companies can use laboratory tests to determine the nutritional value of a food. Unfortunately, lab tests are not as good as feeding trials, because they don't measure the food as it is used or metabolized by the puppy. Therefore, a food could test well but still not adequately nourish your puppy. Foods that are tested by actually feeding dogs (feeding trials) will say so on the label of the dog food. You can also call the company that makes the food—the phone number should be on the label.

The quality of a pet food is also based on the quality of the ingredients. Grains grown in mineral-poor soils will have few minerals to pass on to the puppy that consumes them. Poor quality meats will be less able to nourish the puppy. Less expensive foods contain inexpensive and less nourishing grains and less of the more expensive meats. Again, the puppy's nutrition can and often will suffer.

Many dog owners are also concerned about the preservatives, artificial flavorings and additives in many dog foods. Some of these additives are of questionable value as far as your puppy's nutrition is concerned. If you have a concern about a particular additive or ingredient, call your veterinarian and call the manufacturer of the food. What does each say about that ingredient?

Paws for Thought

Plain label dog foods are inexpensive to buy but expensive in other ways. The University of California at Davis Veterinary College has named a malnutrition syndrome found in dogs fed a poor quality food "generic dog food disease."

Reading the Label

The label on each bag (or can) of dog food will tell you a lot about that particular food. One section of the label lists the percentages of nutrients. Most puppies do well on a food that contains about 28 percent protein and 8 percent fat.

The label will also tell you the ingredients of the food. Ingredients are listed in quantity order. In other words, the first ingredient listed will be what the food has the most of. Therefore, if beef is listed first, followed by rice, corn and wheat, you'll know that there is more beef in the food than rice, and more rice than corn.

Paws for Thought

Ingredient lists are even more important if your puppy develops allergies. Many dogs are allergic to wheat, for example, and their owners must read labels very carefully.

However, this listing can be deceptive. You might see wheat midlings, wheat germ and wheat bran listed in a food, all listed after the meat ingredient. Since they are listed after the meat, does that mean there is more meat than wheat? Not necessarily. There might be more meat than wheat midlings, or more meat than wheat germ. But if all the wheat is added together, there might very well be more wheat than meat. You need to read the label carefully so you know exactly what you are feeding your puppy.

Wet or Dry?

There are basically three types of dog food. Dry, kibbled foods come in a bag and are small pieces of food. These usually contain grains and meats. Dry foods have a good shelf life and most dogs eat them quite readily. They are usually very affordable—some more so than others.

Canned foods are mostly meats or meat recipes. These foods have a high water content. In the can they have a long shelf life, but once the can is opened they must be used right away. Canned foods are very palatable and are more expensive than dry foods.

Puppy Tails

Nutrition is a very complex topic, and I could write a whole book about reading dog food labels and selecting the best diet for your dog. In fact, I did. It's called *The Consumer's Guide to Dog Food,* and it's published by Howell Book House (1996).

Semimoist foods have a higher moisture content than dry kibble foods, but not as high as canned. These foods contain a lot of sugar and salt, as well as artificial colorings—none of which your puppy needs. Many dog treats are semi-moist.

Which is the best form for your puppy? Most veterinarians and breeders recommend dry food. The action of chewing the hard kibble will help keep your dog's teeth clean and healthy. And dry foods provide the most nutrients for the money. Since wet foods are mostly water, your dog has to eat a lot more of them in order to get the nutrition she needs every day. That means more going in, and more coming out—which may not be good news for your housebreaking program!

Pick a Food

Choosing the right food for your puppy can be difficult. Here are some suggestions to help you decide:

1. Read the ingredients. Is there a good variety of foods? Are there complete and incomplete proteins? Is there a selection of carbohydrates and fats? What about additives and preservatives? Do you understand what they are and why they are in the food?

2. What are the protein and fat percentages? Are you comfortable with those levels?

Paws for Thought

When you got your puppy, she was being fed something by her breeder, the shelter or pet store owner. If that is not the food you prefer to feed, mix the old food with the new, gradually increasing the amounts of the new food over a three-week period.

3. If you have any questions about the food, talk to your veterinarian and call the food manufacturer.

The final (and best) test of the food is your puppy. Is she growing well? Is she too skinny? Is she too fat? Does she always act hungry? Does she have enough energy for play? If your puppy is doing well, the food is probably just fine.

What About Supplements?

Most experts agree that a good quality commercial puppy food contains everything a puppy needs. However, many people are still tempted to supplement their puppy's diet. Perhaps you take vitamin and mineral supplements yourself, and think your dog needs them too.

The first thing to remember is that good dog food is probably a lot healthier than the food you eat. It has been carefully tested and balanced for optimum nutrition, and most of us don't do that with our daily meals. Still, if you want to give your puppy extra vitamins and minerals, it probably won't do her any harm. Most dog food manufacturers confirm that as long as the supplements do not exceed 10 percent of the food fed, they probably will not disturb the nutritional balance of the commercial food. Just make sure you follow the manufacturer's directions. More is not better with many vitamins and minerals, and excessive amounts of some can cause serious problems.

Many dog owners also add other kinds of supplements, such as yogurt and brewer's yeast, to their dog's diet. Yogurt has been said to aid digestion by adding beneficial bacteria to the digestive tract. It's nutritious and a good source of fat, and certainly will not hurt your puppy unless she has trouble digesting dairy products.

G-r-r-r!

Too much supplementation can upset a previously balanced and complete diet. Supplement carefully, and if you have any doubts, talk to your veterinarian.

Many dog owners believe brewer's yeast will naturally repel fleas. This has never been proven scientifically, but yeast is a good source of B vitamins, and again, it will not hurt the dog when used as a supplement.

Vegetables, vegetable juice or meat broth can be added to your dog's dry food. They add nutrition and make the food more palatable. Cooked eggs, cheese or cottage cheese can also make dry food more attractive.

Are Preservatives Safe?

Most commercial dog foods are preserved with something in order to extend their shelf life. The idea itself is not a bad one, but some preservatives have been linked with health problems. The most controversial preservative currently used in dog food is ethoxyquin, a chemical that prevents the fat in food from going rancid and the vitamins from losing their potency. Ethoxyquin is approved by the Food and Drug Administration for use in human foods, but it has come under some criticism from the general public. It has been alleged that ethoxyquin has caused cancer, and liver, kidney and thyroid problems. However, this has never been proven scientifically.

Paws for Thought

Most preservatives in dog food, like ethoxyquin and the tocopherols, are antioxidants, which means they prevent the oxidation of fatty acids and vitamins.

If you are concerned about ethoxyquin, look for a food preserved with one of the tocopherols. These antioxidants are naturally occurring compounds of vitamins C and E. Just be aware that tocopherols have a very short shelf life, especially once a bag of food had been opened.

Treating Your Puppy

There are many brands of commercial treats available on the market. Some are pure junk food, full of corn syrup, meat scraps, cereal fillers and sugar. Others are actually good nutrition. But any treat you feed, whether as part of a training regimen or to keep your puppy busy with a toy, must be taken into account when considering her overall diet.

If you're using treats as part of a training program, measure out a portion of treats for the day, and subtract some dog food from your dog's daily ration to compensate. Bits of meat or cheese make good training treats. A carrot makes a good chew treat, and a slice of apple is a much better sweet treat than a commercial treat containing sugar and artificial colors.

G-r-r-r!

Never treat your dog with chocolate. It's lethal to dogs. A 10-ounce milk chocolate candy bar can kill a seven-pound dog.

Of the commercial products, the hard biscuit-type treats are probably best. They give your pup something to chew on, and have fewer artificial colors, additives and flavors and less sugar than the semimoist treats.

When Should Your Puppy Eat?

Most young puppies need to eat three times a day. A big morning meal, a small lunch and a big evening meal usually suit eight- to twelve-week-old puppies just fine. By 12 weeks of age, most puppies will be able to skip lunch and do quite well with just morning and evening meals. That doesn't mean you should start feeding them less. It just means that you can divide their daily ration into two servings a day instead of three.

By 14 to 18 months of age, most young dogs will eat one or two meals a day, and usually indicate by preference how often and what time of day they are more comfortable eating. Some dogs will simply stop eating their morning meal and will eagerly consume the evening meal, while others will do just the opposite. If your dog has a hearty appetite at both meals, that's okay too. Two meals a day is fine for an adult dog.

G-r-r-r!

If your puppy is healthy and growing well, don't force her to eat more than she wants.

How Much Is Enough?

The label on the dog food you buy will have recommendations for how much to feed your puppy. They are a good place to start, but don't take them as the final word. Every puppy is different, and the amount of exercise your pup has had, how cold it is outside and lots of other factors will affect how much your puppy should eat.

Regulate how much you feed your puppy by how she looks and feels. If she is thin and is always acting hungry, give her some more food. If she is fat and doesn't always seem interested in mealtimes, cut back. If she is sleek and active and growing well, you've got it just right. Along the same lines, if she has been working hard, give her a little extra, and if she has spent the day lying around, cut back a bit.

No Free Feeding

Don't leave food out for your puppy to nibble on all day. This is called free feeding, and is not recommended for several reasons.

First, if your puppy does happen to get sick, one of the first questions the veterinarian will ask is, "How is your puppy's appetite? How did she eat this morning?" If the puppy eats sporadically throughout the day rather than at specific times, you won't be able to answer that question.

In addition, housetraining is much easier when the puppy eats at specific times. You know she needs to go outside after every meal. If those meals are at set times, you know when to take her outside. However, if the puppy snacks all day, when should you take her out? It's much harder to tell.

Feeding at set times also helps develop the proper relationship between you and your puppy. As the giver of the food at each mealtime, you assume a very important position in your puppy's life. After all, to the puppy, food is survival.

Food that is set out for free feeding is also easily spoiled. Ants, flies and other insects can soil it, rodents can visit it, and heat or water can spoil it.

Paws for Thought

If your puppy is hesitant about a particular family member, have that person feed her. This will change how that person is viewed in the puppy's eyes.

The Least You Need to Know

➤ A good quality food is important to your puppy's growth and continued good health.

➤ You get what you pay for with puppy food, and the more expensive brands usually are better.

➤ Dry foods are generally better for your dog.

➤ Read the labels when making your decision about which food to buy.

➤ Supplements and treats should be fed sparingly, and only as part of an overall plan for good nutrition.

➤ Free feeding is not a good idea. Feed your puppy on a regular schedule.

Chapter 15

Pay Attention to These Health Concerns

In This Chapter

➤ Fleas, ticks and mites can bug your puppy and you

➤ Internal worms and parasites can be really disgusting

➤ There are a few diseases you need to know about

➤ Genetic health problems could affect your puppy

Caring for your puppy does entail some less than pleasant chores. Puppies can pick up fleas, ticks and mites. Controlling these insects is sometimes difficult, but is absolutely necessary. Puppies can also have internal parasites. Roundworms, for instance, are very common in puppies, and your veterinarian will help you identify and eliminate these pests.

You should also be familiar with the diseases your puppy can be exposed to, especially those that can threaten his health. Certain genetic disorders are more prevalent in some breeds than in others, and you should be aware of them.

Hopefully, you will never need this chapter and your puppy will remain parasite-free and healthy. However, this information is here for you if you should need it.

Those Pesky, Pesty Bugs

External parasites—fleas, ticks and mites—are insects that are uniquely suited to bug your dog. The fleas and mites that thrive on dogs would greatly prefer a canine host to a human one. That's not to say these insects won't take a nibble out of you; often they will. It's just that they would rather munch on your dog instead.

Fleas, ticks and mites have a long history of devastation, too. Fleas have been blamed for innumerable plagues throughout history, including the bubonic plague that decimated Europe centuries ago. Today, fleas are still dangerous pests that can threaten your dog's comfort and health. The good news is that we have a much better arsenal available to combat them.

Puppy Tails

Fleas can jump six feet in one hop. But despite their talents, most flea circuses (remember those?) never contained any live fleas. The so-called fleas were either dead and glued into place, or were so small they were invisible!

Fleas

A flea is a small, crescent-shaped, six-legged insect with a big abdomen and a small head. It has flat sides so it can slip through hair with ease. When caught, it will pop under your fingernail like a tiny balloon. If that sounds gross, you obviously haven't dealt with too many fleas. Fleas cause dogs so much torment, it can be very satisfying to pop the little pests!

Fleas live by biting your dog and taking a drop or two of blood each time they bite. A heavy infestation can cause anemia from the blood loss, especially for small, young puppies.

But the blood loss isn't the worst of it. Fleas carry a wide variety of diseases. And many dogs are so allergic to flea bites, the poor things will scratch and chew themselves raw. Think about the worst bug bite you've ever had, and then multiply it thousands of times. That's what a flea-infested allergic dog feels like. An allergic dog could end up with flea bite dermatitis or open sores, which could then develop secondary infections.

If you're aren't sure whether your dog has fleas, have him lie down on a solid-colored sheet. Brush the dog's coat thoroughly, then let him up. If you see residue that looks like salt and pepper, your dog has fleas. The residue is fecal matter (the "pepper") and eggs (the "salt").

In the past, insecticides and pesticides in the form of collars, dips and sprays were the only products available, and you had to use those with caution. If you weren't careful, you could easily end up poisoning yourself and your dog before you killed off all the fleas. Luckily, in the last few years several products have been introduced to make flea control easier and safer.

Paws for Thought

Fleas are also the intermediate host for tapeworms. If your dog has fleas and swallows an infected flea, he can then become infested with tapeworms.

The new products on the market attack fleas in two ways. Some kill adult fleas (which are the only ones that bite). Others are called insect growth regulators, and they stop the immature flea from developing or maturing. It then cannot reproduce. To be really effective, most of the newer flea control products combine the insecticide with an insect growth regulator.

The new products are systemic, meaning they enter the dog's body systems, and generally come in tablets and liquids. The tablets release the product into the dog's bloodstream, where the flea ingests it every time it bites. The liquids are poured along the dog's neck and back, where they are absorbed into the dog's skin to repel fleas.

To control fleas, you must attack them in three ways: on the dog, in your house and in your yard. Leave out any one of the three and your control efforts will not be successful. However, with the new products available, flea control is now possible. A few years ago, the battle was on-going, with the fleas often winning!

Some control methods include:

➤ **In the yard,** use a spray designed for outside use that contains an insect growth regulator. Repeat the applications according to directions.

➤ **In the house,** use a spray with insect growth regulator designed for inside use. If your house is infested, use a spray with a quick-kill ingredient as well as an insect growth regulator. Use all products according to directions.

G-r-r-r!

Mixing different flea control products can be deadly. Do not use a flea spray on the dog as well as a flea collar, for example. Read the labels carefully and follow the directions.

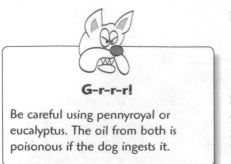

G-r-r-r!

Be careful using pennyroyal or eucalyptus. The oil from both is poisonous if the dog ingests it.

➤ **On the dog**, use a systemic such as Program or Sentinel. Do not use insecticides on the dog, or flea collars, unless the labels on both products specify that it is safe to do so.

Some owners prefer to use more natural products to control fleas. Some of those products include feeding garlic, yeast, B complex vitamins and other combinations of similar products. These will not hurt the dog when given in appropriate dosages. However, they are usually not entirely effective in controlling fleas when used alone. They can, of course, be used in conjunction with other flea control methods.

Cedar or eucalyptus shavings, or pennyroyal are also supposed to help repel fleas, especially in the dog's bedding. They can also help with flea control, but again, are not usually effective by themselves.

Ticks

A tick is an eight-legged, oblong insect with a head that imbeds into the skin. Ticks feed on the host's blood and, when engorged, will drop off. Ticks, like fleas, are known carriers of disease. In the United States, Rocky Mountain spotted fever was a concern for many years. This acutely infectious disease is characterized by muscular pains, high fevers and skin eruptions. It can be found all over western North America.

Rocky Mountain spotted fever is still a danger, but a new disease has emerged that is even more frightening. Lyme disease affects dogs as well as people, and is transmitted primarily by ticks. A lingering fever and joint pain (sometimes quite severe) are characteristics of this disease.

Paws for Thought

Ask your veterinarian if Lyme disease is a problem in your area. If it is, there is a Lyme disease vaccine. Ask your vet if he recommends it.

Although some flea products are partially effective on ticks, they are rarely totally effective at killing or keeping ticks off your dog. During tick season (spring and summer) you will have to examine your dog daily and remove each and every tick. Check your dog all over, but favorite spots for ticks to hide are behind or in the ears, in the armpit area of the front legs and around the neck.

Never remove a tick with your bare fingers. Use tweezers or wear rubber gloves. Grab the tick down close to the skin and pull gently but firmly, with a slow twisting motion. Don't flush the tick down the toilet—it will survive its trip downstream. And don't squish it between

Golden Retrievers

German Shepherds

Cavalier King Charles Spaniel

Soft Coated Wheaten Terrier

Siberian Huskies

Pointers

Australian Cattle Dog

Spinone
Italianos

Labrador Retriever

Bichon Frise

Bloodhound

*American
Staffordshire
Terrier*

Miniature Schnauzer

Pembroke Welsh Corgi

Border Collie

Wire Fox Terriers

your fingers, because you will be exposed to whatever diseases it is carrying. The best way to kill a tick is to burn it. Put a little antibiotic ointment on the wound where the tick was embedded.

Mange Mites

Mange is usually associated with stray dogs that have no one to care for them, but this isn't necessarily so. Many well-loved dogs have come down with mange one way or another.

There are two types of mange seen most often in dogs. Sarcoptic mange is contagious to people and other pets. Its primary symptoms include red welts that the dog will be scratching continuously. Sarcoptic mange usually responds well to medical treatment.

Demodectic mange is not as easily transmitted to people or other pets. It shows up as bald patches, usually first on the dog's face. There may not be any scratching or itching. Demodectic mange often appears in young dogs and will clear up with treatment. However, in older dogs treatment can be long and drawn out, and is sometimes not effective at all.

G-r-r-r!

Mange is *always* a case for your veterinarian. Do not try to treat it yourself.

Ringworm isn't really a worm at all, but instead is several different kinds of fungi. These very contagious fungi infest the skin and cause ring-shaped, round, scaly, itchy spots. These round spots are the trademark identification of ringworm.

Ringworm usually responds well to veterinary treatment, but care must be taken to strictly follow the treatment plan set up by your veterinarian, because this is very, very contagious to people and other pets.

Internal Parasites

Internal parasites are just as disgusting as external parasites, but can be more threatening to your dog's health because they are not as easily seen. You will see fleas on your dog, for example, but he could have worms for quite a while before you see any signs of poor health.

Most internal parasites can be detected by taking a small piece of your dog's stool to the veterinarian's office. The stool will be prepared and then examined under a microscope. Parasites, their eggs or larvae can then be detected and your veterinarian can prescribe appropriate treatment. After treatment, your veterinarian will ask you to bring in another stool sample—usually in two to three weeks—to make sure the treatment was effective.

Roundworms

Most puppies must be treated for roundworms. These long, white worms are fairly common in puppies, although they can also be found in adult dogs and humans, as well as other animals. An adult female roundworm can lay up to 200,000 eggs a day, most of which are passed out of the host animal through the feces.

G-r-r-r!

Roundworm eggs can be picked up via the feces, so your puppy should be discouraged from sniffing other dogs' feces.

A roundworm infestation in an adult dog is not always dangerous, especially a light infestation. However, a heavy infestation can threaten a dog's health. A young puppy with roundworms will not thrive and will appear thin, with a dull coat and a pot belly. Often you will see worms in the stool.

Roundworms can be detected by your veterinarian through a fecal analysis. Good sanitation is important to prevent an infestation. Feces should be picked up and disposed of daily.

Hookworms

These parasites live their lives in the small intestine, where they attach to the intestinal wall and suck blood. When they detach and move to a new location, the old wound continues to bleed for awhile, so bloody diarrhea is often a symptom of a hookworm infestation.

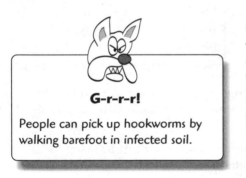

G-r-r-r!

People can pick up hookworms by walking barefoot in infected soil.

Hookworm eggs are passed through the feces and are either picked up from stool, as with roundworms, or, if conditions are right, hatch in the soil and attach themselves to the feet of their new host. They burrow through the skin of the feet, then migrate to the intestinal tract where the cycle then repeats itself.

The eggs can be detected in a fecal analysis. Treatment often needs to be repeated two or more times before finally ridding the host of the parasites. Good sanitation is necessary to prevent a re-infestation.

Tapeworms

These parasites also live in the intestinal tract and attach to the wall to absorb nutrients. They grow by creating new segments. Usually the first sign of an infestation is small rice-like segments found around the dog's rectum or in its stool.

Tapeworms are acquired when the dog eats an infected flea, the intermediate host. A good flea control program is the best way to prevent a tapeworm infestation.

Whipworms

These worms live in the large intestine, where they feed on blood. The eggs are passed in the feces, and can live in the soil for a long time—years, even. A dog that eats the fresh spring grass or buries his bone in the infected soil can pick up eggs.

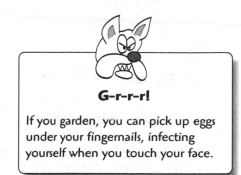

G-r-r-r!

If you garden, you can pick up eggs under your fingernails, infecting yourself when you touch your face.

Heavy infestations can cause diarrhea, and the dog will appear thin and anemic, with a poor coat. Whipworms are not as easily detected through fecal analysis, because they do not shed eggs in the stool as frequently as do roundworms and hookworms. Several stool samples may need to be checked to be certain they have been dealt with.

Heartworms

These parasites live in the upper heart and greater pulmonary arteries, where they damage the vessel walls. Poor circulation results, which in turn damages other body functions. Eventually the heart fails and the dog dies.

The adult worms produce thousands of tiny worms, known as microfilaria. These circulate throughout the bloodstream until they are picked up by mosquitoes, the intermediate host. The microfilaria continue to develop in the mosquito. Then, when they're ready, they are transferred to another dog when that mosquito bites the dog.

Dogs infested with heartworm can be treated when the infestation is in its early stages. However, heavy infestations are difficult to treat, because the treatment itself is risky. Preventive medications are available, and that is the best way to deal with this problem. They are easy to administer and are very effective. Talk to your veterinarian about heartworm preventives and whether heartworm has been found in your area.

Giardiasis

This is not a worm, but it is a parasite. The protozoa giardia is common in wild animals. If you and your dog go camping or hiking and take a drink from a clear mountain stream, you can both pick up giardia. Diarrhea is one of the first symptoms.

Paws for Thought

If you come home from a camping trip feeling ill, tell your physician and veterinarian you've been in the wild, and have yourself and your dog tested for giardia.

Coccidiosis

This is another parasitic protozoa. This one is often carried by birds. Symptoms include coughing, a runny nose, eye discharge and diarrhea. It can be diagnosed through a fecal analysis.

Dangerous Diseases

Many of the diseases that threaten your puppy can be prevented with vaccinations. However, it's important to know why your puppy needs these vaccines, and why the vaccines were developed in the first place. In addition, some puppies will still get sick. Perhaps the puppy's immune system is not functioning properly, the virus causing the disease mutated or the vaccine itself was ineffective.

Hopefully, your puppy will be healthy and disease-free and you will never see any of the diseases I'm going to describe in this section. But you should know what to look for, just in case.

Distemper

This is a very contagious, viral disease that used to kill thousands of dogs. The new vaccines should be able to prevent distemper, but unfortunately some dogs still die from it.

The virus is passed through the saliva, urine and feces. Dogs with distemper have a fever, are weak, depressed, have a discharge from the eyes and nose, cough, vomit and have diarrhea. Most infected dogs die.

The vaccination usually prevents the disease. However, vaccines work by stimulating the immune system. If the immune system is threatened or if the puppy does not receive the complete series of vaccines, he may not be adequately protected.

Infectious Canine Hepatitis

This is another highly contagious viral disease. It primarily attacks the liver, but can also damage the kidneys. It is not related to the human forms of hepatitis. The virus is spread through the saliva, mucus, urine and feces. Initial symptoms include depression, vomiting, abdominal pain, fever and jaundice.

Mild cases can be treated, but the mortality rate is very high. Vaccinations can prevent this disease.

Coronavirus

This virus is rarely fatal for adult dogs, but can be very dangerous for puppies. Symptoms include vomiting and loose, watery diarrhea. The virus is shed in the stools. Dehydration from the diarrhea and vomiting is the primary danger for puppies. Vaccinations can prevent this virus.

Parvovirus

This virus, commonly called parvo, is a terrible killer of puppies. It attacks the inner lining of the intestines, causing bloody diarrhea. This diarrhea has a very distinctive smell that veterinarians and breeders who have dealt with the disease quickly learn to recognize. In young puppies, the disease also attacks the heart, causing death, often with no other symptoms. The virus also moves very quickly, and dehydration can lead to shock and death within a matter of hours.

Paws for Thought

Cancer is the leading cause of non-accidental death for pet dogs in the United States—if you don't count shelter euthanasia deaths.

The vaccination for parvo is usually effective, although this virus has been known to mutate, rendering the vaccine useless. The vaccine is often given in conjunction with other vaccines, and many vets and breeders believe it should be given alone for the best results.

Leptospirosis

This is a bacterial disease, not a virus, and is passed in the urine. The bacteria attack the kidneys, causing kidney failure. Symptoms include fever, loss of appetite, jaundice and sometimes diarrhea.

Antibiotics can sometimes treat lepto, but often the outcome is not good because of the tremendous damage the bacteria causes. Vaccinations will usually prevent lepto, but care must be taken to not spread this highly contagious disease. It is not limited to dogs, and can also spread to people.

Kennel Cough

What is commonly referred to as kennel cough or canine cough is actually a group of respiratory diseases, including tracheobronchitis, adenovirus and parainfluenza. All three of these diseases cause a lot of coughing, sometimes with a fever, sometimes without.

Most healthy adult dogs can recuperate from these diseases without veterinary care. However, young puppies and older dogs need careful monitoring, as a secondary respiratory infection can occur. In some cases, pneumonia develops.

Vaccinations usually prevent these diseases, but viruses can and do mutate. Often, vaccinated dogs will still come down with some form of kennel cough. What strain or variety they have is usually unknown.

Bordetella Bronchiseptica

This is a coughing disorder caused by bacteria, and is another one of the infections sometimes known as kennel cough or canine cough. The bacteria is spread through mucus and saliva, often through droplets coughed out by an affected dog. A vaccination can prevent this disease.

Rabies

This virus is carried by infected wildlife, and is highly contagious. Rabies is transmitted in the saliva, either through a break in the skin or by a bite. This virus is always fatal.

Vaccines, however, have been very effective in preventing the disease. Rabies vaccines are required by law before obtaining a dog license.

Genetic, Congenital and Other Health Problems

Genetic health problems are inherited from the puppy's ancestors. Either the mother or father had the gene carrying the problem, or both parents had the genes. Research has been ongoing and will probably continue for many years into how genetic diseases are passed from generation to generation, but many questions remain to be answered.

Paws for Thought

Congenital health problems are also called birth defects.

Congenital health threats are present at birth but are not hereditary. Identifying which health problems are genetic and which are congenital is also the subject of much study. For example, hip dysplasia is a crippling disease of many medium to large breeds of dogs. The causes of hip dysplasia have been said to be environmental, nutritional, genetic and congenital. Too much exercise has even been said to be the cause of hip dysplasia. It is easy to assign blame, but it is much more difficult to scientifically prove the cause.

Because many of these health threats are still being investigated and the causes have not yet been definitively determined, I will not lay blame. However, I will tell you which breeds tend to have a predisposition for some problems. This does *not* mean that all dogs of that breed have that problem. But it does mean you should ask your puppy's breeder about them before you get a dog.

I'll also tell you a little about the health threats themselves. When dealing with all of these health threats, contact your veterinarian for appropriate treatment.

The Nervous System

Epilepsy: Most seizures fall into the broad category of epilepsy. Seizures may be mild, as when the dog freezes up and doesn't or can't move. They may also be severe, with strong convulsions (called a *grand mal* seizure). And they can fall anywhere in between. Epilepsy can be found in all breeds, but is more often seen in all sizes of Poodles, Beagles, St. Bernards and German Shepherds.

Wobbler syndrome: This is caused by a malformation of the vertebrae in the neck, causing pressure on the spinal cord. It is more often seen in Great Danes and Doberman Pinschers.

Breed Bits

German Shepherd progressive myelopathy begins as a weakness of the legs, and is progressive, which means it eventually spreads throughout the body. It almost always shows up in German Shepherds that are over five years old.

The Eyes

Juvenile cataracts: These occur in young dogs, usually less than three years of age. They are seen more often in Standard Poodles, Afghan Hounds, Miniature Schnauzers, Cocker Spaniels, Golden Retrievers, Boston Terriers, Labrador Retrievers and Bull Terriers.

Cherry eye: On a dog with this condition, the third eyelid becomes enlarged and swollen and is very red. Cherry eye is more often seen in Cocker Spaniels, Beagles, Bloodhounds, Bulldogs, Bull Terriers, Chinese Shar-Pei, Newfoundlands and St. Bernards.

Collie eye anomaly: This is actually several eye defects, including detached retina, optic nerve disorders and a loss of retinal cells. Collie eye anomaly is seen more often in Collies, Shetland Sheepdogs, German Shepherd Dogs and Australian Shepherds.

Entropian eyelids: With this condition, the lower lid rolls inward so that hairs scrape along the eyeball. This can occur in any breed, but is most often seen in Chinese Shar-Pei, Poodles of all sizes, most of the Spaniel breeds, Rottweilers and Great Danes.

Glaucoma: As with people, this is a disease that causes increased pressure within the eyeball. It is seen more often in Afghan Hounds, Cocker Spaniels, Basset Hounds, Fox Terriers, Dalmatians and Poodles.

Progressive retinal atrophy: In dogs with this disease, the retina deteriorates and vision decreases. Lesions can be detected on the retina. This is seen most often in Collies, Norwegian Elkhounds, many of the Spaniel breeds, Irish Setters, Golden Retrievers, all sizes of Poodles and Miniature Schnauzers.

Puppy Tails

The Canine Eye Registration Foundation (CERF) maintains a directory of dogs whose eyes have been examined by a licensed veterinary ophthalmologist. Thus, breeders can eliminate from their breeding program dogs with eye defects such as progressive retinal atrophy or dogs that have produced puppies that later developed eye defects.

The Skin

Allergies: Dogs can be allergic to many things, including grass, pollen, dust mites, flea bites, and even flea collars. Allergies can be found in any breed.

Collie nose: With this condition, raw lesions appear above the nose on the muzzle, where dogs have little pigment. The skin appears to sunburn, peel and reburn, and then lesions develop. This is most often seen in Collies, Shetland Sheepdogs and other dogs with a white muzzle.

Puppy acne: Also known as impetigo, small white pustules appear on the lower chin. They may open and drain much like acne in humans. It usually disappears with maturity, but may remain into adulthood, especially in Bulldogs, Shar-Pei, Boxers, Great Danes and Doberman Pinschers.

Schnauzer comedo syndrome: Also known as Schnauzer back, because it is usually seen in Schnauzers, the skin along the back erupts in hives. Crusty bumps will be evident, along with hair loss. The skin may be oily and will smell.

Breed Bits

Some health threats are related to structure. For example, brachycephalic dogs (those with round, wide skulls and flat faces) are more prone to respiratory problems, including asthma.

The Bones

Disc disease: Discs act as shock absorbers between the vertebrae, and if one is damaged or ruptures, severe back pain results. The breeds with long backs are at particular risk for disc disease, including Basset Hounds, Dachshunds and Corgis, although any dog can injure his back.

Hip dysplasia: This is a deformity of the hip joint. The dog may show lameness and may not want to move. It is seen in many breeds, including most of the larger breeds. Labrador Retrievers, Gold Retrievers, German Shepherds, Rottweilers and many other breeds can be affected.

Elbow dysplasia: This is a deformity of the elbow, similar to hip dysplasia, and will show up as lameness and a desire not to move. It is seen in many large breeds, including Golden Retrievers, Labrador Retrievers and German Shepherds.

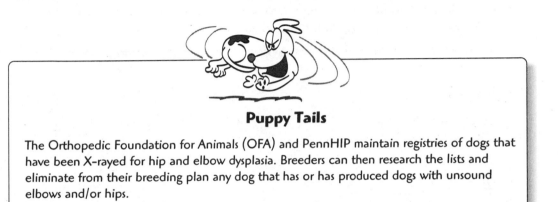

Puppy Tails

The Orthopedic Foundation for Animals (OFA) and PennHIP maintain registries of dogs that have been X-rayed for hip and elbow dysplasia. Breeders can then research the lists and eliminate from their breeding plan any dog that has or has produced dogs with unsound elbows and/or hips.

Luxated patella: In dogs with this condition, the kneecap (patella) is not held in place properly, causing the dog to hop and skip. This is more often seen in the smaller breeds, including Miniature and Toy Poodles, Papillons, Maltese and several of the other toy breeds.

The Circulatory System

Cardiomyopathy: This disease damages the muscles of the heart, weakening it. Eventually, the heart is no longer able to adequately pump blood, and other organs begin to fail as well. It can be found in all breeds, but is seen more often in Boxers, Great Danes, German Shepherds, Irish Wolfhounds, Irish Setters, Springer Spaniels, Greyhounds and Doberman Pinschers.

Patent ductus arteriosus: This is a disorder where the blood being pumped from the heart bypasses the lungs, and therefore is not properly oxygenated. It is seen in several breeds, including all sizes of Poodles, German Shepherds, Cocker Spaniels, Shetland Sheepdogs and Pomeranians.

Von Willebrand's disease: This is a bleeding disorder, similar to hemophilia in people. Injuries will bleed significantly and the blood will not clot as it should. It has been found in some breeds more than others, especially in Doberman Pinschers. Other breeds with a proclivity to Von Willebrand's disease include German Shorthaired Pointers, Scottish Terriers and Chesapeake Bay Retrievers.

The Least You Need to Know

➤ External parasites are more than just nuisances. They can transmit disease and potentially endanger your puppy's life.

➤ Internal parasites are nasty and often difficult to get rid of—and some can be transmitted to people.

➤ Although vaccinations can prevent many deadly diseases, their effectiveness depends upon the health of your puppy's immune system.

➤ Many breeds are affected by a variety of genetic and congenital disorders.

Chapter 16

What to Do in an Emergency

In This Chapter

➤ Know your veterinarian's emergency procedures

➤ Put together an emergency first aid kit

➤ How to restrain your puppy

➤ What to do in the most common puppy emergencies

You can be the most careful puppy owner in the world, making sure your yard and house are safe, and emergencies will still happen. Someone may trip over the puppy, she may fall off the sofa and hit her head, or your puppy may chew on something that makes her sick. It's always scary when your puppy gets hurt, but if you are prepared for emergencies, you will be able to handle them with a little bit less stress.

Your Vet's Emergency Procedures

Don't wait until there is an emergency to find out what your vet's policies are. Ask now so you know. Some veterinarians do not handle after-hours emergencies at all. Instead, they refer their clients to emergency animal hospitals. Other vets take all calls no matter what the hour. There's no right or wrong policy—what's important is that you understand the policy and know who to call when there is an emergency.

If your vet refers emergencies to a local animal hospital, do you know where it is? Can you find it right away without having to search for it? If you aren't sure, you should drive around and find it now. Again, don't wait for the emergency to happen. Be prepared.

Paws for Thought

Some dog owners set aside a credit card just for emergencies. That way it's never over-extended when an emergency arises.

What are your veterinarian's policies regarding payment for emergency care? What are the policies of the emergency animal hospital? Many require complete payment when they treat your dog. If that's the case, can you pay the bill? Emergency care can be very expensive. What happens if an emergency occurs between pay days?

Post the vet's telephone number and the emergency animal hospital's number in several prominent locations. Put it on the refrigerator, in your telephone book, in your wallet and in your canine first aid kit.

A Canine First Aid Kit

I put together my first canine first aid kit more than 20 years ago, and am always glad I did. It has been used for a few big emergencies, and numerous small ones. I used it to take care of my dogs, cats and reptiles, as well as friends' and neighbors' dogs. It has come in handy more times than I can count.

I use a large fishing tackle box to hold all my first aid supplies, because it is big and has a lot of little sections to hold small items. The table has a list of some supplies you'll probably want to include.

Your Canine First Aid Kit	
Large and small tweezers	Gauze pads of different sizes, including eye pads
Rounded-end scissors and pointed, sharp scissors	Elastic to wrap around bandages
Disposable razors	Instant cold compresses
Nail clippers for dogs	Antiseptic cleansing wipes
Thermometer	Sterile saline eye wash
Safety pins	Alcohol prep pads
Mirror	Small bottle of hydrogen peroxide
Pen and pencil	Benadryl tablets
Paper for notes and directions	Bactine
Tape of various sizes, widths and types	Bacitracin ointment
Butterfly adhesive bandages	Kaopectate tablets or liquid
Rolls of gauze or fabric of different widths	Spare leash and collar

I also keep a gallon jug of water in my van, a dog bowl and an old sheet that can be used as a stretcher.

You should check this kit often, to replace materials that have been used and materials or medications that have expired. Most medications have an expiration date, and you shouldn't use them after that date.

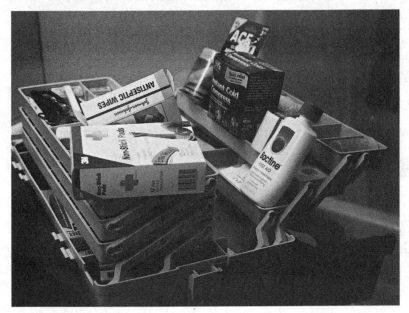

You can combine human and canine first aid kits in a big tackle box. Many items will be the same for both.

Restraining an Injured Dog

You must know how to restrain your puppy if she gets hurt. This is necessary so that she doesn't continue to hurt herself by struggling, and so that she won't hurt you either when you try to help her. As much as we love our dogs, and as much as they love us, they are still dogs; when a dog is hurt, she doesn't stop to think about how her actions may hurt herself or you. She struggles because she is frightened and in pain. Therefore, you need to know how to restrain her.

Prevent Her From Biting

The first thing you need to learn is how to muzzle your pup. By closing her mouth gently but firmly, you can make sure she doesn't bite anyone when she's afraid or hurt. You can make a muzzle out of just about anything that is long and soft. A leash works very well, as does a bandanna or a length of gauze from your first aid kit.

G-r-r-r!

Watch your dog carefully when she's muzzled to make sure she can breathe. If she's having trouble breathing or is getting even more anxious, loosen the muzzle slightly.

Take the length of leash or material and wrap it quickly around your dog's snout at least twice. Wrap it gently—not too tight—but firmly. Then pull the ends back behind your dog's ears and tie it behind her neck. If you gently pull on the material around the snout, it shouldn't slip off.

Practice this muzzling technique on your puppy every once in awhile. Make a game out of it by using a happy tone of voice. Give her a treat and make a big deal out of it when you take the muzzle off. She's not going to care for it no matter what you do, but the practice will be good for you. And if she's felt the muzzle before, it won't be quite so traumatic if you need to do it for real.

You can use a scarf or a length of bandage to make a muzzle, as shown.

Paws for Thought

I also have dog leashes in several different places, including in the car and the first aid kit. I don't want to have to go searching for a leash when there's an emergency.

Be Still!

Another skill to teach your puppy is to be still while lying on her side. Lay her down with her feet away from you so her head is near your right hand. Use your hand to keep her head down as you tell her, "Be still!" If she's thrashing around or trying to fight you, talk gently to her and rub her tummy. As she relaxes, tell her quietly what a good puppy she is.

This is an important skill for times when you may need her to be still and quiet, especially in emergencies, so be sure to practice this every once in awhile.

Canine CPR

CPR—a combination of cardiac massage and assisted breathing—has saved thousands of people's lives, and it can do the same for many dogs. If you know how to perform canine CPR, you may one day be able to save the life of either your dog or someone else's treasured pet.

The best way to offer CPR is with two people: one to do the heart massage and one to do the breathing. But you can do it alone, if need be. But before you do anything, when you see a dog lying still you will want to make a quick evaluation. Then, if there's no heartbeat or she's not breathing, here are the steps to take:

➤ Check to see if there is a heart beat.

➤ Check to see if she's breathing.

➤ If she's not breathing, clear her mouth of any obstructions.

➤ Pull her tongue out and to the side of her mouth so that it doesn't block the airway.

➤ Close her mouth and pull her lips over the teeth to help make her mouth airtight.

➤ Inhale a deep breath, and then exhale into the dog's nose. Watch her chest to check that it rises after you blow.

➤ Repeat every 10 seconds for big dogs and more often (if you can without hyperventilating) for smaller dogs.

Paws for Thought

In many areas, the Red Cross offers classes for pet CPR, just as they do for CPR on humans. Call your local Red Cross to find out if one is offered in your area.

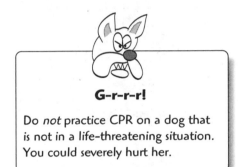

G-r-r-r!

Do *not* practice CPR on a dog that is not in a life-threatening situation. You could severely hurt her.

➤ After 10 breaths, stop and do chest compressions. Place her on her side, and clasp your hands together, one on top of the other. Place your hands over the dog's heart, lean over, and push down in short bursts.

➤ Compress the chest five times and go back to assisted breathing. Do ten breaths, then five chest compressions, then repeat the cycle.

Once you start CPR, continue it until your dog begins breathing on her own, until you can get your dog to help, or until it seems very obvious that it is vain. But don't stop too soon—many dogs have been saved by canine CPR.

Shock Is Life Threatening!

A dog (like a person) will go into shock after a traumatic injury or during a serious, sudden illness. By itself, shock is life threatening. When it's combined with whatever caused the shock in the first place, your dog is in serious danger. Symptoms of shock include:

➤ Faster, often irregular heartbeat.

➤ Panting or very rapid breathing, often gasping.

➤ Dilated pupils, a staring, glazed look to the eyes and no eye response to movement.

You cannot treat shock, other than keeping your dog warm and still and getting her to a veterinarian right away. This is not the time to watch the dog and hope she'll come out of it on her own. She needs help right away!

Heatstroke

Dogs do not sweat through pores in their skin, as people do. Instead, dogs lose heat by panting and by sweating through the pads of their feet. Because these are small areas on a dog's body, they can overheat much more quickly than people do.

Breed Bits

Bulldogs have a tough time in hot weather. Their short muzzle and crooked nasal passages make breathing and panting difficult. Severely limit a Bulldog's activities in hot weather.

The number-one cause of heatstroke in dogs is being left alone in cars. Never, ever leave a dog shut in a car on a warm day—not even for a moment. A car will heat up to over 100 degrees in just minutes, even if it's in the 70s outside.

A dog that is overheated will lie down, often flopping herself down, or will pace back and forth in agitation. She will pant heavily and may go into shock. Her body temperature will rise rapidly.

You need to cool her down *immediately*. Immerse her in cool water or pack her in ice and get her to the vet's office right away.

Bleeding

Bleeding accompanies most kinds of injuries. How it should be treated depends upon the type of bleeding and its severity.

If the skin isn't broken, there may be bleeding under the skin. This can result in a bruise if the injury is small. A bruise can be treated with an ice pack. Use the ice pack on and off at 15-minute intervals until it seems that the bleeding under the skin has stopped.

After 24 hours, use a heat pack to improve blood circulation and healing to the injured site.

Bleeding from small scrapes, scratches and small cuts is usually not a danger. Wipe it off, and apply pressure with a gauze pad if it's still oozing. When the bleeding stops, rinse it off with hydrogen peroxide. Check the wound for a few days to make sure it's not infected and that it's healing well.

If the wound is red and oozing, rinse it several times a day with hydrogen peroxide and carefully rub an antibiotic ointment on it. If you're concerned, make an appointment to bring your dog in to see the vet. This is not, however, an emergency.

A continuous, oozing type of bleeding is more serious. You will need to put pressure on the wound, using layers of gauze pads and pressure from your hand, and you'll want to get the dog to your veterinarian right away. Stitches will probably be required, and if the dog has lost too much blood, additional treatments will be needed.

Bleeding that comes out in spurts is very dangerous. It means a major blood vessel has been broken and your dog is in immediate danger of bleeding to death. Use a length of gauze or a shoelace to make a tourniquet above the wound, between the wound and the heart. Wrap the shoelace around the dog's leg, then tie a small stick to the knot. Twist the stick so that it tightens the knot and the shoelace around the leg. You are trying to cut off circulation so that the bleeding slows.

Tourniquets *must* be loosened every 10 to 15 minutes, or the tissue in the leg will die from lack of blood. Loosen it, let the blood flow for a couple of minutes, and then tighten it again.

Internal bleeding is less obvious and is very dangerous. If your dog has been in some kind of rough accident, watch her behavior. If she stops moving, acts restless or cries, get her to the vet's office right away. Other symptoms of internal bleeding include pale gums, a distended abdomen, bloody diarrhea, bloody vomit or blood in the saliva.

Paws for Thought

If you don't have an ice pack handy, use a bag of frozen vegetables.

G-r-r-r!

Watch your dog carefully. Too much blood loss can trigger shock and cardiac arrest. Get her to the vet's office right away!

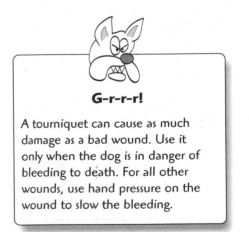

G-r-r-r!

A tourniquet can cause as much damage as a bad wound. Use it only when the dog is in danger of bleeding to death. For all other wounds, use hand pressure on the wound to slow the bleeding.

Choking

Puppies put stuff in their mouth all the time. After all, they don't have hands, and tasting and chewing on things is one of the ways puppies discover their world. Unfortunately, that means puppies (and adult dogs) are in danger of choking. If your dog seems to be choking, coughing or gagging:

➤ Open her mouth and try to see what is blocking her airway.

➤ If you can reach it, do so and pull it out. Sometimes tongs (such as salad tongs) will help you grasp round things, like a ball.

➤ If you can't, try the canine version of the Heimlich maneuver. Stand above and behind your dog, reach under her belly just behind the ribcage and pull up quickly several times.

➤ If this doesn't work, don't wait around. Her life is at stake—get her to the nearest veterinarian right away.

Paws for Thought

You can get your puppy to vomit by giving her several teaspoons of hydrogen peroxide.

Poisons

I know you puppy-proofed your house, yard and garage before you brought home your puppy, and all the dangers you could think of were removed from her reach. Unfortunately, accidents can still happen, and more than one puppy has been poisoned because she was too curious and stuck her nose where it didn't belong.

Symptoms of poisoning can vary depending upon what the puppy ate. Some of the more common symptoms include extreme salvation and drooling, vomiting, diarrhea and muscle tremors. The puppy's eyes may be dilated or she may suffer seizures.

The table lists some of the more common substances found around the house, and what you should do if your puppy gets into them.

Emergency Treatment for Common Poisons

Poison	Treatment
Anti-freeze	Induce vomiting and get your puppy to the vet's office right away.
Bleach	Induce vomiting and take your puppy in to your veterinarian soon, although if she has vomited it is no longer an emergency.

Chocolate	This is poisonous to dogs, so make her vomit and then call your vet.
Gasoline	Make her vomit, give her some vegetable oil to block absorption and take her to the vet's office right away.
Ibuprofen	Make her vomit and get her to the vet's office right away.
Insecticides	If ingested, get her to the vet right away. Do not induce vomiting unless your vet recommends it. If there was skin contact, wash her thoroughly, then get her to the vet's right away.
Rodent, roach or snail poisons	Induce vomiting and get her to your vet's office right away.

With any case of poisoning, after doing what you can at home, get your puppy to the veterinarian right away.

Bring with you whatever it was your puppy got into. If at all possible, bring the label with the name of the product and any ingredients. The more information you can give your vet, the better.

Paws for Thought

A 24-hour poison hotline called the National Poison Control Center for Animals is available at (900) 680-0000. No credit card is needed; your phone bill will be charged.

Burns

Puppies can get burned in a variety of ways. Thermal burns are those caused by heat, and puppies can be burned if they stick their nose on the outside of the charcoal grill after you light it or investigate a candle or knock over the iron. Electrical burns occur when the puppy chews on an electrical cord or a battery or licks an electrical outlet. Chemical burns happen when the puppy makes contact with a corrosive substance that causes a burn, such as bleach, gasoline, liquid drain cleaner, paint thinner or road salt.

If you suspect your puppy has been burned, follow these directions:

➤ If it's a chemical burn, rinse your puppy thoroughly. Also treat it as a potential poisoning.

➤ For any burn, put an ice pack on the spot.

➤ If the burn is not severe and the skin is simply red, keep it clean and watch it carefully to make sure it doesn't get infected.

➤ If the burn has damaged layers of skin, is blistered, bleeding and oozing, or if the burn has damaged all the layers of skin, cover it lightly and take your puppy to the vet's office right away.

Gastric Torsion (Bloat)

This condition is more prevalent in large breed dogs with deep chests, such as Great Danes, Rottweilers, German Shepherds and Labrador Retrievers. However, it can happen in just about any breed. When a dog has bloat, the gases that are normally produced in the stomach cause the abdomen to distend. If there is too much pressure, the stomach can actually twist (torsion). Shock follows quickly, and the dog dies.

If you notice your dog has an enlarged abdomen or is pacing, showing extreme restlessness, or gagging without throwing up (especially soon after eating), get her to the vet's office right away. Bloat can be treated if the dog arrives at the vet's office soon enough.

Paws for Thought

No one is sure what causes bloat, but you can lessen the likelihood by keeping the dog quiet for an hour after each meal, feeding two or three small meals instead of one large meal, and limiting water intake for an hour after each meal.

Insect Bites and Stings

Any puppy that spends any amount of time outside will someday run up against a bug that doesn't want to play with her. Most insect bites and stings are simply an annoyance and are no real health threat. However, some dogs are allergic to bee stings, wasp stings or spider bites. If your dog is allergic, this could be a potentially life-threatening situation.

If you suspect your dog has been stung or bitten by an insect, first try to find where on your dog's body the bite or sting is. If there is a stinger, scrape it out. Don't grab it and pull it—that will squeeze more venom into your dog's skin. Scrape it out with a fingernail.

If you need to, shave away some of the dog's hair so you can see the sting or bite. Wash it off, pour some hydrogen peroxide on it and watch it. Some signs of allergic reaction include:

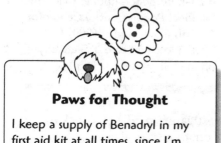

Paws for Thought

I keep a supply of Benadryl in my first aid kit at all times, since I'm allergic to bee stings myself, as are two of my dogs.

➤ Swelling at the site of the bite or sting and in the body tissues surrounding it

➤ Redness or extreme whiteness

➤ Fever

➤ Muscle aches, joint pain and lameness

➤ Vomiting

➤ Diarrhea

If your puppy is showing any of these allergic reactions, call your veterinarian right away. He or she may recommend that you give your puppy a Benadryl antihistamine immediately. The vet will also want to see your puppy as soon as you can bring her in.

Animal Bites

If your puppy is bitten by another puppy during organized play time and the bite is a simple puncture made with baby puppy teeth, don't be too worried. Simply wash the bite, pour some hydrogen peroxide over it and watch it. If it looks red and like it may be infected, call your veterinarian.

However, if your puppy is attacked by an unknown dog, call your vet immediately, as this could pose a real health threat. If you can, try to find the dog's owner to make sure the dog is vaccinated, especially with an up-to-date rabies vaccine. Some bites may need special treatment, including antibiotics, draining or stitches, to make sure they heal properly.

G-r-r-r!

Wild animals carrying the rabies virus are not that uncommon. Skunks, raccoons, bats and squirrels are all possible carriers. The best prevention is to make sure your puppy is vaccinated.

If your dog is bitten by a wild animal, you must get her to the veterinarian's office right away. If your puppy has received her rabies vaccination (usually given between four and six months of age), that worry will be eliminated. However, if your puppy has not yet received that vaccine, there could be serious consequences. Your vet will also want to treat the wound itself, and may recommend antibiotics.

Snake Bites

Contrary to their reputation, most snakes are not very aggressive. In fact, most of the time you won't see the snakes that are close to you—they will slither away before you know they are near. However, many snakes will defend themselves when threatened, and when your puppy decides to use a snake as a play toy, the snake will consider that a threat! Luckily, the vast majority of snakes are not poisonous (non-venomous).

If your dog is bitten by a non-venomous snake, just wash the wound with hydrogen peroxide and watch it to make sure the wound doesn't get infected.

If your dog is bitten by a venomous snake, don't panic. First of all, many snakes do not automatically inject venom. Your dog is not a natural dinner item, and the venom is used to subdue prey. Therefore, the snake may strike to scare away your dog without actually injecting venom.

If venom is injected, the bite site will begin to swell. If your pup was bitten on the leg, the leg will swell. Unfortunately, most dogs are bitten on the face, because they stick their nose down into the snake's space and whap!—the snake strikes the dog on the nose or muzzle. If the nose or muzzle begins to swell, the dog is in great danger of suffocating. In any case, get her to the veterinarian's office right away. Call ahead so the vet can make arrangements to get the anti-venom.

Before leaving for the vet's office, take a good, hard look at the snake—without getting bit yourself, of course! Make sure you can describe it or identify it in a book. There is no universal anti-venom that works for all snakes. Each species has its own anti-venom, and you need to be able to identify the particular species.

While getting her to the vet's office, you need to stay calm so you can keep your dog calm. Keep her quiet, too, because limited movement will help slow down the spread of the venom in her system.

What if you don't know whether or not the snake was poisonous? Take a good look at the snake, wash the dog's wound, and then watch her *very* closely. The instant you see swelling or any signs of distress, get her to the vet.

Natural (and Other) Disasters

Where do you live? In Southern California where I live, we must deal with wildfires and earthquakes. In the Midwest, dog owners must put up with tornadoes. Families in the Southeast must be able to survive hurricanes. Natural disasters are a fact of life, and you need to make preparations so that you can take care of your puppy as well as your family.

Paws for Thought

My dogs always wear a buckle collar with a tag with my name and phone number on it, as well as their license tag. They are also tattooed and microchipped for identification.

I keep my canine first aid kit (which is stocked with human first aid supplies, too) easily accessible. When on vacation or a trip, the first aid kit is in my van. I also have on hand a gallon jug of water—more if we're traveling in the desert. Extra leashes and collars are always in my van, too.

In my garage, within reach of the side door, is my emergency kit in case of earthquakes or fires. It has some canned dog food that will keep a long time, a can opener, water, a smaller first aid kit and a variety of other supplies that are recommended for people.

A few of my neighbors think I'm either a little neurotic or overly concerned, but my husband and I have lived in this area for many years and twice have been evacuated due to wildfires. When you're ordered to evacuate, you don't have any time to pack up. You grab what you can and leave. My emergency kit has come in handy both times we had to leave in a hurry, and it's there for any future emergencies.

The Least You Need to Know

➤ Know what your veterinarian's emergency procedures are before there's an emergency. Make sure you know where the emergency animal hospital is located, too.

➤ Practice restraining and muzzling your puppy before an emergency. Make a game out of it for your puppy, but know how to do it.

➤ Put together a first aid kit, and keep it stocked and handy.

➤ Familiarize yourself with first aid for a variety of emergencies, so you'll know what to do.

➤ In any emergency, after you administer aid, take your puppy to the veterinarian immediately.

Part 4

Let's Teach You How to Train Your Puppy

Dog training isn't really a good description of what we'll be doing in this section. You will be learning just as much (if not more) than your puppy. You need to know how to communicate with your puppy, how to motivate him so he wants to be good, and how to let him know when he's made a mistake.

You will be teaching your puppy the basic commands, such as sit, lie down, stay and come. We'll discuss how to prevent and solve problems, including jumping on people, biting, chewing and digging. You will also learn how to teach some advanced commands and some fun tricks. There is so much you can do with your puppy once you learn how to teach him, so let's get started!

Chapter 17

All About Dog Training

> **In This Chapter**
>
> ➤ Training offers you and your puppy many benefits
> ➤ There is a variety of training techniques, methods and styles
> ➤ What are training tools and how do you use them?
> ➤ How to find the best training help for you

Each year in this country, thousands of dogs are given up by their owners because of behavior problems. Sometimes the owner gets fed up because the dog chews on the furniture or digs up the backyard. Parents get upset because the dog jumps on the children and nips at their clothes. The dog may dash out the gate one time too many, and this last time no one chases after him. Unfortunately, many of those dogs given up for bad behavior will never be adopted; they will be destroyed at the local shelter.

The fact that so many healthy dogs are euthanized is tragic, and it's not the only sad part. It's also sad that many of those problem behaviors could have been prevented if the dog's owners had looked for help. If the dog had been enrolled in a puppy training class, the owners could have learned how to prevent or correct any troublesome behaviors. They could have established some control over the dog. Very often, dog training makes the difference between whether a dog remains in his home or not.

The Benefits of Training

Dog training is not something you *do to* your dog—it is something you and your dog *do together*. You and your dog will both be learning. You learn how to teach your dog, how to motivate him so that he wants to be good and, when necessary, how to let him know he's made a mistake. Your dog learns to look to you for directions and permission. He also learns to control himself, and to restrain himself from doing things he might want to do.

Paws for Thought

Good dog training rewards desired actions or behaviors and discourages or ignores undesired actions.

Paws for Thought

A well-trained dog will seem as if he is able to read your mind. He is so attuned to your body language, emotions and habits that he will anticipate your commands.

While you train between the two of you, you will also strengthen the bond between the two of you. As you both learn and do things together, you will learn more about each other—about both your strengths and your weaknesses because, after all, neither one of you is perfect! Your weaknesses could even be offset by your dog's strengths. If you are shy with strangers and your puppy is an extrovert, for example, you will find yourself talking more to strangers because your puppy likes to visit with them!

During training, your puppy will learn to look up to you as his leader. Mutual respect, love and affection will follow. Training is a process that you both go through.

A trained dog and an educated owner can do many more things *safely* than can an untrained dog and an irresponsible owner. The owner of an untrained dog may allow her dog to run around off leash, but the owner of the trained dog knows when it is safe to do so and when it isn't. The owner of the trained dog also knows that her dog will come back to her when she calls him.

The trained dog is a joy to have around the house because he won't dash out through an open door. He won't stop on the stairs, tripping his owner. He will lie quietly while his owner is talking on the telephone. The trained dog may bark when people come to the door, but will stop when he's told to be quiet. The trained dog will not chew on the furniture, steal the kids' toys or have housetraining accidents when left alone.

The trained dog is welcome around people because he won't jump on them. He will sit quietly while people are talking, he won't beg under the table and he won't steal food off the counters.

The trained dog can participate in other activities, including Frisbee games, herding tests, obedience trials or carting demonstrations. The trained dog has the world at his feet. There is nothing he and his owner can't do!

Training Techniques and Methods Galore

Every dog trainer has his or her own method of training. Some follow a method designed by someone else. Some combine a number of different techniques until they find something they like. Other trainers come up with their own method. If you talk to a thousand different dog trainers, you will hear a thousand different variations on dog training.

In addition, if you read books or magazines, or watch training videos, there are another thousand (or more!) techniques available.

Why So Many Techniques?

There are several reasons for all this variation. First of all, dog training is not an exact science. Every single dog is different and responds to training in his own unique way. Sure, most Border Collies have certain characteristics in common, just as most Doberman Pinschers, Cocker Spaniels or Mastiffs have some common characteristics, but they are also each unique individuals. When you add in the fact that each dog owner is also a unique individual, you have a profession that cannot be an exact science. Instead, training must respond to that uniqueness in each dog-and-owner team. The best trainers use a method that reflects this uniqueness and allows for variations in training techniques.

Puppy Tails

As with any profession, dog training has its fads. Sometimes a new technique will become very popular before it has been really proven, and everyone wants to try it. Most experienced dog trainers look upon new fads with skepticism. They may experiment with a new technique, but in the long run they want to see if the fad stands the test of time. Good trainers develop their techniques from what works in the long term.

In addition, dog training as a profession is constantly evolving. We are always learning more about how people (and dogs) learn. We are also learning more about teaching both people and dogs. As trainers explore different ideas, what they learn is passed on to other trainers. These trainers explore their new knowledge and pass on what they have learned. When someone tries something new and has great success with it, other people try it too, and it becomes a new technique. Thus, the profession is continuing to evolve and grow.

The dog trainer's own personality will also affect which training method is used. A trainer who is very soft may dislike using corrections, while a trainer with a demanding personality may be demanding of her canine clients, too.

Training methods can vary significantly. What one trainer uses as standard procedure can be completely disregarded by another. That doesn't make either one right or wrong, and both may have success with dogs. I'll describe some of the more widely used methods for you, so you can understand them better and start to get an idea of what technique you might be most comfortable with.

Paws for Thought

Many psychologists, psychiatrists, teachers and other experts in behavior believe aggression begets aggression. A forceful, compulsive training technique may instigate aggressive behavior from your dog.

Compulsion Training

This is probably the oldest training method. The compulsion method requires the dog to do as he is told, and if he doesn't, he is corrected. For many years, this was believed to be the only way to train dogs, oxen or horses. The old adage "Spare the rod and spoil the child" embodies the same philosophy as this training method.

Today, compulsion training is still used by some trainers who consider it very effective for some dogs. But it is not as popular as it used to be. Many people feel uncomfortable being that harsh or punitive with their dog.

Positive Training

Techniques based on positive reinforcement (praise, food treats, petting) are very popular now. The dog is rewarded when he does something right, rather than corrected when he does something wrong. Many people are very comfortable with this type of training, especially people who are uncomfortable using corrections.

Clicker training is a positive training technique that is receiving a lot of attention at the moment. The dog learns to associate the sound of a clicker with positive reinforcement. The clicker is then used to teach him when he's done something right.

Combination Techniques

Most dog trainers use a combination of both positive and compulsion techniques. These trainers use positive reinforcements when the dog has done something right and corrections to let the dog know when he's made a mistake.

This type of training offers a lot of flexibility. Individual dog owners can vary the amounts of positive reinforcements or corrections to suit their individual dog, or their own personality.

Combination techniques also help owners communicate very clearly to their dogs. When desired behaviors are rewarded and undesired behaviors are corrected, the dog is not left wondering what is and is not allowed.

Training Tools

Training tools are things you can use to help train your dog. Your voice is a training tool to both praise and correct. A leash is a training tool, as are food treats and toys. Anything that you use during the course of training your puppy can be considered a training tool.

Paws for Thought

Watch how a trainer uses the tools he or she prefers. If you are uncomfortable with a particular training tool, ask questions. And remember, the final decision to use any tool is yours.

Different trainers will use a variety of training tools, and which ones you choose is often decided by the training method you are using. Most trainers have very firm beliefs about what training tools should be used. That's fine, but, as I mentioned, there are thousands of different ways to train dogs. You, as your puppy's owner, must also be comfortable with the training tools being used.

Leash

The leash is not just for taking the puppy for a walk. Instead, think of the leash as an umbilical cord between you and your puppy. Most trainers will tell you to use the leash around the house so you can help the puppy learn to listen to you, and so you can prevent the puppy from getting into trouble. Most trainers suggest a four- or six-foot leash to start.

You may also want a long leash or long line. This is usually 20 to 30 feet long. It is used to help teach the dog to come from a distance. It can also be used when the dog is playing anywhere other than within a fenced yard, to make sure he responds to the come command.

Motivators or Positive Reinforcements

You will use something to help your puppy learn what is right and to help motivate him to want to be right. Positive reinforcements can include your voice (in a happy tone), food treats, toys or even a tennis ball. Some trainers emphasize a particular motivator more than others. Some trainers do not like to use food in training, while other trainers emphasize the importance of food.

Collars

There are several types of collars available for dogs, and most trainers feel pretty strongly about one or the other. A simple buckle collar, made of either nylon or leather, is usually the first type of collar a puppy wears. You can put your puppy's identification tags on this collar. This collar is soft and provides very little in the way of correction.

A chain slip collar, often called a choke chain or a training collar, can be a very effective training collar when used properly. However, when used improperly it can choke the dog. Because of this, a slip collar should never be left on the dog when he isn't supervised.

A variety of training tools is available to help you train your puppy.

A prong or pinch collar doesn't choke the dog, but instead gives a pinching correction. This collar looks like a medieval torture device, but it can be an effective training tool for some dogs. It is *not* recommended for puppies.

Head halters work like a halter on a horse, following the principle "Where the head goes, the body will follow." These do not choke the dog, nor do they give a hard correction. Instead, the dog is guided to do the right thing.

Private Training or Group Classes?

There are pros and cons to both private training and group classes. Although some trainers offer both, most have a preference for one or the other.

With private training, you and your dog have the trainer's undivided attention. You can ask as many questions as you want without feeling like you're the only person with questions. Private training also allows you to make the training more personalized. You can address specific problems.

On the down side, you are working alone with no other students to practice with, help out or motivate you. Your dog is also alone, with no socialization to other dogs and people. There is also very little in the way of distraction.

In a group situation, dog owners find out they are not alone with their problems—many problems are shared by other dog owners. This group-therapy setting can be a great morale booster. In a group setting, dogs also learn to listen to you even with distractions—things going on around them—and that's a good skill to have.

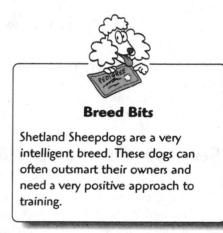

Breed Bits

Shetland Sheepdogs are a very intelligent breed. These dogs can often outsmart their owners and need a very positive approach to training.

Personally, I enjoy group classes. And although I used to teach privately, I don't anymore. I like teaching groups and enjoy the dynamics and different personality of each class. I love to see the progress that each class makes. However, many trainers really enjoy the personal relationship that develops over time between the trainer and private clients.

You will need to decide what is important to you and what you will be comfortable with. Some dog owners will combine both, taking private lessons first and attending a group class later.

Breed Bits

Basset Hounds originated in France. *Bas* means low, and refers to the breed's short legs. Bassets do well with a more positive training method, but can be very stubborn. Some corrections are usually needed.

Training Goals

Different trainers also emphasize different things in their training programs. Some trainers use the American Kennel Club's obedience competition requirements as guidelines for training. For example, in the first level of obedience competition, the dog must heel (walk in a specific position by your left side), stand for an examination and perform several other very specific exercises. These trainers teach these exercises, even if the dog owner has no intention of ever competing in AKC obedience trials.

Other trainers teach their classes with a specific goal in mind. If a trainer is very interested in promoting the Canine Good Citizen program, therapy dog certification, herding trials or other dog activities, her training may be oriented toward that end result.

Most dog owners today need a training program that has as its end goal a well-trained family pet. This functional training emphasizes good social skills, household manners and basic obedience. The technique should be friendly to both the dog and the owner, and should be easy for the owner to implement.

Setting Your Priorities

Before you enroll in a training class or hire a trainer, you need to decide what is important to you. Do you have some strong beliefs about how your puppy should be trained, or do you have an open mind? How do you feel about corrections? What about using food treats in training? What are your goals? You need to think through the answers to some questions before you go looking for a trainer.

➤ What do you expect from the training program?

➤ What do you want to teach your puppy?

➤ What do you want to learn how to do?

➤ What obedience commands do you want the puppy to learn?

➤ Are there some problem behaviors you want to change?

➤ What type of training or training method do you prefer?

➤ Do you prefer private lessons or group classes?

➤ Is the cost of the training a factor in your decision?

➤ Is driving distance to the training important?

➤ Is a specific day or evening better than any other?

Answer these questions—even if just to yourself—before you call any trainers. Then, if the issues are important to you, keep them in mind as you talk to the trainers in your area.

Finding a Trainer

In Chapter 6, I mentioned that a trainer is one of those professionals you need to find before you bring home your new puppy. If you did, you already have someone reputable to call if you have problems housetraining the puppy or if other problem behaviors surface. However, if you haven't yet found the "perfect" trainer, let's review the process.

G-r-r-r!

Hiring a trainer is not the time to shop for bargains. Don't be afraid to pay a *reasonable* amount for a good trainer. On the other hand, a high price tag is no guarantee of quality.

Often the easiest way to find trainers in your community is to call the local veterinarians. Ask whom they recommend. Veterinarians and their staff know which dogs behave themselves and which dogs don't, and often they know which trainer trained the dogs in both groups. They also hear their clients mention this trainer or that trainer, and describe who teaches a good class and who doesn't. If you call several veterinarians and one or two trainers' names keep coming up, you will know where to start your research.

If you see a nicely behaved dog walking with his owner, ask the owner where they went for training. Ask your neighbors, too, where they attended classes. Personal referrals are a good endorsement for any trainer.

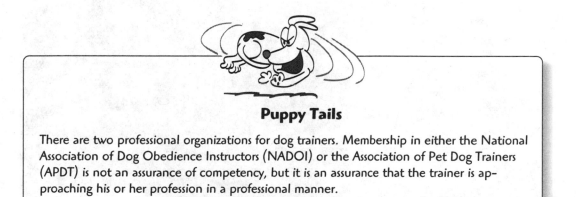

Puppy Tails

There are two professional organizations for dog trainers. Membership in either the National Association of Dog Obedience Instructors (NADOI) or the Association of Pet Dog Trainers (APDT) is not an assurance of competency, but it is an assurance that the trainer is approaching his or her profession in a professional manner.

Once you have two or three trainers on your list, call them and ask some questions:

➤ Do you offer private training or group classes?

➤ Do you teach puppy classes as well as regular beginners' classes?

➤ What type of training do you do (pet, competition, etc.)?

➤ What training method or style do you use?

➤ What training tools do you use?

➤ Where do you teach?

➤ How much do you charge?

➤ May I watch a couple of classes?

➤ If I sign up for training, can I call you for help between sessions?

➤ Can the whole family attend the training sessions?

Many instructors encourage the entire family to come to class, so that everyone learns the same way of doing things.

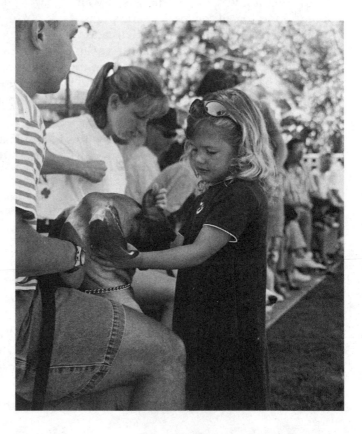

If all the questions are answered thoroughly, plan on watching a couple of this trainer's classes. Don't interfere with the class, don't ask questions during the class and certainly don't make any comments. After all, at this point you are not a paying customer.

Watch how the instructor handles the class. Is everyone being helped? Are directions clear and understandable? Do the dogs appear to be under control? Are they learning? Most important, would you be comfortable working in this class?

Puppy Kindergarten Class

Many years ago, it was understood that a dog shouldn't start training until it was eight months to a year old. Before that, trainers believed, the puppy wouldn't have the concentration to apply to training and the owner's time would be wasted. Today, most trainers recommend that puppies start training at 10 to 12 weeks of age, or as soon as the puppy has had two full sets of vaccinations.

Why the big change in training philosophy? Granted, young puppies often do have trouble concentrating, but that doesn't mean they can't learn. It just means the owner has to learn how to teach the puppy. By starting training early, puppies learn how to be good without learning bad habits. The owner also learns—not just how to teach the puppy, but also how to prevent problem behavior.

A puppy kindergarten class will give you and your puppy a chance to learn together alongside other puppies and their owners.

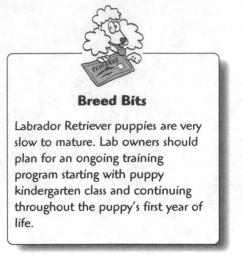

Breed Bits

Labrador Retriever puppies are very slow to mature. Lab owners should plan for an ongoing training program starting with puppy kindergarten class and continuing throughout the puppy's first year of life.

Puppy class also includes a lot of socialization, both to other people and other puppies. This socialization is a vital part of puppyhood (Chapter 10 explains why), and has a great influence on the puppy's adult personality.

Puppies that never get this important socialization will grow up with character flaws. They can be aggressive and nasty to other dogs, as well as to people, or can grow up fearful, timid and shy. Puppy socialization is just as important as training.

When You Need a Trainer's Help

There may be certain instances when you will need a trainer's help. Obviously, the puppy kindergarten class is very important. However, before and after that class you may need some additional help.

Call the trainer if any of these situations comes up:

➤ Your puppy bites you or any other person.

➤ Your puppy growls at you.

➤ Your puppy guards his food.

➤ Your puppy throws a temper tantrum—screaming, biting, throwing himself around—when you try to get him to do something.

➤ Your puppy regresses from previously good behavior.

➤ You are feeling overwhelmed.

➤ You feel your puppy is smarter than you.

Don't be embarrassed to ask for help. When you need help, don't be afraid to call. A trainer's job is to help you, and she may be able to answer your questions on the telephone. However, if she says she needs to meet with you, do it. She will charge you for the private training, of course, but if you have a problem, the money will be well spent.

The Least You Need to Know

➤ Training is beneficial to you so you learn how to teach your puppy and how to prevent problem behavior. It's also good for your puppy, who will learn what you expect of him, how to control himself and to look to you as his leader.

➤ There is a variety of training methods, techniques and tools, and many of them work just fine.

➤ Find a trainer who will teach in a style you will be comfortable with.

➤ Choose a trainer who will help you meet your training goals.

➤ Don't be afraid to call a trainer if you need help.

Chapter 18

How to Be Your Puppy's Teacher

In This Chapter

➤ Learning how to use your voice and other training tools

➤ How to train so that you set your puppy up to succeed

➤ Some tips to make your training more successful

➤ Finishing a training session on a high note

Training your puppy involves much more than telling her to sit. Training is a process that involves both you and your puppy. You need to know how to teach your puppy so that she *wants* to be good for you. Your puppy wasn't born knowing how to be good, or even wanting to be good for you; she must learn that, and it's your job to teach her.

Training should (ideally) be as positive as you can make it—as positive as your puppy will allow you to make it. When you can set your puppy up for success and prevent as many problems as possible from happening, you and the puppy will both enjoy your life together much more.

Learn How to Teach Your Puppy

Your puppy was born understanding canine communication. She understands canine body language, facial expressions and verbalizations. Living with people, she must translate everything she sees and hears into this language, much the way you'd have to if you were dropped into a totally foreign civilization.

Paws for Thought

Every time you interact with your puppy, you teach her something and it may (or may not) be what you want her to know! Think about it: What are you teaching her right now?

To make teaching easier, you want to communicate with her so there is as little misunderstanding as possible. But that's hard because if the puppy misunderstands you, you understand her even less. It is impossible for people to think like dogs—we just can't do it. Oh, we can try. And we can make some relatively educated guesses, but we are always thinking like people, and that affects everything we do with our dog.

However, we can try to communicate as simply as possible, and that's our goal. If your puppy understands you, then what you're doing is working.

Using Your Voice

Your voice is your most important training tool. With all of my dogs, my ultimate goal is to teach my puppy to listen to my voice, to pay attention and to respond to verbal commands when off leash. For example, if my puppy is playing out in a field, sniffing and chasing rabbits, I want to be able to call her back to me; I want her to listen to that command and to respond to it right away with no hesitation.

I also want her to listen to me around the house, in the car and in the backyard. I want her to understand that I don't just jabber on for no reason, and that she should pay attention to me when I talk to her.

To make it easier for your puppy to understand, you will be imitating some of the mother dog's verbalizations—or at least her tone of voice. When your puppy was still with her mom, she would interact with her and her littermates using verbal sounds as well as body language. If she wanted to play, her bark was higher in pitch. If a littermate or her mom responded to her play invitation, their barks were also higher in pitch.

We can make a safe assumption that play invitations are higher in pitch than the normal speaking voice, and we can use that to our advantage. When praising your puppy, say "good girl!" in the tone of voice you used to say "ice cream!" as a child. This should be higher in tone than your normal speaking voice, but not as high pitched as a yelp that might suggest you are hurt.

When your puppy was corrected by her mom—for example, if she bit her with her needle-sharp baby teeth—mom would growl at her. That deep growl meant, "You made a mistake! Don't do it again." We can use this sound, too, to our advantage. When your puppy makes a mistake, you can use a deep voice to make a sound such as "Acckk!"

It's traditional to correct a dog using the word "no," but I find that can get confusing. "No" what? Are you saying no to the kids or to the puppy? Are you answering a question or making a correction? Use a sound that will apply only to the dog and no one else—a sound such as "Acckk!" Then you can teach your puppy a specific vocabulary, such as "No bark!" or "No bite!"

Of course, there is no way you can sound like a dog—even with lots of practice! What you are trying to do is use your voice in the same way your puppy's mom used hers: higher pitched for happy; very high pitched for hurt; and deeper sounding for corrections. By using tones much like the ones she used, you are hoping to keep confusion to a minimum during training.

If you are normally soft spoken and are concerned about using your voice to control your puppy, don't worry. Use your normal speaking volume (loudness) but vary the tones. You are teaching your puppy to listen to you, and if you are naturally soft spoken, that's fine. Your puppy can hear you very well.

G-r-r-r!

Don't correct your puppy with a deep voice and then giggle. You will lose all authority.

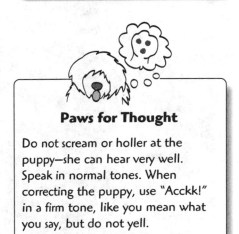

Paws for Thought

Do not scream or holler at the puppy—she can hear very well. Speak in normal tones. When correcting the puppy, use "Acckk!" in a firm tone, like you mean what you say, but do not yell.

Striking a Balance Between Positive Reinforcement and Correction

Dogs do not learn what to do by being corrected. A correction can let your puppy know when she has made a mistake, but it cannot tell her what to do instead. However, positive reinforcements do let your puppy know when she did something right.

For example, if your puppy is jumping up on you, you can tell her "Acckk! No jump!" as she leaps up. But that alone is not enough to stop the problem. If you follow that up by shaping her into a sit and telling her, "Good girl to sit!" and pet her while she's sitting, she learns an acceptable alternative.

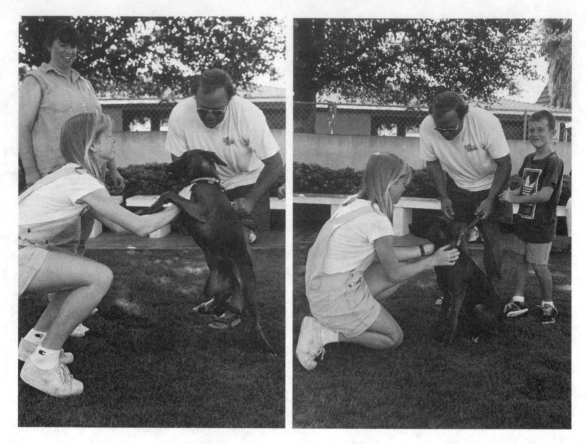

Jumping up on people is rude. Teach your puppy instead to sit when she meets people.

Let's look at it this way:

➤ She's jumping on you for attention.
➤ Correct the jumping when she leaps up.
➤ Show her a better way: Have her sit in front of you.
➤ Praise and pet her for sitting.

Much of your puppy's training can be approached in this manner. Let her know when she's made a mistake, and then show her what she can do instead. Show her the right way and praise her enthusiastically for doing it.

Your Training Tools

Training tools help you teach your puppy pay attention to you and listen to what you have to say. If your puppy had been born understanding human language and full of the desire to do what you tell her, you wouldn't need training tools. However, your puppy needs to be taught to listen to you and needs to be motivated to do what you ask her. That's why you need training tools.

Using the training tools I described in Chapter 17 is not difficult. Let's take a another look at them.

Paws for Thought

When your dog is doing something right, *always* praise her. If she's lying on the floor quietly chewing on her toy (and *not* chewing on your nearby shoes) praise her for chewing on her toy.

Buckle Collar

A buckle collar holds your puppy's identification tags. In training, it is used to connect the leash to your puppy and will restrain her, and that's about it. Its use as a training tool is primarily as a place to hook the leash.

Training Collar

This collar is often referred to as a slip chain collar or a choke chain. It works with a snap and release motion—you snap up and release down. *Never* jerk this collar hard and *never* hold it tight. Don't allow your puppy to pull it tight either, as it can choke her.

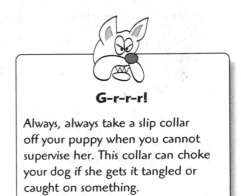

G-r-r-r!

Always, always take a slip collar off your puppy when you cannot supervise her. This collar can choke your dog if she gets it tangled or caught on something.

When you use this collar to give a correction, always use your voice as well. "Acckk! No pull!"—snap and release. Otherwise your puppy may think the snap is simply a movement that has no meaning.

Prong or Pinch Collar

This collar also works with a snap and release, but a snap with much less force than the slip or training collar. Again, always use your voice when you use this collar to give a correction.

Some owners are afraid the prong collar will give their dog a severe, hurtful correction. However, when it's being used by a skilled trainer, the collar allows for much less force when giving a correction. While prong collars have been used in

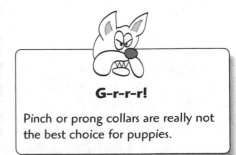

G-r-r-r!

Pinch or prong collars are really not the best choice for puppies.

the past, their use is declining as newer products like head halters come on the market that allow more control without the use of pain.

Head Halters

People unfamiliar with a halter may think it's a muzzle. In fact, it's more like a horse's halter. Your puppy can even drink water with it on. Halters are not used with any kind of snap or release. Instead, they work with a gentle guiding motion. As with the collars, always use your voice to teach the dog what you want her to do.

Paws for Thought

If your puppy likes to chew on her leash, dip it in vinegar before hooking it up to her collar. She'll take one bite and spit it out.

Leash

A leash attaches to the collar or halter so that you have a means of using the collar or halter to teach the puppy. A collar alone won't do much—you must be able to use it, and that's where the leash comes in.

Motivators and Positive Reinforcements

These are things your puppy likes that you will use to motivate her to learn. They can be food treats, squeaky toys, furry toys or even a tennis ball. They can be used to help your puppy do what you want (as a lure, for example), or can be a reward for doing something right.

A treat is a wonderful motivator. Blue's owner uses a treat to encourage Blue to follow him while walking on a leash.

To keep a motivator special, give it to your puppy only when you are working with her. Never give it to her for no reason.

Using Your Training Tools

These tools, no matter what they are, should be used as much as possible. If you use the training tools only during training sessions, your puppy will think the behavior she is learning during those sessions is also only for use then. If you use the training tools often during your daily routine, your puppy will understand that good behavior is part of her daily routine.

Here are some examples of how to use one of the simplest of your training tools, the leash:

Breed Bits

Golden Retrievers need to have something in their mouth almost all the time. Unfortunately, that often seems to be something of yours—a sock, a shoe or a piece of clothing. Teach your Golden to pick up a dog toy instead.

➤ The leash can be used too as an umbilical cord to your puppy. If she decides to sneak away from you to a back room where she might get into trouble, use the leash to keep her with you.

➤ If your puppy likes to play keep-away, dashing back and forth but never letting you touch her, simply step on the end of the leash and stop the game.

➤ If your puppy likes to steal things of yours or the children's, use the leash to stop her from running away with the stolen item.

I will give you additional examples of how to use your training tools around the house and yard as we go along.

The Agony of Negative Attention

Some dogs, just like some children, will actually work for corrections. These confused souls have discovered that they get attention when they misbehave, and are willing to put up with the yelling, collar corrections and other negative attention because, after all, it *is* attention.

Usually a puppy like this has some problem behaviors and is often in trouble. Her owners yell at her more than anything else, so the puppy soon equates yelling with owner attention. She continues to get into trouble just so she can get attention—any attention, even negative attention.

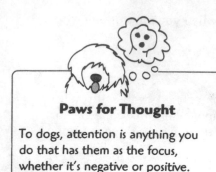

Paws for Thought

To dogs, attention is anything you do that has them as the focus, whether it's negative or positive.

To change this scenario, you must focus on giving the puppy attention for good behavior. This might be difficult in the beginning, because the bad behavior should be ignored, but not corrected (remember, correction is attention!). However, when the negative attention decreases and the good behavior is rewarded, the dog's focus will change.

Putting It All Together

When you teach your puppy, you will use your training tools to do so. Although it may seem right now that there is a lot to remember about these tools, it isn't that difficult. Once you get some practice, it will become second nature to you.

You have:

➤ A collar or head halter

➤ A leash, either regular length or a long length

➤ Motivators and positive reinforcements

➤ Your voice

In the next few chapters, as I show you how to teach the individual exercises, I will also show you how to use your training tools for each command or exercise. Right now just make sure you are comfortable with your training tools.

You Must Be Your Puppy's Leader

You are not your puppy's best friend—at least not yet—nor should you try to be. Instead, you must be your puppy's leader. If she were living with other dogs instead of people, an older dog would assume the leadership position. This dog would demand certain behaviors or actions from subordinates, and your puppy would be one of the subordinates.

Now, naturally, you are not a dog and your puppy is not living in a dog pack. But your puppy is comfortable with that pack structure and will actually feel safer and more secure if you are the leader. Here's what she expects:

➤ The leader is confidant. If you are not yet confidant about training, at least act like it!

➤ The leader of the pack always eats first and best. You should always eat first, even if it's just an apple.

➤ The leader always goes first. Don't let the puppy dash through doorways ahead of you. Don't allow her to dash out of the house or into the house ahead of you. Make her wait at all doorways, car doors and the gate.

➤ The leader establishes the rules. It's your house, you pay the bills and you have every right to set some rules.

The leader, according to your puppy, is the biggest, strongest, fastest and smartest. Now, not all leaders actually are those things, but if they aren't, they act like they are. Many small dogs are the leaders of much bigger dogs. What they lack in actual size they make up for in attitude. So, act like the leader!

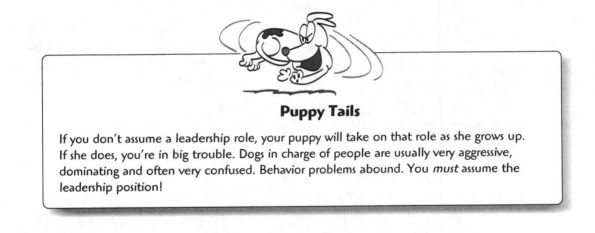

Puppy Tails

If you don't assume a leadership role, your puppy will take on that role as she grows up. If she does, you're in big trouble. Dogs in charge of people are usually very aggressive, dominating and often very confused. Behavior problems abound. You *must* assume the leadership position!

Make Your Training Successful

There are some basic principles that apply to all dog training. Following them will help make your training more successful.

➤ Show your puppy what to do, help her do it and praise her when she does it correctly.

➤ Always give only one command. Do not repeat the word over and over and over again. If you repeat it, which one counts? Which one should she respond to?

➤ Consistency is important. Once you establish some rules—such as keeping the puppy off the furniture— you must consistently enforce them.

➤ Timing is critical to your training success. Praise your puppy *as* she is doing something right. Correct your puppy *as* she makes a mistake. Praise and corrections that happen later are not effective.

➤ Corrections (any corrections, including voice, collar or any other training tools) should be forceful enough to stop unwanted behavior, and *that's all*. Excessive corrections or punishment after the fact will not teach the puppy effectively and could easily cause her to shy away from you or avoid you.

➤ You don't need to yell, scream or shout at your puppy. A loud, frightening voice will not stop unwanted behavior and will threaten your relationship with your puppy.

G-r-r-r!

Don't train your puppy when the pressures of the day will cause you to take out your frustrations on her.

➤ You do have to mean what you say. If you correct the puppy and giggle, or laugh when she makes a mistake, your puppy will not take you seriously. Believe in what you are doing.

➤ Keep in mind that bad behavior is *not* directed at you personally. Your puppy is *not* chewing on the sofa and thinking, "Ha! I'll chew up this and that will teach her to go off to work and leave me alone!"

➤ Never train your puppy when you are drunk, stoned, tipsy or buzzed. Don't train your puppy when you're angry.

Praising and petting your puppy are wonderful ways to reward good behavior.

Always End on a High Note

Always finish a training session with a success. Stop when your dog has successfully learned something or when she does something very well. You and she will both finish the session feeling good.

If your puppy is having a hard time with a particular lesson, ask her to do something you know she can do well. After she does it, stop the training session there. You can then still end on a high note.

Paws for Thought

Be patient. It will take time for your puppy to learn new things and even more time for her to figure out that these new things are important to you.

The Least You Need to Know

➤ Your voice, the leash and collar, and the things you use to motivate your dog are your training tools.

➤ Training tools should be used all the time, and not just during training sessions.

➤ You must be your puppy's leader. It's natural and she expects it.

➤ Set up your training so that your puppy is given every opportunity to succeed.

➤ Always end your training sessions with something you know your puppy can do well.

Chapter 19

Basic Training

> **In This Chapter**
>
> ➤ How to teach your puppy the basic commands
> ➤ Why are these commands important?
> ➤ How can you use them at home?

The eight basic obedience commands should be a part of every dog's vocabulary. When a dog understands these commands and the dog's owner knows how to use them, many potential behavior problems are eliminated. For example, when the dog knows how to walk nicely on a leash, he isn't dragging his owner down the street, choking himself and pulling her arm out of the socket. The other commands—including sit, lie down, stay, come, heel and watch me—are just as important and just as useful.

Because there are so many different ways to teach your puppy, I will be explaining more than one way to teach each command. Just as different children learn in different ways, so do different puppies. By offering a couple of different training techniques, I'm sure you'll find one that will work for your puppy.

Paws for Thought

The eight basic commands are sit, release, lie down, stay, come, watch me, let's go and heel.

Breed Bits

Siberian Huskies are very leader oriented. They need to know you are in charge. Training should begin early in puppyhood and continue through adolescence.

Let's Start with the Basics

The eight basic commands teach your puppy several skills, all of which are important for his behavior at home and out in public. Some of the commands teach your puppy to control himself—to be aware that there are consequences to his actions. He will learn that if he controls himself, does what you ask of him and restrains his desires to run and jump and play (at least for the moment), he will be praised. If he doesn't restrain himself, there will be no praise and there might be a correction.

In other situations, a command may serve as an alternative behavior to prevent problems. For example, your puppy cannot jump on people if he learns to sit for praise and petting. He cannot drag you down the street if he learns to walk nicely on the leash while watching you.

Any training you decide to do later with your puppy rests on these basic commands. He will need to understand these thoroughly before he can go on to any advanced training or any dog activities or sports.

Teaching Sit

Teaching your puppy to sit is relatively easy. Teaching him to sit still is a little harder, but we'll take this in small steps and set him up to succeed. I'm going to pretend your dog's name is Sweetie (he is one, isn't he?), but you can just fill in the right name.

Method one: With your puppy on his leash close to you, show him a treat. When he reaches up to sniff the treat, move it over his head and back toward his tail as you tell him, "Sweetie, sit." When his head comes up and back to follow the treat, his hips will go down. After he sits, praise him and give him the treat.

Method two: If he spins around trying to get the treat, rather than sitting, put the treat away in your pocket. Put one hand on his chest where the chest and neck meet. Tell him "Sweetie, sit," and at the same time, push that hand slightly up and back (thereby pushing his chest up and back) as the other hand slides down his back toward the hips and tucks his hips down and under. Think of a teeter-totter: up and back at the chest and down and under at the hips. When he's sitting, praise him.

Put one hand on the puppy's chest, and slide the other back as you say, "Sweetie, sit!" Then praise your puppy.

You want the puppy to understand that the word "sit" means "Put your hips on the ground, keeping your front end up, and be still." Obviously, you cannot tell your puppy this and expect him to understand, so you must teach him that's what it means. You can do this using your voice. When he does sit, praise him in a higher-than-normal tone of voice, "Good boy to sit!" When he begins to move from position—not after he's gone, but right when he starts to move—use your growling tone of voice, "Acckk!" and put him back in the sit position.

How Useful Is Sit?

Sit is a very useful command, not just as the foundation for more advanced commands, but also for everyday use around the house.

➤ Have the puppy sit to greet people, especially if he likes to jump on people. He can't jump up and sit at the same time.

➤ Have him sit when you fix his dinner. He can't jump on you and knock the bowl out of your hands when he's sitting.

➤ Have him sit when you hook up his leash to take him outside. If he's sitting, he can't be spinning around in circles out of excitement.

Have your puppy sit for everything he wants: for petting, for his dinner, for treats and for toys. When he comes up to you and nudges you to pet him, have him sit first.

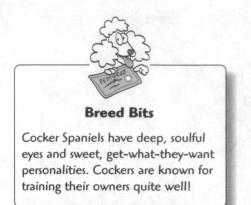

Breed Bits

Cocker Spaniels have deep, soulful eyes and sweet, get-what-they-want personalities. Cockers are known for training their owners quite well!

When he drops his tennis ball at your feet, have him sit first. By teaching him to sit for everything he wants, you are setting up some rules for behavior and giving him structure (which is important to a young puppy), and you are giving him a job to do. Keep in mind that most dog breeds were developed to do a job of some kind. As a pet, this job is missed. Sitting for everything he wants can be your puppy's first job!

Teaching the Release

Once your puppy is sitting, what do you do next? Do you just let the puppy get up? How does he know when he's done with the sit? The release command "Okay!" means, "You're done now, you can move." With this command, the puppy knows exactly when he's allowed to move from position.

Paws for Thought

Use both a touch and a verbal command for the release. If you use only a word, the puppy could release himself whenever he hears that word used in conversation.

Method one: With your puppy sitting, pat him on the shoulder as you tell him "Okay!" in a high-pitched tone of voice and encourage him to get up from the sit by raising your hands high. If you lift your hands up and bounce a little yourself, he will probably bounce up, too, copying your movements.

Method two: With your puppy sitting, pat him on the shoulder as you tell him "Okay!" in a high-pitched tone of voice. Use the leash to gently move him from the sit.

The primary purpose of the release command is to alleviate confusion: The puppy knows exactly when he's done.

Teaching Lie Down

Teaching your puppy to lie down can be easy, but just as with the sit, lying down and being still can be a little harder!

I use the phrase "lie down" because "down" by itself is used for so many other things. If you tell your puppy "down" when he jumps on you and "down" when you want him to get off the furniture, which meaning should he respond to? And neither one of those uses is exactly the same as lie down. Each command must have only one meaning. You can't expect a puppy to understand the nuances of context.

Hold a treat in one hand and tell your puppy, "Sweetie, lie down."

Lead his nose to the ground with the treat.

When he's down, praise him and give him the treat.

229

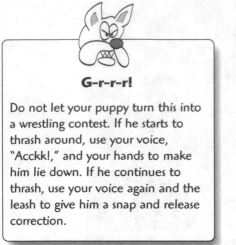

G-r-r-r!

Do not let your puppy turn this into a wrestling contest. If he starts to thrash around, use your voice, "Acckk!," and your hands to make him lie down. If he continues to thrash, use your voice again and the leash to give him a snap and release correction.

Method one: Have your puppy sit. With a treat in one hand and another hand on the puppy's shoulder, tell him "Sweetie, lie down," as you let him sniff the treat. Move the treat directly to the ground in front of his front paws. (In other words, lead his nose down with the treat.) As he starts to move down, the hand on his shoulder can assist him in this downward movement. However, don't push! If you push, he may simply push back. When he's down, give him the treat and praise him.

Method two: Have your puppy sit. Tell him "Sweetie, lie down," as you gently scoop his front legs up and out, laying him down. You can do this by reaching over his shoulders with one arm to grasp the front leg away from you, while your other hand grasps the closest leg. Gently lift both legs up, forward and then down.

Lie Down Can Be a Handy Command

The lie down command is very useful, both at home and out in public. You can use the lie down in conjunction with the stay command, which you'll learn next. You'll find it's a very handy way to get your puppy to settle down.

Paws for Thought

The lie down command is a good exercise to help establish your position as leader. Have your puppy lie down at your feet while you are sitting or standing above him. Do this at least once (more is better) every single day.

➤ Have the puppy lie down during meals so that he isn't begging under the table. Place him where you can see him, but away from the table.

➤ Have him lie down at your feet while talking to guests. He can't be jumping all over them or knocking their drinks over if he's still lying at your feet.

➤ Have him lie down and give him a toy to chew on when you would like to have some quiet time to read or watch television.

➤ Have him lie down while you're talking to a neighbor.

➤ Have him lie down while you get your mail out of the box and sort through it.

As you practice with this command, you will find other ways to use it. For example, have your puppy lie down in the bathroom while you're taking a shower; he can't get into trouble in another room if he's there with you. The important thing is that you use the command. Find out where it can help you with your puppy, and then be sure to use it.

Teaching Stay

The stay command is used with sit and lie down. You want your puppy to understand that stay means, "Remain in this position while I walk away, and stay here until I come back to you and release you." The sit and lie down commands by themselves teach the puppy to hold that position until you release him, but only while you are with him. With stay, you will be able to walk away from him.

Stay means, "Don't move from this position."

Method one: Have your puppy sit. Hold your open palm in front of his face about two inches from his nose. Tell him "Sweetie, stay!" Take a step or two away. If he moves, use your voice, "Acckk!" and put him back in position. Wait a few seconds and then step back to him. Have him remain still while you praise and pet him, then release him with the release command.

Method two: Have your puppy on leash and tell him to sit. Hold your open palm in front of his nose and tell him "Sweetie, stay!" In one hand hold the leash up from his neck, without holding it tightly. Take a step away while you continue to hold the leash up. If he moves, tell him "Acckk!" as you give him a snap and release correction with the leash. Put him back in position. Wait a few seconds, then step back to him, praise him and then give him the release command.

After practicing the stay with sit, try it with lie down. The training methods are the same, except that you begin by telling the puppy to lie down. You should be the one who decides this. If you ask him to sit-stay and he decides to lie down, correct him and help him back up into a sit. He doesn't get to choose the exercise, you do.

Breed Bits

Jack Russell Terriers are very intelligent, independent, active little dogs. Teaching the stay command can be hard because they don't like to hold still. It's important you find the right motivation so that they *want* to hold still for you.

How Long Can a Puppy Stay?

Don't be in a hurry to move away from your puppy or to have him hold the stay for longer time periods. It is very difficult for puppies to hold still, and right now it's more important that your puppy succeeds in his training. Here are some reasonable expectations for sit-stays for a young puppy 12 to 16 weeks old:

➤ First week of training: one to two steps away for 10 seconds

➤ Second week: three to four steps away for 10 seconds

➤ Third week: three to four steps away for 15 to 20 seconds

➤ Fourth week: six to eight steps away for 20 seconds

The lie down–stay will be a little easier for most puppies, and your progress could be quicker. However, if your puppy is making mistakes, you're pushing too hard. Back up, and practice a little closer for shorter time periods. Then gradually—*very gradually*—begin increasing the time and distance again.

Many Uses for Stay

Use stay around the house in conjunction with sit and lie down.

➤ When guests come over, have the puppy lie down by your feet and tell him to stay. Then he cannot be tormenting your guests with demands for attention.

➤ When you want him to stay away from the table while you're eating, have him lie down and tell him to stay.

➤ Tell him to sit and stay while you're fixing his dinner so he doesn't jump up for his dish.

➤ Have him sit and stay at doorways, gates and at the curb so you can teach him to wait for permission.

There are lots of uses for these commands. Just look at your house, your routine and where you might be having some problems with your puppy's behavior. Where can the stay help you?

Teaching Your Pup to Come

Come is a command that could one day save your puppy's life. When I teach my dogs to come when called, I want them to understand that come means, "Stop what you're doing and come back to me right now, with no hesitation, as fast as you can run." This instant response might save your dog from a dangerous situation—perhaps a dog fight, being hit by a car or a snake in the grass. Situations come up every day that could cause your puppy harm. A quick response to the come command could save him.

Puppy Tails

My dogs were in the front yard with me one day as I was washing my car. I heard my older dog growl, so I looked up. The dog down the street, who is known for being quite dog aggressive, was heading our way. I told my older dogs to stay, but as I reached for my puppy, she was already heading toward the dog! I called her, "Kes, come!" As I got ready to chase after her, I realized she had already stopped, turned around and was heading back to me. The training worked!

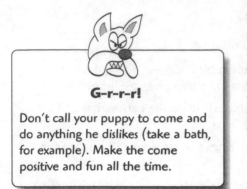

G-r-r-r!

Don't call your puppy to come and do anything he dislikes (take a bath, for example). Make the come positive and fun all the time.

Method one: Take a small plastic container, such as a margarine tub, and put a handful of dry kibble dog food in it. Put the top on. If you shake it, you will hear a nice rattling sound. With your puppy sitting in front of you, have the shaker in one hand and some good treats in the other. Shake the shaker and tell your puppy in a happy tone of voice "Cookie!" (or whatever word he knows for treats), and then pop a treat into his mouth.

You are building a relationship in your puppy's mind between the sound of the shaker and the word "cookie," and between the word "cookie" and the fact that he's going to get a treat. Practice this two or three times, and then stop for this training session. You can come back and do it again later in the day.

After two or three days of this training, stop using the word cookie and say "come," but keep everything else the same. Start with your puppy sitting in front of you (he's not going or coming anywhere). Shake the shaker, say "Sweetie, come!" and pop the treat into his mouth. Now you're changing the equation. The sound of the shaker equals the word "come," which equals the treat popped into his mouth. Practice this for several days, two or three times per session.

When he's sitting in front of you with his mouth open, waiting for the treat, start backing away from the puppy as you say "Sweetie, come!" Lure him with the treat in front of his nose as you back away. After a few steps, pop the treat into his mouth and praise him, "Good boy to come!"

G-r-r-r!

Never correct your puppy for anything to do with learning the command come. Timing is vitally important, and if he misunderstands a correction, he could learn that coming to you is bad and results in a correction.

In a week or two, depending upon how enthused your puppy is, you can stop having him sit in front of you. Instead, when he's across the room from you, pick up the shaker, call him and when he charges across the room to you, praise him and pop the treat into his mouth.

Method two: Have your puppy on a leash. Hold the leash in one hand and have some treats in the other. Back away from your puppy as you call him, "Sweetie, come!" Make sure you back up a few steps so he gets a chance to chase you. If he doesn't come to you right away, use the leash to make sure he does. Praise him when he does come to you: "Good boy to come!"

As your puppy learns to come and is responding to it well, add some games to the practice. Call him back and forth between two family members and offer him a treat each time he comes. Make sure you keep it fun and exciting.

If your puppy hesitates about coming to you—especially if something is distracting him—there are some tricks you can use to make him come. First, don't chase him. That will only make him run farther and faster away from you. Instead, call his name in an exciting (not scolding) tone of voice and then run away from him. He will turn and chase after you.

Some other tricks will bring your puppy in closer to you. You can lie down on the ground, hide your face and call him. Or bend over and scratch at the ground as if you're looking at something very interesting. Ask your puppy, "What's that?" in an "ice cream" tone of voice. When he gets up to you, don't reach out and grab him: You'll never fool him again. Instead, continue to talk to him in an excited tone of voice as you gently take hold of his collar and praise him for coming to you.

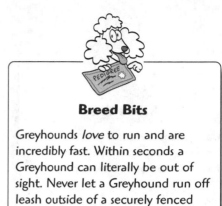

Breed Bits

Greyhounds *love* to run and are incredibly fast. Within seconds a Greyhound can literally be out of sight. Never let a Greyhound run off leash outside of a securely fenced area.

Teaching Watch Me

Training your puppy can be very difficult if you can't get him to pay attention to you. Most puppies will focus on their owner at home, but when out in public, the puppy wants to pay attention to everything else. You can help your puppy succeed by teaching him how to pay attention.

When you tell your puppy "Watch me," you want him to look at your face, and preferably at your eyes. He should ignore any distractions and focus on you. In the beginning, this focus may only last a few seconds. But later, as the puppy gets better at it and as his concentration improves, he should be able to focus on you and ignore distractions for minutes at a time.

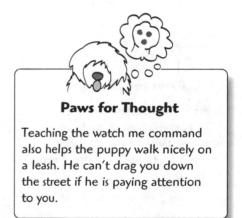

Paws for Thought

Teaching the watch me command also helps the puppy walk nicely on a leash. He can't drag you down the street if he is paying attention to you.

Method one: With your puppy sitting in front of you and with treats in one hand, tell your puppy, "Sweetie, watch me!" At the same time, let him sniff a treat and then move it up to your chin. This movement and position are important. First let the puppy sniff the treat so he knows you have it. Then take it up to your chin slowly, so that as he watches the treat, his eyes follow your hand to your face. As he looks at the treat and then at your face, praise him. After you praise him, "Good boy to watch me!" pop the treat into his mouth. If he gets distracted and looks away, take the treat back to his nose and get his attention back on you.

Method two: Put your puppy on a leash and have him sit in front of you. Hold the leash in one hand and treats in the other. Teach "watch me" as I described in method one, except that if the puppy gets distracted or looks away, use a quick snap and release of the leash and collar to let the puppy know he's not to look away. Snap and release—"Acckk! Watch me!" As soon as he acknowledges the correction and looks back to you, praise him, "Good boy to watch me!"

As the puppy learns the command, you can start making it more challenging. Tell your puppy, "Sweetie, watch me!" and then back away so that he has to watch you while walking. When he can follow you for a few steps, back up in a zigzag pattern. Back up quickly, then slowly. Add some challenges. Of course, when the puppy can do this and has fun following you, you should praise him enthusiastically.

Teaching Let's Go

Good on-leash skills are necessary for all dogs. When on a leash, a dog should respect the leash without fighting it, pulling on it or choking himself. The let's go command will help teach those skills.

Method one: Have your puppy on the leash, and hold the end in one hand. Show him a treat, tell him, "Sweetie, let's go" and simply back away from him. If he watches you, praise him. If he follows you, praise him even more. However, if he sniffs the ground, looks away from you or tries to pull in the other direction, use a snap and release of the leash and a verbal correction, "Acckk! No pull!" (or "No sniff!" if that's appropriate). After the correction, if he looks back up to you, praise him.

Back away from the puppy several times in several different directions. Each time he follows you and each time he looks up at you, praise him. Every time he pulls away, sniffs the ground or ignores you, correct him.

Method two: With your puppy on the leash and the leash held securely, walk forward as you tell him, "Sweetie, let's go!" If your puppy dashes past you to pull forward, simply make an about-turn so that you are going in the opposite direction. Without saying anything to your puppy, just hold the leash securely, turn and go. Your puppy will hit the end of the leash as you turn, and when he does, act surprised, "Wow! What

Show your puppy the treat and tell him, "Sweetie, let's go."

Back up, encouraging him to follow you.

After a few steps, stop and praise him.

Paws for Thought

As you train your puppy, watch his eyes and ears. He'll tell you whether he's alert and eager to do these things (his body language will be up and forward), or whether he's worried (his body language will be down and slinky).

happened?" When he turns to go with you, praise him. However, if he dashes past you again, turn around again, repeating the entire exercise.

You may have to go back and forth a few times. However, pretty soon he's going to figure out that it's to his advantage to pay attention and walk where you walk.

Your goal with either method is to keep the leash slack as your puppy follows you, paying attention to your every move. And of course, when he does, you will praise him enthusiastically!

Teaching Heel

The command "heel" means, "Walk by my left side with your neck and shoulder area next to my left leg, maintaining that position no matter what I do." With that definition, if you walk fast, jog, walk slowly or simply amble, your puppy should maintain the heel position. If you have to walk through a crowd and zigzag around people, your dog should still maintain that position.

Teaching the heel requires a great deal of concentration on your puppy's part. Do *not* start teaching it until your puppy has been doing the watch me command for several weeks (not days—weeks!) and has been doing let's go very well for at least two weeks with regular practice.

Method one: With your puppy on a leash, hold the leash in your left hand and some treats in the right. Back away from your puppy as you tell him, "Sweetie, let's go!" As he follows you, let him catch up with you as you back up slightly and turn so that you are facing the same direction he is and he ends up on your left side. Walk forward together as you show him a treat and tell him, "Sweetie, heel!" Stop after a few steps, have him sit and praise him as you give him the treat.

Breed Bits

Rottweilers are working dogs, bred to perform a job. Training can fulfill that need, so make it a part of their daily routine and make sure the training sets them up to succeed.

Repeat this several times, keeping each walking session short, enthusiastic and fun. Make it challenging by turning, walking fast, walking slowly and going in different directions.

With this method, at this point in the training always start with the let's go command and tell the puppy to heel as he arrives at your left side and you begin walking forward together.

Method two: Have your puppy sit by your left side, on a leash, and hold the leash in your left hand. Have some treats in your right hand. Show the puppy a treat and tell him, "Sweetie, watch me!" When he's paying attention to you, tell him, "Sweetie, heel!" and walk forward. If he pulls ahead, use the leash to give him a snap and release correction as you tell him, "Acckk! No pull!" When he slows down, backs off the pulling and looks back to you, praise him and repeat the watch me command. When he watches you, praise him enthusiastically.

This method requires a little more concentration, so make sure you keep the sessions short, upbeat and praise the puppy's successes.

When you take your puppy for a walk, don't ask him to heel the entire way. Instead, go back and forth between let's go and the two different methods of teaching the heel. Offer some variety and some challenge. However, once you start this training, do not let your puppy pull on the leash—*ever!* Whenever he is on leash, he is to respect it and never, ever pull on it.

Tips for Top Training Sessions

Keep your training sessions fun. Make sure your puppy learns what he needs to learn, and don't allow him to ignore you. This way, you can enforce your leadership position and still have fun training.

With my puppy Kes, a training session might go like this:

➤ We'll start with several sits and watch me's, so I make sure I have her attention.

➤ We'll practice the let's go with some back-aways, some turns and some fast-paced walking.

➤ We'll do a few quick, short heels, and then I'll release her and praise her.

➤ I'll toss her tennis ball a few times and call her to come as she brings it back.

➤ I'll then have her do a sit-stay, followed by a down-stay.

➤ I'll do another quick heel, and then we're through for this training session.

Every training session will be different, but in all of them I try to keep the training upbeat yet enforced. I want my dogs to *want to* be good and to *want to* do these things for me, so I keep it fun. But I also want them to take it seriously. Training is not a game, so I always enforce my rules.

It's also important to practice these commands in the house, in the yard, in the car and out in public. Make sure your puppy understands they are in effect *all* the time—not just during training sessions.

The Least You Need to Know

➤ The basic commands are the foundation for everything you will ever teach your puppy in the future.

➤ There is more than one way to teach your puppy, and no one technique is right for every dog. Try the different methods and use the one that is more effective with your dog. Or use them both.

➤ The eight basic commands—sit, release, lie down, stay, come, watch me, let's go and heel—have many useful applications at home and out and about.

➤ Keep your training sessions fun and upbeat but under control.

➤ Use these commands everywhere, not just in training.

Chapter 20

There's More You Can Teach

The eight commands in the previous chapter are the foundation for your puppy's training. But once you have laid the foundation, there's so much more you can teach your puppy. In this chapter I'll explain how you teach the next level of commands—the first floor, so to speak. Later you can go on to teach your puppy even more—maybe even to build a skyscraper. With each level of training, you gain more control over your puppy, your puppy learns more self-restraint and you both learn more about each other. There is no limit to the dog sports, activities and games you can play together as you explore your puppy's capacity to learn. It all starts right here.

Teaching Wait

When you taught your puppy the stay command, you wanted her to understand that stay means, "Hold this position until I come back to you to release you." The key phrase right now is "until I come back to you to release you." When taught properly, this is a very secure command. You want your puppy to be able to hold the stay so that if you drop a glass in the kitchen, you can tell her to lie down and stay in the hall, and she'll do it while you clean up the broken glass.

"Wait" means "Don't walk forward with me, but pay attention: I'm going to give you another command."

However, in some situations it may not be easy for you to go back to release her (remember, the release is done with a touch as well as a verbal command). For example, you may want to take the trash cans out through the gate. You don't want her to dash through the gate, so you'll give the sit command. But when you have taken the trash out, you're going to get in your car and leave for work. If you told her to stay, you should really go back to her to release her, right? You don't expect her to do a sit-stay in the yard all day. So what can you do?

Paws for Thought

The words "wait" and "stay" sound a lot alike, but your puppy's hearing is very good. Speak clearly when teaching her, and she'll quickly learn the difference between the two words.

The wait command is a temporary hold. You want the dog to understand that wait means, "Hold this position as I walk away from you, but pay attention because another command is going to follow." The other command will be given at a distance. With the trash and the front gate, you'd do it this way: Have your puppy sit, tell her "wait," open the gate, take the garbage cans out (closing the gate behind you) and then tell your puppy, "Sweetie, okay" from outside the gate.

Three Ways to Teach Wait

Method one: Have some treats and the shaker you used to teach the come command. Have your puppy sit, tell her "Sweetie, wait," and step away. Shake the shaker, call your puppy to come and back away a few steps. Praise her for coming. If she breaks the wait, moving before you call her, tell her "Acckk!" and put her back in her original position. Practice this in different places, always using the come command and the shaker, and reward her with verbal praise and a treat.

Method two: Have your puppy on a leash and have some treats in your pocket. Tell her to sit, then say "Sweetie, wait" and step away from her. Call her to come, use the leash to make sure she does, and praise her when she comes to you. Give her a treat. If she breaks the wait, moving before you call her, tell her "Acckk!" and use a snap and release of the leash. Put her back in the original position.

Method three: Have your puppy sit, tell her "Sweetie, wait" and step away from her. Wait a few seconds, then tell her, "Sweetie, okay, you can move!" and encourage her to get up with your body language (bounce up and lift your hands high). Praise her when she moves.

Using Wait in Real Life

Look at your daily routine. Where can you use this command? I think it has a lot of practical uses.

➤ Have your puppy wait at the door until you give her permission to go inside or outside.

➤ Have her wait at the gate before you go out for a walk.

➤ Have her wait before you give her permission to jump into or out of the car.

➤ Have her wait at the curb before you walk across the street.

Paws for Thought

I can't emphasize this enough: Use your puppy's training around the house. The more you use it, the better the end result.

Teaching Your Puppy to Respect Boundaries

Boundary training means teaching your puppy to respect physical boundaries. You can teach her to remain in the front yard with you (always with you, never alone) and to remain within the boundaries of the yard. You can teach her to respect the gate, the garage door and outside doors. By teaching her to respect these boundaries, there is less chance of her dashing out through the gate or running away.

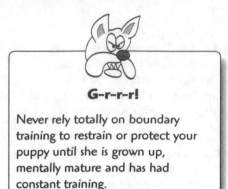

G-r-r-r!

Never rely totally on boundary training to restrain or protect your puppy until she is grown up, mentally mature and has had constant training.

Boundary training is very difficult for puppies. If a cat is grooming itself just beyond the boundary of your yard, your puppy is not going to be able to resist that temptation. She's going to make a dash for the cat. If it's that hard, why are we even trying to teach it? Because if you start teaching it now, when your puppy is grown up the training will work. You just have to keep teaching, enforce the boundaries and be patient while your puppy grows up.

How to Teach Boundary Training

Method one: Start in a spot where the boundary is very obvious, such as a gate. Put your puppy on a leash and have her sit in front of the closed gate, inside the yard. Tell her, "Sweetie, wait," and step up to the gate. If she moves, correct her, "Acckk!" and put her back in position. Open the gate. If she moves, correct her and put her back where she started. If she waits, go back to her and praise her.

Paws for Thought

Work on boundary training and let your puppy know that you expect her to honor it, but don't trust it until she's grown up.

Repeat the exercise a few times, closing the gate each time before you start again. When she will hold the wait while you open the gate, step through the gate. If she moves, correct her and put her back. Continue this way, opening and closing the gate, walking through and walking back, over several days and training sessions. When your puppy is doing well and not making any mistakes (still on leash, of course), start the exercise all over at another location—such as the garage door.

Method two: Sit your puppy at the gate, inside the yard. Fasten a long leash or a 20-foot length of clothes-line rope to your puppy's collar. Tie the other end to something secure in the yard, such as a tree. Have a little bit of slack in the line, but not too much. Tell your puppy "Sweetie, wait," and open the gate. If she dashes through, let her go and hit the end of the line. When she does, go to her and tell her, "Well, that was dumb!" in a matter-of-fact voice. Walk her back to where she started, close the gate and repeat the whole exercise.

When she's figured out that dashing won't work when you open the gate, leave her, open the gate and then walk through. When she's reliable there, move to another boundary and repeat the entire exercise.

There's More You Can Do with Come

Because come is such an important command, I like to teach it in a variety of ways. In Chapter 19 I showed you how to train the come with a shaker—emphasizing the sound and treats—and the come on a leash, which gave the puppy no chance to ignore you. But there is more you can do with the come command.

You can use come with the shaker to teach the puppy to come to you from a distance. This is best taught with two people in a large fenced area where the puppy can't get into any trouble. Have the shaker with you and some special treats that she really likes. Have one person hold the puppy as you let her sniff the treat. Walk away from her (don't say wait or stay) and hold out the treat so she can see you still have it. When you're 20 or 30 yards away, bend down, open your arms, shake the shaker and call your puppy. She should be running to you as fast as her legs can carry her. Praise her, hug her and tell her what a wonderful puppy she is!

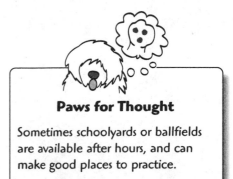

Paws for Thought

Sometimes schoolyards or ballfields are available after hours, and can make good places to practice.

Repeat the exercise with you holding the puppy while the other person walks away. Have her go back and forth two or three times, and then quit. *Always* quit *before* she's tired and before she loses interest. As she gets bigger and stronger, with more stamina, go farther away. But again, always stop while the game is still fun.

Practicing with Distractions

When the puppy is doing really well and is coming to you with no hesitation, start adding distractions. Call her when there are some kids playing on the other side of the yard, or when some kids are in-line skating outside the yard. Have a family member lie on the ground (presenting an interesting distraction) while you call the puppy. Have some of the puppy's toys out on the grass nearby when you call her.

Paws for Thought

You know your puppy better than anyone else. What distracts her? Practice with those distractions, but as you do, make sure you are also setting her up to succeed.

Distractions are a part of life, and your puppy must learn to ignore them. However, remember you need to set your puppy up for success. If she has trouble ignoring certain distractions, have her come to you on the leash for awhile instead of calling her across the yard without the leash. Use the long leash or a length of clothesline to help her do it right. Make sure she can do what you're asking her to do.

Sarah calls Kes to come.

Kes races to Sarah as fast as she can.

When she reaches Sarah, Kes sits in front of her.

Teaching Stand

Stand is not a difficult command to teach, but it is sometimes very hard for puppies to do because it requires them to stand still. The still part is hard!

Method one: Have your puppy on a leash. Hold it in one hand while you have a treat in the other. Ask your puppy to sit and praise her. Hold the treat in front of her nose, and as you tell her, "Sweetie, stand" slowly pull the treat away from her so that she follows it. When gets up onto all four paws, praise her, "Good to stand!" and give her the treat. Pat her on the shoulder to release her, just as you did to release her from the sit and lie down.

Method two: With your puppy on a leash, ask her to sit and praise her. Using your right hand, take hold of her collar under the neck in front of the chest. Tell her, "Sweetie, stand" and gently pull her forward so that she steps forward. As she steps forward, use your left hand under her tummy to keep her from sitting again. Praise her for standing.

Once the puppy is standing easily (using either method), you can add the stay to it. It is then, "Sweetie, stand. Good to stand. Stay." When you're ready, you can go back to her, praise her and release her.

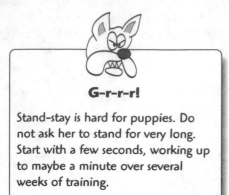

Using the Stand Command

Once your puppy knows how to do this, you'll find many uses for stand:

G-r-r-r!

Stand-stay is hard for puppies. Do not ask her to stand for very long. Start with a few seconds, working up to maybe a minute over several weeks of training.

➤ Have your puppy stand if she's been out in the rain or has been playing in the lawn sprinklers. It's much easier to towel her off when she's standing and, hopefully, standing still.

➤ If your puppy is a breed that needs professional grooming, your groomer will appreciate it if you teach her to stand. She does have to stand nicely on the table while being groomed.

➤ Your puppy will also need to know how to stand nicely at the veterinarian's office, both on the scale to be weighed and on the examination table.

➤ If your puppy has a long coat or a thick one that needs regular combing or brushing, you can teach her to stand while you brush her.

Puppy Tails

I like to challenge my dogs to listen to my commands, to think and to respond. I will tell them to sit, to lie down or to stand, but I will give the commands in different orders. For example, I may say stand, sit, lie down, sit, stand. If the dog does it right, I praise her after each command. If the dog has trouble or gets stuck, I will help her. If the dog is doing very well, listening carefully and trying hard, I *really* praise her and give her some treats.

Teaching Your Puppy to Go to Bed

Go to bed is a command that doesn't have much use anywhere except at home, but it's still useful. In Chapters 6, 7, 8 and 9 I discussed the need for kennel crates, their uses and how to teach the puppy to use a crate. I briefly mentioned teaching the puppy a command that means, "Go put yourself to bed," but during crate training you are always there to make sure the puppy goes into her crate and then you close the door behind her.

It is very nice to be able to sit on the couch in the evening, tell your puppy, "Sweetie, go to bed" and have your puppy get into her crate on her own. Eventually, you won't even have to follow her down the hall to make sure that she does it—she just will.

My youngest dog, Kes, who at this writing is just about a year old, has been putting herself to bed reliably for about four months. When she was younger, she would go to the crate, but if I didn't close the door behind her she would come back out, waiting for me to send her in again. To her it was a big game. She likes her crate (after all, it is her bed) and going in and out was fun. Now, though, she's taking her training more seriously and understands that "Go to bed" means go there and stay there.

You can start teaching this command by emphasizing the words as you put your puppy to bed at
night. When you know she understands the
words, say "Go to bed" as you are walking toward
her crate. If she dashes ahead to the crate, praise
her. If she dashes to the crate and puts herself
inside, *really* praise her.

G-r-r-r!

Don't overdo this command. If you
do it too often (more than twice a
day) your puppy will regress, lose
interest or enjoyment in the crate
and will refuse to go to it.

When she's at that point, start telling her earlier.
As you are walking down the hall, give her the
command. Then give her the command as you are
getting up from the couch. Always follow up by
going to the crate and praising her. If you just
send her to the crate now, she will come back to
you looking for the praise.

However, at some point you will see your puppy go to her crate on her own and lie down. When she's doing this, you will know that she enjoys taking refuge there and the crate itself will begin to be a reward for going inside. At that point, you can start sending your puppy there without following her. However, you should still call out to her and tell her she's good. She still needs some praise.

Teaching Leave It

Puppies put everything in their mouths. After all, they don't have hands. However, puppies are not very smart about what goes into their mouths, and often it's some-thing that could hurt them or make them sick. That's why I teach the leave it command.

I want my dogs to immediately ignore or turn away from whatever interests them when I say "Leave it!" That means if a chicken bone is on the ground and smells really

Paws for Thought

Make sure you say "Leave it!" first and then use the treat to turn her away. You don't want her to think "leave it" is a new name for treats.

Breed Bits

Most terriers are very tenacious, and once their minds are set on something, it's hard to make them stop. The leave it command is very important so that you can control what these dogs grab when you're out on a walk.

inviting, I want Kes to immediately turn away from it when she hears that command. This is hard for her, but it could save her life some day.

Method one: With the leash on your puppy, drop something on the ground that will get her interest and that she is normally not allowed to touch—a smelly sock, a leftover sandwich or something similar. Have the leash in one hand and treats in the other. Walk your puppy toward the item on the ground. Watch her carefully. When she sees it and begins to move toward it, tell her "Sweetie, leave it!" as you put the treat under her nose and lead her (using the treat) in the opposite direction. Praise her and give her the treat.

Method two: Have the puppy on a leash and drop the interesting item on the ground. Walk toward the item and when your puppy sees it, tell her "Leave it!" as you turn sharply away from it, snapping the leash so that the puppy quickly follows you. Praise her.

With both methods, practice with different items on the ground so the puppy learns that the command applies to anything you tell her to ignore.

What Else Would You Like to Teach?

You can teach your puppy almost anything, as long as you can communicate with her about what it is you want. What is important to you? What would you like her to do (or not do)? Teach her using the same techniques we've used so far.

➤ Show her what to do, helping her if she needs help.

➤ Teach her a word (command) for it.

➤ Praise her when she does it right, even if you've helped her.

➤ *Really* praise her when she does it right all by herself.

➤ Correct her or let her know when she makes a mistake.

➤ After she's made a mistake, help her do it right.

➤ Repeat the training often.

The Least You Need to Know

➤ The eight basic commands were just the foundation for everything else. There is a lot more you can teach your puppy.

➤ Practice the come command some more, using these new techniques. Keep it fun and exciting.

➤ Other commands can be useful around the house, in the yard or out in public.

➤ What else would you like to teach your puppy? You can do it using the basic training techniques you've learned so far.

Chapter 21

Why Does My Puppy Get into Trouble?

> ### In This Chapter
>
> ➤ Ideas on preventing problems in the first place
> ➤ The common causes of problem behavior
> ➤ Why changing problem behavior requires a commitment from you
> ➤ Some common problems and their solutions

More dogs are given up by their owners for behavior problems than for any other reason. These problems include housetraining accidents, leg lifting and marking, barking, digging, chewing and a range of other behaviors. Many dogs with problem behavior exhibit several different problems.

Many of these problems are not simply bad behavior on the part of the dog. A dog's owner has a lot to do with any behaviors the dog might develop. That's why solving behavior problems requires a team approach, with both dog and owner on the team.

Why Does He Do That?

Most behaviors that we consider problems are not problems to the dog. Dogs bark because they have something to say; they are communicating, just as we do. Keep in mind that some people talk too much, just as some dogs bark too much!

Dogs dig because the ground smells good or because you have gophers. Dogs chew because it's fun or because they're teething. They raid the kitchen trash because there are wonderful tidbits in there. All of these things are natural for dogs—they are not problems to a dog!

Other things can also affect problem behavior, sometimes quite significantly. Let's take a look at some of them.

Paws for Thought

Many behaviorists and dog trainers believe at least 20 percent of all behavior problems are related to the dog's health in some way.

Health Problems

If your dog has been well-housetrained and suddenly begins having accidents in the house, make an appointment with your veterinarian. A urinary tract infection or some kind of stomach upset can cause housetraining accidents. If the dog is in pain, he may be distracted or even aggressive. Other health concerns can trigger problem behavior, too, so a thorough exam is always a good idea.

When you make your appointment, make sure you tell the vet that you are working on some problem behaviors and want to pin-point or eliminate any potential health problems. Don't just ask for an exam and leave the vet guessing as to why he's examining your dog.

Lack of Leadership

As I have mentioned several times throughout this book, you must be your puppy's leader. If you aren't the leader, someone else needs to be—after all, there must be a leader! If you won't do it, your puppy will, especially if your puppy has a dominant or assertive personality.

Dogs lacking leadership can develop a host of problems. Leg lifting, marking, mounting, humping and other unacceptable behaviors are frequently seen. Aggressive behavior towards family members is common, as is destructive behavior around the house. Food guarding, toy guarding and similar behaviors are also common.

If you have not yet convinced your puppy you are his leader, you need to change how he looks at you. Here's how:

➤ Feed him at set times, giving him his food and taking it away after 15 minutes. Do *not* free-feed, leaving food out all the time.

➤ Make him sit for everything he wants. Give just one command to sit, and then help him do it.

➤ Have him lie down and stay at your feet (with you either sitting or standing) at least twice a day.

➤ You go through doorways and gates first. You go up and down stairs first. Make him wait for you.

➤ Do *not* let him sleep in bed with you.

➤ Do *not* play rough games with him. No tug-of-war and no wrestling. Play games that make him work for you; retrieving games are good.

➤ Think like a leader—think assertive. Stand tall and act confident.

G-r-r-r!

If your adult dog thinks he's the leader and you are trying to change things, be careful—he may try to bite you. If you even *think* you could be bitten, hire a trainer or behaviorist to help you.

Do not allow your dog to engage in a power struggle with you. If he argues with you, use his leash and collar to help him do what you want. Never, ever allow him to use his strength against you—it would be too easy for him to win.

Dogs with delusions of dominance can easily become aggressive dogs. As adults, they can be very difficult to handle. Nip this behavior right in the bud. Let your puppy know that you are in charge.

Boredom

Boredom is the plague of dogs in modern times. Most of today's dog breeds were developed to perform a job. Border Collies herded sheep, Bernese Mountain Dogs pulled milk wagons and Doberman Pinschers patrolled alongside law enforcement officers. These, and all the other breeds designed to do a job, are now pets with no obvious work to do. All the years of working instincts are sitting idle, and you know that old saying, "Idle hands are the devil's tools." Idle paws are, too.

A bored dog is going to get into trouble. What he does may vary: some dogs bark, some dig and some chew. You need to figure out how to alleviate this boredom. Here are some suggestions:

➤ Increase his exercise so that he's more likely to sleep when left alone.

➤ Give him a toy before you leave: a rawhide, a paper bag with treats in it, a Kong or a Buster Cube. Kongs are hard rubber hollow toys that look like rubber balls that have been squashed together. Fill the hollow center of the Kong with peanut butter and give it to

Paws for Thought

Take a small brown paper lunch bag and put in a variety of small items. A slice of apple, a dog biscuit, a carrot and a cracker with peanut butter on it are all good. Just before you leave the house, give this to your dog. You'll have to clean up the paper bag when you get home, but your dog will be so interested in the treats, he'll forget you're leaving.

A run through an obstacle course or around a playground allows the puppy to use up his energy and engage his mind.

your dog just before you leave home. The Buster Cube is a plastic cube dog toy with an adjustable hole in one side where you can fill the cube with kibble. Many dogs are occupied by this for hours at a time.

➤ Keep his obedience skills sharp. This challenges his mind.

➤ If you are gone for long hours during the day, hire a dog walker, a neighbor or the neighbor's teen-ager to come over and spend some time with your dog while you're at work.

Paws for Thought

If you do switch foods, take your time. Add a little of the new food to the old and gradually—over two to three weeks—add more and more of the new food.

Diet

Dog foods that are very high in protein and fat or diets that are over 50 percent carbohydrates are known to cause hyperactivity in some dogs. Foods high in certain sugars and starches also cause behavior problems in some dogs. Many dogs are also very sensitive to some food colorings, preservatives or other additives.

If you suspect a food-related problem, read the label of the food you are giving your puppy. Most puppies do very well on a dry food that is about 28 percent protein and 8 to 10 percent fat. Make sure most of the protein is from meat and not from grains and cereals. Feed a food that does not contain a lot of sugar and artificial preservatives, colorings and additives.

Lack of Exercise

Lack of exercise causes many problems. A dog that hasn't gotten enough exercise may, literally, bounce off the walls. A healthy young dog needs to run, explore and use up his energy. If he doesn't get a chance to do that, he's likely to burn up all that energy doing things you'd rather he didn't. These may include running around the house, pacing, digging, barking and destructive behavior.

A dog that doesn't get enough exercise has other problems, too, including health problems. Just as we are getting more sedentary, so are our dogs. Experts say that more people are overweight today than at any time during recorded history, and veterinarians say the same thing about our dogs. An overweight dog is not happy, nor is he healthy.

Regular aerobic exercise can help use up your dog's excess energy and can keep his weight at a healthy level.

Breed Bits

The amount of exercise needed will vary from dog to dog. A nice one-mile walk around the neighborhood would be enough for a Miniature Dachshund, but a five-mile jog would be better for a young Labrador Retriever.

A healthy puppy needs good, vigorous exercise every day.

What We Do to Our Dogs

Unfortunately, behavior problems can also be caused by us, our personality and how that personality affects the relationship we have with our dog. Behavior problems caused by dog owners are often the hardest to solve because it is very difficult for us to recognize what we are doing wrong. After all, we may know that we have a personality "quirk" or two, but we don't want to admit that our quirk could be causing problems in our dog!

Our behavior can affect our dogs in many ways:

➤ Overprotective owners take away the dog's ability to cope with the world around him. By "protecting" him from everything, the dog often becomes fearful— sometimes aggressively fearful.

➤ Overemotional owners who are quick to get excited or quick to react often end up with dogs just like them. Unfortunately, during episodes of excitement these dogs can get out of hand.

➤ Overpermissive owners don't set enough rules, and when they do set rules, they do not enforce them. These owners are not the dog's leader, and many problem behaviors can develop as a result.

➤ Demanding owners would prefer the dog to be a furry robot that follows each and every order exactly as given. Dogs, of course, are just as fallible as people are, and will make mistakes. Dogs that belong to these owners will never measure up.

➤ Mean owners overpower their dogs, or make their dogs fearful or fearful aggressive. Because aggression begets aggression in certain dogs, these owners often wind up with a dog as mean as they are.

Puppy Tails

The owner of a destructive terrier once told me, "He knows he's bad because he looks guilty when I come home." That look isn't guilt; the dog is simply anticipating a correction. He has learned that he often gets yelled at when his owner comes home, so his body language is submissive. Submissive body language would stop or lessen a correction given by a more dominant dog. Unfortunately, the owner sees this cowering as guilt. Dogs live in the moment, and *must be corrected the moment they do something wrong.* They don't understand the reason for a correction that comes even 15 seconds after they've done something.

➤ Shy, timid owners tend to have dogs with one of two personality types. Many timid people get a large, extroverted dog who can project their bolder self. This dog may become over-protective of his timid owner, sometimes dangerously so. Or the shy owner may get a dog just like himself, and the two will go through life very quietly and fearfully.

We also contribute to our dog's problem behavior by training him inconsistently or incorrectly. Our dogs want to be good, and if we clearly show them what we want, they will comply.

Changing Problem Behaviors

Changing problem behavior requires a commitment from you. You are going to have to be involved in the process, which may require you to make some changes. You may have to make some physical changes around the house or yard, or you may have to make some changes in your daily schedule. If you make the effort, your chances of success are greatly increased. Most canine behavior problems can be changed, and if not cured, at least controlled.

Here's where to start:

➤ Make sure your puppy is healthy. Don't assume he is healthy—make an appointment with your veterinarian.

➤ Make the time to play and have fun with your dog. The time spent with you is important, and so is laughter!

➤ Make sure your puppy gets enough appropriate exercise.

➤ Prevent problems from occurring when you can. Put away the trash cans, pick up the children's toys and put away the cushions for the lawn furniture.

Paws for Thought

Preventing problems from occurring may mean limiting your puppy's freedom. Don't let him have free run of the house, and supervise him more carefully.

➤ If your puppy is getting into a lot of trouble in the yard, build him a dog run.

➤ Teach the puppy an alternative behavior. He can't jump on you if he learns to sit for petting. He can't dash out the front door if he has been taught to sit and wait at the door.

➤ Set the puppy up to learn. Purposely arrange things so he makes a mistake when you're there to teach him.

Common Puppy Problems and Some Solutions

Every puppy is a unique individual, just as you are. Therefore, there are no solutions that work for every person, every daily routine and every puppy. However, over the years I have found a few solutions that do work for a great number of puppies.

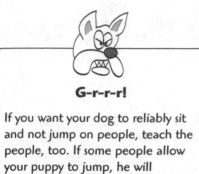

G-r-r-r!

If you want your dog to reliably sit and not jump on people, teach the people, too. If some people allow your puppy to jump, he will continue to do it. Don't let them sabotage your training.

Jumping on People

One of the most common methods of correcting jumping is to knee the puppy in the chest. Many trainers still use this method, but I don't understand why. It may teach the puppy to jump on his owner's back instead of in front of him, but it doesn't teach the puppy what to do so he can get attention from his owner—which is why the puppy is jumping in the first place. Needless to say, I am *not* a fan of kneeing any puppy!

Instead, teach the puppy to sit. This may seem very simple, but when the puppy learns to sit for attention, including petting from you, he will sit in front of you, quivering in anticipation of petting, and will have no need to jump on you. If you consistently reward him for sitting, the jumping will disappear.

You will also have to teach him to sit for other people. Use his leash and do not allow him to jump on other people. When he tries to jump, use a snap and release correction, tell him, "Acckk! No jump!" Then make him sit and don't allow other people to pet him until he's sitting.

Paws for Thought

Make sure everyone in the house is aware that the puppy likes to dash out. If everyone watches the puppy and keeps him away from open doors, you can stop the behavior from occurring while you are teaching him.

Dashing Through Doors and Gates

This problem is easily solved by using the boundary training I explained in Chapter 20. Take another look at it, and begin training your puppy to wait when you open a door or gate. You can use either method, but if your puppy tries to dash through the doors a lot, try using both methods.

Barking

Dogs bark for a number of reasons. Protective dogs bark to warn you of trespassers—real or imagined. Social dogs bark to communicate with you and the world

Puppy Tails

I want my dogs to warn me when people come up to the house, but I don't want any problem barkers. That's why I have a Three Bark Rule. When someone comes to the gate or door, the dogs can each respond with three barks. After that, I have trained them to stop. However, if there is a genuine emergency, such as the time someone tried to steal my husband's car, they can bark as much as they like. When they do bark that way, I know something is really wrong.

around them. Dogs bark at the kids playing out front, the birds flying overhead and the neighbor's dog barking down the block. Unfortunately, a barking dog is also a nuisance—sometimes a major nuisance.

Start correcting barking in the house when you are close by. Make up a squirt bottle filled about an eighth of the way with white vinegar and the rest with water. Make sure the solution is primarily water with just a little vinegar; one-quarter cup vinegar to one-and-three-quarters cups water is good. You want just enough vinegar so you can smell it. Any stronger and the vinegar could sting your puppy's eyes.

When someone comes to the door and your dog barks, walk quietly to the dog and tell him "Quiet!" firmly but without yelling. Squirt the vinegar water towards him. He will smell the vinegar, stop barking, back off and maybe even sneeze. When he stops barking, tell him, "Good boy to be quiet!"

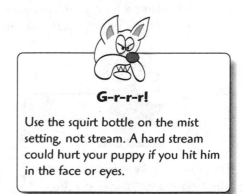

G-r-r-r!

Use the squirt bottle on the mist setting, not stream. A hard stream could hurt your puppy if you hit him in the face or eyes.

If you yell at your dog to stop barking—which is most people's first reaction—you're making lots of noise at the front door, which is the same thing he's doing. To your dog, you're barking too! Of course he isn't going to stop, since he thinks you're joining in.

However, when you calmly tell him to be quiet as you spray this nasty-smelling vinegar water, it is difficult for him to continue barking and he'll hear your command. Dogs have a sensitive sense of smell, and very few dogs enjoy the smell of vinegar.

Make sure you praise him for being quiet when he does stop barking. You don't want to just correct, you must also tell him what is right.

Once your puppy has learned what the word "quiet" means, start asking him to be quiet in a variety of situations. Whenever he starts to bark inappropriately, tell him to be quiet and back up your command with a spray of vinegar water. Again, always praise him for being quiet when he does.

If your dog barks when you're not home, you may have to set up a situation so you can catch him in the act. Go through all the motions of leaving: get dressed, pick up your purse, wallet or briefcase, get in the car and drive down the block. Park the car down the block and walk back with squirt bottle in hand. When your puppy starts to bark, surprise him with "Acckk! Quiet!" and a squirt! If you set him up a few times, he will quickly learn that you have much more control than he thought.

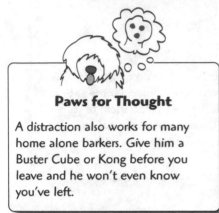

Paws for Thought

A distraction also works for many home alone barkers. Give him a Buster Cube or Kong before you leave and he won't even know you've left.

I do *not* recommend any of the electronic anti-bark collars for puppies. If you feel you have a serious barking problem and would like to try one of these collars, resist the urge. Call a trainer or behaviorist for help instead. You never have to hurt your dog to train him.

There is a new anti-barking collar on the market that is more humane. It has a vibration sensor, and when your dog barks, it squirts a small stream of citronella in the direction of his nose. Citronella is safe, but its smell is as unpleasant to dogs as vinegar.

Destructive Chewing

This isn't a hard problem to solve if you follow a few guidelines. First, consistently correct the puppy each and every time he puts his mouth on something he shouldn't.

Follow up each and every correction by handing him one of his toys. You show him what's wrong—"Acckk! No!"—and take the wrong item away as you tell him, "Here, this is your toy. Good boy!" and hand him his toy.

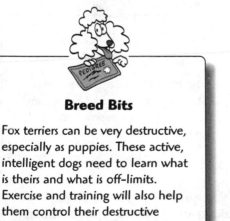

Breed Bits

Fox terriers can be very destructive, especially as puppies. These active, intelligent dogs need to learn what is theirs and what is off-limits. Exercise and training will also help them control their destructive tendencies.

In addition, as much as possible you must prevent chewing problems from developing. That means never allow your puppy to have unsupervised access to things that can be destroyed. Don't let him have free run of the house when you aren't watching him. Section off the garage so he can't get into stuff. Put away the kids' toys, the garden tools and the pool supplies. Prevent destructive chewing from happening!

As a puppy, everything goes in the mouth and everything is to be chewed on. That's why you have to

Dax learned to chew on her toys instead of the furniture. She even learned to share them with Tigger.

prevent it from happening as much as possible. Never assume that your puppy knows what he may chew and what he may not. He'll understand later—that's why you're teaching him now.

Digging

Does your backyard look like an Army artillery range? Puppies dig for a number of reasons, all of which could leave your backyard looking like a war zone.

Most digging occurs when you're nowhere to be seen. You will rarely see your dog busy excavating, and that's too bad, because to correct it, you have to catch him in the act. Correcting him later, when you come home and discover his handiwork, does no good at all and is even cruel.

To stop the digging, you need to prevent it from happening. When you're not home, don't let the puppy have free access to the lawn and gardens. Build him a dog run where he can do anything he wants! Make it big enough so that he can play, make sure it's covered, that he has shelter from the weather and has water in an unspillable dish. This can be his place when you're gone. He'll be

Breed Bits

Many terriers, including Scottish Terriers, are especially enthusiastic about digging. This makes sense, because many of the terrier breeds were bred to hunt rodents in their underground dens.

safe there and can play without getting into trouble. Then, when you're at home, you can let him run around the backyard and when you see him start to dig (or sniff the gopher holes), you can interrupt and teach him, "Acckk! No dig!"

With many dogs, you can control digging by giving the dog a place where he can dig. Find a spot in the yard, perhaps behind the garage or in an out-of-the-way corner, where he can dig up the soil. Using a shovel, loosen the dirt really well. Take half a dozen dog biscuits and stick them in the dirt so they are only partially covered. Invite your dog to find the biscuits and to dig there. As he finds the biscuits, completely bury a few so he has to dig for them, and in the beginning, help him do so. For the first few days, continue to bury something in this spot and invite him to find it. When he digs elsewhere, correct him and take him back to his spot. He'll learn.

Mouthing and Biting

When your puppy was still with his mother and his littermates, he learned to play by wrestling. Since he doesn't have any hands, he would bite and grab his brothers and sisters. If he bit too hard, a sibling would yelp or cry and he'd back off. Using his mouth to grab something is very natural to him.

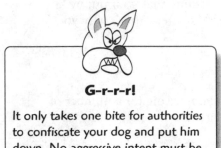

G-r-r-r!

It only takes one bite for authorities to confiscate your dog and put him down. No aggressive intent must be proved, either. Legally, a bite is a bite no matter what the dog's intent.

Unfortunately, human skin is much more fragile than dog skin covered in a fur coat, and your puppy's teeth can easily cause harm. In addition, as your puppy grows up, he will become more powerful and a playful puppy grab could turn into a serious bite.

The Centers for Disease Control in Atlanta, Georgia, has declared a dog bite epidemic, with more than 800,000 dog bite cases reported yearly. When you consider that this only includes the bites requiring medical attention, the numbers of actual bites is probably two to three times this number.

The American Veterinary Medical Association has also declared the problem alarming enough to form a Task Force on Canine Aggression and Human-Canine Interactions. The group is working on developing a multifaceted, community-oriented model program to address canine aggression and injuries caused by dog bites.

Every puppy must learn that touching teeth to skin or clothing is absolutely forbidden. You need to teach this lesson right away, starting the day you bring your puppy home. Here's how:

➤ Be consistent. Don't allow the puppy to bite you during play and then correct him for nipping in other situations.

➤ Don't play games that teach him to use his strength against you. No tug-of-war and no wrestling.

➤ Don't allow the puppy to chase the children and don't allow the puppy to "herd" the kids, nipping at their heels or clothing.

➤ Teach the children to play quietly with the puppy. There should be no running and screaming.

➤ Don't allow the puppy to grab at his leash, chew on it, mouth it or pull against it with the leash in his mouth.

There are several ways to correct mouthing and biting. No correction is better or worse than the others. Each is most useful in certain situations.

Use the squirt bottle (one-eighth vinegar to seven-eighths water) for those instances where the puppy is nipping at your legs, heels or clothes. Have the squirt bottle in hand in those situations when you know he is apt to do it. When he nips at your heels, spray him as you tell him, "Acckk! No bite!" When he backs off, praise him quietly, "Good boy."

Paws for Thought

Like a child, a puppy can have temper tantrums. He might throw himself around, crying, growling or screaming, and may try to bite you. A temper tantrum is bad behavior. Do not give in. If he wanted you to stop brushing him, for example, when the tantrum is over continue brushing him.

If you have your hands on your puppy, perhaps when hooking up his leash, playing with him or petting him, and he tries to mouth or bite you, correct him right away without hesitation. With one hand, grab his buckle collar or the scruff of his neck (as a handle) and with the other hand simply close his mouth. Tell him firmly, "Acckk! No bite!" Do not let go of his muzzle until he takes a deep sigh and relaxes. If you let go and he continues to try to mouth or bite you, close his mouth again, correct him again and wait him out.

When you're teaching him, don't lose your temper. Aggression begets aggression, and if you get angry and lose your temper, your puppy will too. He may try to fight you even more. If you lose your temper often, his behavior may mirror your own, becoming more aggressive in response to you. When you correct puppy biting and mouthing, correct him fairly and firmly—just as you did any other behavior—without losing your temper.

When your puppy tries to mouth or bite you, keep in mind he has to learn that it isn't acceptable to bite people. It *is* natural behavior to him, but it's behavior we simply cannot tolerate. You have to teach him, and you have to be consistent with your teaching. Never, ever allow him to touch skin or clothing with teeth.

Suggestions for Other Problems

As your puppy grows up, other behaviors may appear that you don't want to live with. If that happens, don't panic. Many behaviors can be changed or prevented with a minimum of fuss.

➤ **Digging under the fence.** Bury some rocks in the holes he digs. Then, ask yourself why he is digging under the fence. Make sure he's getting enough exercise, playtime and attention from you.

➤ **Chasing cars, bikes and kids on rollerblades and skateboards.** Keep him on leash, and when he tries to chase, correct him with the leash and have him sit. Enforce the sit and sit-stay. If he can't sit still, turn around, walk in the other direction and if he doesn't walk with you, let the leash correct him—*hard!* Praise him when he does walk with you.

➤ **Barking in the car.** Use your magic training tool, the squirt bottle. As you're driving, when your puppy barks, don't even turn to look at him (that could cause you to run off the road or into the back of another car). Just grab the squirt bottle and spray a sweeping mist in the direction of your dog as you tell him, "Sweetie, quiet!"

Let's Go Over the Steps Again

As I mentioned earlier in this chapter, more dogs are given up by their owners for problem behavior than for any other reason. This is tragic when so many problems can be stopped or controlled. When your dog has a behavior you consider a problem, follow these steps:

1. Why is your dog doing this? Try to look at it from his point of view, not yours! Is he getting enough exercise? Are you spending enough time with him? Does he have a health problem that might be causing it? Are neighborhood kids teasing him?

2. Can you prevent the problem? Will having a dog run help? How about a crate? Do you need to supervise him more closely?

3. How can you teach him? Set him up so that you can catch him in the act and correct him. Make sure you praise him if he decides not to do it!

4. Make sure you are your puppy's leader.

5. Practice his obedience commands regularly and use them around the house and yard. Incorporate them into your daily routine.

The Least You Need to Know

➤ Problem behaviors are not a problem to the dog; to the dog they are very natural behaviors.

➤ Problem behaviors usually happen for a reason. Try to find out why your dog is doing what he's doing.

➤ Prevent problems from happening if you can, especially when you aren't there to teach him.

➤ When you are at home, teach him what is wrong and, most importantly, teach him what is right!

Part 5

There's So Much More to Do!

Once you've learned how to teach your puppy, there is so much more that you can do with him. Tricks are a lot of fun, and can be entertaining and a great way to relieve stress during regular training sessions. Games are fun, too, and can be good exercise as well as a wonderful way to spend time with your dog. If you like having fun with your dog, there are a lot of dog activities and sports; let's look at them.

Many dog owners often find themselves confused by their dog. If he has such a sensitive sense of smell, why does he drink out of the toilet? He's picky about the food he eats, yet is more than willing to eat garbage on the street. Why? I'll answer those questions for you, along with some other puzzles of canine behavior.

Chapter 22

Twelve Tricks Your Puppy Will Love

In This Chapter

➤ Tricks are fun for you and your puppy

➤ Trick training will make you a better dog trainer

➤ Amuse your family and amaze your friends

When you're teaching your puppy the basic commands in Chapter 19, training can get boring. Your puppy can only sit so many times, and you can only reinforce it so many times without both of you going crazy. However, training doesn't have to be that way. If you train a few sit-stays and then train a few tricks, you will find that you and your puppy will both have a lot more fun. You'll look forward to your training sessions, and so will your puppy. You'll practice your skills more, and as a result, your puppy's overall training will be much better. All because of a few tricks!

Trick Training Skills

Trick training really isn't any different from basic command training, except it's more fun. Most people don't expect to have fun with basic training—which is a shame, because you actually can have fun with that, too. But if you add trick training to your regular training sessions you will find both of you are having more fun.

You will teach your puppy tricks by using the same training techniques I introduced in Part 4. You will show the puppy what to do, help her do it, and praise and reward her for getting it right. Correct the puppy only when she's defiant, or when she knows what to do and refuses to do it.

Paws for Thought

With their parents' permission, hire the neighborhood kids to be your audience. With cookies and lemonade in hand, have them be your audience for a trick training session. Have the kids clap and yell, providing distractions for your training session.

Make sure you use lots of praise when teaching tricks. All of this enthusiasm will help encourage the puppy to work harder and do the things you want her to do. The enthusiasm will make it more fun for you, too.

With all of these tricks, you will start teaching by leading the puppy with a treat (used as a lure) and by using a verbal command. As the puppy learns the trick, you can leave out either the signal or the verbal command, so that she's doing the trick for one or the other. However, don't be in a hurry to do this; make sure your puppy really understands the trick first.

Practice your trick training in front of other people. If you practice it when you and your puppy are alone and your puppy isn't used to an audience, when you try to show off her tricks she may not be able to concentrate. If your family gets tired of the tricks, show off to friends and neighbors.

Some Easy Tricks

We'll start with the easy ones first: Tricks that build on a behavior your dog already knows. Your puppy is a lot smarter than you think, and now she's going to prove it.

Paws for Thought

Have your puppy sit, preferably in front of an audience. Tell her "shake" and praise her quietly. Then, for your audience's ears, tell her, "Now give me your other paw!" Praise her. People will think your puppy is very smart!

Shake

➤ Start with your puppy in a sit.

➤ Reach behind her front paws and lightly tickle her right paw. As she lifts that paw, tell her, "Sweetie, shake!" and shake her paw in your hand.

➤ Praise her and give her a treat.

After a few training sessions, your puppy will begin to lift her paw before you tickle her. When she does, praise her!

The Other Paw

Once she can shake with one paw, teach her to shake with the other front paw. Instead of saying "shake," which means specifically the right paw, tell her "other paw!" Teach it the same way—just make sure she's giving you the left paw. If she doesn't get it at first, help her by gently touching the left paw.

Wave

When your puppy is shaking hands well, tell her to shake but don't grasp her paw to shake it. Instead, just let her barely touch your fingers and keep lifting your hand higher so that she has to reach up and out to give you her paw.

➤ Tell her, "Wave!"

➤ As she reaches out to your hand, praise her, "Good to wave!"

➤ If you want her to move her paw, move your hand back and forth. As she reaches toward your hand, moving her paw, praise her.

Over several training sessions, let her touch your hand less and less. With practice, she will wave on your verbal command without your hand's cue.

Spin

In this trick, you are teaching your puppy to circle in front of you.

➤ With your puppy standing in front of you, show her a treat.

➤ Tell her, "Sweetie, spin!" and lead her in a small circle, with the treat right in front of her nose. When she follows the treat, praise her.

➤ When she is willingly moving in a circle following your hand, teach her, "One more spin!" and have her circle again.

When she gets good at this, you can take away the treat and just use a spin of your finger as a cue. Remember to give her plenty of praise when she gets it right.

Some Intermediate Tricks

Let your puppy feel comfortable with the easy tricks before you move on. Don't try to teach her too many too soon.

Paws for Thought

Trick training is wonderful combined with therapy dog work. A dog visiting someone in a nursing home or hospital can do a few tricks and make people smile and laugh.

Crawl

You will be teaching your puppy to do a belly crawl.

➤ Have your puppy lie down but do not tell her to stay.

➤ Put your left hand on her shoulder, and with your right hand hold a treat or a favorite toy in front of her nose. Tell her, "Sweetie, crawl!" and slowly pull the treat along the ground away from her.

Lead her by her nose and encourage her to crawl after the treat. Your hand on her shoulder can discourage her from actually getting up.

➤ Praise her as she moves, "Good girl to crawl!"

➤ After she has crawled a few steps, give her the treat.

After she learns the command, you can take your hand off her shoulder. When she's really good at the crawl, you can take away the treat lure and simply use a hand signal.

Use a treat or toy your puppy really likes to teach her to crawl on command.

Roll Over

This is a classic dog trick. You want your dog to lie down and roll over.

➤ Have your puppy lie down. With a treat in one hand, lead her nose in a circle (from her nose up and over in the direction you want her to roll) as you tell her "Sweetie, roll over!"

➤ If she doesn't quite understand what you want, help her roll over with your hands.

➤ As she does it, praise her.

Two Roll Overs, Three Roll Overs

Show your friends that your dog knows how to count. Teach your dog—by helping her—that "two roll overs" means roll over two times and "three roll overs" means roll

Roll over is a fun trick that most puppies learn very easily.

over three times. You don't have to tell your friends that your dog really doesn't know how to count! Teach this by telling your dog "two" or "three" as you help her do the correct number of roll overs. As you do it, emphasize the appropriate word. "Roll over" means one, while "*two* roll overs" means two and "*three* roll overs" means three.

Beg

Your goal is to have your puppy sit up on her hips, balance herself and hold the position for a gradually increased period of time—a few seconds to a minute.

➤ Have your puppy sit but don't tell her to stay.

➤ Hold a treat over her nose. As you tell her, "Sweetie, beg!" pull the treat straight up from her nose just a few inches. Lead her by the nose so that she pulls her front feet off the ground and balances her body on her hips.

➤ Praise her and give her the treat.

➤ Release her and praise her.

Paws for Thought

Begging requires body coordination and strength. A young puppy may be able to pull herself up but may not be able to hold the position. Keep each exercise (and the training session) short and sweet, making sure the puppy can succeed.

Start with just a few seconds before you give her the treat and praise her. Slowly work up by adding a few seconds more.

Go to Sleep

Your goal is to have your puppy lay her head on the floor as if she were asleep.

➤ With your dog in a down, move a treat from her nose to the ground as you tell her, "Sweetie, go to sleep." Use your other hand to encourage her to keep her head down.

➤ When she puts her head on the floor and relaxes, praise her!

➤ Release her and praise her.

As she learns the command, you can have her hold her head down and still for gradually longer times—from a few seconds to a minute.

Special Tricks

A well-trained puppy is always impressive, but these are the tricks your friends and neighbors are dying to see.

Play Dead

➤ Have your puppy lie down.

➤ Tell her, "Dead dog!" as you help her over to her side. Gently put her head down so she's flat on the ground. Keep a gentle hand on her as you tell her, "Good dead dog!"

➤ Wait a few seconds as she lies still, then release her and praise her.

As she learns that "dead dog" means, "Lie flat on your side with your head down and remain still," you can start teaching it from a sit or a stand. You can also add other cues, such as a toy gun or your finger pointed at her like a gun. Simply point your finger at her and tell her "Sweetie, dead dog!"

Puppy Tails

One day I was out with my German Shepherd, Michi, and was talking to one of my neighbors who had just graduated from the police academy. He was showing the neighborhood kids his uniform. I congratulated him and then turned to my dog and said, "Michi, would you rather be a police officer or a dead dog?" Down went Michi, flat on her side!

Take a Bow

Your goal is to have your dog stand, and then, on command, lower the front half of her body, keeping her hips in the air, as she lowers her head and shoulders. She'll look like she's taking a bow in front of an audience.

➤ Start by having your dog stand. Keep one hand under her tummy to show her she needs to keep her hips high.

➤ With a treat in the other hand, tell her, "Sweetie, take a bow!" and move the treat from her nose to the floor, the way you did when you taught her to lie down. As her head and front end go down, keep her hips high and praise her.

➤ Take your hand out from under her tummy only when you aren't needed to remind her and she'll keep her hips high by herself.

➤ After a short few seconds, release her, give her the treat and praise her.

Weave

In this trick, you will teach your puppy to weave through your legs as you're walking with exaggerated large steps. As you take one step forward, your puppy will move under that leg to your other side. And as you take another step forward, your puppy will come back under that leg. The end result is your puppy weaving back and forth.

➤ With a treat in your hand, step forward and, reaching under your leg, lead your puppy under your leg as you tell her, "Weave!"

➤ Step forward with the other leg, and lure the puppy to switch directions and go under that leg.

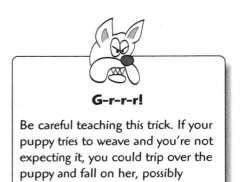

G-r-r-r!

Be careful teaching this trick. If your puppy tries to weave and you're not expecting it, you could trip over the puppy and fall on her, possibly hurting both of you.

As your puppy learns, make the steps a little faster. You will be able to decrease the signal, too, as she gets better at it.

Set the Stage

Once your puppy knows a few tricks, put them together into a routine. Have one trick follow another as you tell a little story, and you can entertain friends and family. Or, if your dog does therapy dog work, you can entertain the people you are visiting.

For example:

You, the narrator, tell the story, "Kes, our heroine, was asleep (use the command "go to sleep"), when she smelled smoke. Knowing the family was in the house, she crawled to the bedroom (have her crawl) to avoid the smoke. She found the baby (a doll) and, picking up the baby, crawled out of the house (have her crawl again). When she was outside, Kes made sure she wasn't on fire by rolling over (roll over), and then rolled again just to make sure (two roll overs).

"Our heroine then went for help. She saw a friendly face (an audience member) and asked for help (have her bow). The person didn't understand, and Kes felt desperate (have her spin). She felt more desperate (have her spin again)! Finally, she figured out how to get the person's attention (have her wave). Kes led the person to the burning house, where help was called. Exhausted, our heroine lay down with the baby she saved (dead dog) and waited for the fire engine to get there. When all was well, the firemen thanked Kes for a job well done (shake hands)."

And There's More!

The tricks you teach your puppy are limited only by your imagination. If you use your training skills, you can teach her just about anything. For example, a friend of mine made some wooden blocks with A, B, C, 1, 2 and 3 written on the blocks. She taught her Welsh Terrier, Zippy, to recognize the marks on the blocks. She could then tell Zippy, "Go get the A," and Zippy would. People were absolutely convinced that Zippy *knew* A, B, C and 1, 2, 3! And Zippy did know them—not what they meant or signified, of course, but she did know they were different and could retrieve the appropriate block. All because her owner figured out how to teach her.

Teach your puppy to give kisses, to speak, to whisper, to sing or to sneeze. Teach her to jump through your arms held in a circle or to jump up in your arms. Teach her to stand on her back legs and dance with you.

There is so much you can do. Just follow the fundamental training steps, figure out how to show your dog what to do and have fun doing it! And don't forget the praise. Your puppy lives for your approval. Make sure you give it to her.

Puppies are smart. We just have to figure out how to teach them.

The Least You Need to Know

➤ Training doesn't have to be serious all the time. You and your puppy should have fun with it.

➤ Train tricks using your training skills: Show your puppy what to do, teach her a word for it, help her do it, and praise her for doing it.

➤ Have fun with your training. Show off for your neighbors, friends and family.

➤ Put some tricks together in a little routine. It's fun!

Chapter 23

The Best Games and Toys for Your Puppy

In This Chapter

➤ Good games to teach your puppy

➤ Some games you should not teach your puppy

➤ Good toys you want your pup to have

➤ Bad toys, and those that should be used with caution

Most people get a dog for companionship, and that companionship can take many forms. You and your dog can go for walks or jogs together. You can go hiking, camping or just strolling along the beach. Your dog can sleep at your feet while you're reading or watching television. All of these things are great. But wouldn't it also be wonderful if you and your dog *really* had some *fun* together? What better way to spend some time with your dog than to play games with him?

What Makes a Game Good?

I can see it now: You're wondering how can there be "good" games and "bad" games? Well, there really are games that are better for your puppy (and you), and games that are not so good. The difference is between games that teach your puppy the lessons you want him to learn and games that teach him what you would rather he *not* learn.

Every time you do anything with your puppy—anything at all—he learns something. If you're lucky, he is constantly learning that you are in charge, and that you are kind, caring and fair. However, sometimes he learns that you are slower than him, not as strong and really stupid in the ways of dogs (we all are, unfortunately). You can try to up the odds in your favor by paying attention to the games you play with your puppy. Good games are those that teach your puppy to work for you, to do something for you that can still be fun.

Konrad Lorenz, the Nobel Prize-winning expert on animal behavior, said that play develops a dog's mind. By stimulating the dog's mind during play, you can actually create a more intelligent dog. That's another reason for playing good games.

Paws for Thought

Retrieving games are great exercise as well as lots of fun. If you have a high-energy puppy that needs to use up some of that energy, retrieving games are good for you both.

Paws for Thought

Roll the toy rather than throwing it in the beginning, because the puppy can visually track a rolled toy much more easily. Watching a thrown toy is more difficult for a young puppy.

Retrieving Games

Retrieving games are great fun once your puppy has learned how to retrieve. Some dogs are natural retrievers and will charge after, grab and bring back anything that is thrown. Retrieving games are easy with these dogs. However, some dogs need to be taught how to retrieve. Luckily, this isn't hard to do.

I like to use a lot of praise while teaching the retrieve, because I want the puppy to consider this fun. We are going to approach the training using very small baby steps, so that your puppy gets a lot of positive reinforcement. Use your "ice cream!" tone of voice for this activity.

➤ Sit on the floor with your puppy. Bounce a toy around a little, so you make the puppy look at it. When he looks at it, tell him "Good!"

➤ Roll the toy a few feet away. Encourage the puppy to chase after it and praise him when he does. When he goes after it, tell him "Sweetie, take it!"

➤ If you're lucky enough that he goes after the toy, grabs it and brings it back, really praise him!

➤ If he goes after it but seems confused about what to do with it, see if you can get him to pick it up by encouraging him to do so in a happy tone of voice and with your hands. If he does, back up a little and tell him "Bring it here!" If he does, praise him! You may have to play with the toy a little yourself to get him interested. Right now your puppy has no idea why you're playing this new game or why you're interested in this toy.

➤ Increase the distance you roll the toy very gradually. If your puppy hesitates or stops going after it, go with him to encourage him, and next time don't roll it so far.

➤ When your puppy is going after the toy enthusiastically, start throwing it—again, just short distances—and keep it exciting.

As your puppy learns this game is fun and exciting, you can start playing with different toys (make sure they are safe to throw) and very gradually increase the length of the throws.

Paws for Thought

Puppies invite play by bowing, nudging, pawing and by bringing you toys. Once your puppy learns you like to play retrieving games, he'll invite you to play!

If your puppy brings the toy back but doesn't want to give it to you, take hold of the top of his muzzle and *gently* press his upper lips against his upper teeth as you tell him, "Sweetie, give!" He will open his mouth automatically and you can take the toy and praise him for giving it to you. He'll soon learn that giving up the toy means you will throw it again, and the fun of continuing the game will become his reward.

If your puppy likes to play keep-away with the toy, getting it but not bringing it all the way back, then play with several toys. He will drop one to get the others, and you can then just walk around the yard, picking up and throwing the various toys.

Hide-and-Seek Games

Games that teach your puppy to use his natural scenting abilities are also good ones to play. All dogs have these scenting abilities, and smelling the world is probably more important than seeing it for a dog.

Hide-and-seek games also give you a chance to teach the puppy the family members' names: Go find Dad or Mary, or Joanne or sister. Why is this useful? Because my dogs know our names, when my husband needs a screwdriver, I can hand that to Dax and tell her, "Take it! Go find Paul!" and she'll take the screwdriver to my husband. She gets a chance to work and be praised for it, and it saves me some effort!

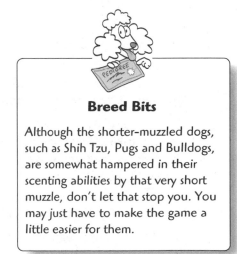

Breed Bits

Although the shorter-muzzled dogs, such as Shih Tzu, Pugs and Bulldogs, are somewhat hampered in their scenting abilities by that very short muzzle, don't let that stop you. You may just have to make the game a little easier for them.

➤ Hide-and-seek is best played with two people and the puppy. Have one person hold the puppy while the second person (who has some treats) runs away to hide. Make the hiding place close and easy at first, so your puppy is sure to succeed.

Paws for Thought

Search and rescue training begins with similar games, called run-aways, where someone will run away from the dog and hide. As the dog's skills develop, the hiding spots become more difficult.

➤ The first person should tell the puppy "Go find Dad!" (or whoever is hiding) and let the puppy go. Dad can be quietly calling the puppy to encourage him to succeed.

➤ When the puppy finds Dad, he should praise him enthusiastically and offer a treat.

➤ When you can see the puppy is using his scenting abilities instead of listening for the call, have the hidden person stop calling the puppy. You'll know this because your puppy will have his head down, nose to the floor, rather than up and listening. Again, when the puppy finds the hidden person, praise him!

As the puppy gets better at the game, make it harder. Have the person who is hiding walk around a little first, leaving a scent trail. Have the person who is hiding go into a different room or down the hall. Make it slightly more challenging, but do so gradually so the puppy can still succeed.

The game can also move outside. Dad can hide around the corner of the garage or behind some bushes. Hold on to the puppy in the front yard and Dad can go around to the back of the house. Again, make it more challenging but easy enough for the puppy to succeed.

The Name Game

When your puppy will retrieve a few different toys, you can teach him the name game. Your goal is to teach him to recognize the different toys by their names. (This is the same game I described in Chapter 22—the one my friend taught her Welsh Terrier Zippy.)

➤ Organize a few toys that the puppy will retrieve. Put them within your reach, but out of the puppy's sight.

➤ Sit on the floor with the puppy and one toy. Send him after the toy, calling it by name, "Sweetie, get the tennis ball!" Praise him when he goes after it and again when he brings it back. Do this two or three times.

➤ Put the tennis ball away and bring out another toy. Send the puppy after this, again, calling it by name, "Sweetie, get the porcupine!" Praise him when he goes after it and when he brings it back. Do this two or three times.

➤ Now put the porcupine out and, with your puppy watching, roll the tennis ball past it. Tell the puppy to go after the tennis ball. If he does, really praise him. If he goes after the porcupine, don't say anything (no corrections!), just start all over again.

➤ When he will go after the tennis ball and not the porcupine, reverse the game, sending him after the porcupine and not the tennis ball. Don't be surprised if there is some confusion here!

Paws for Thought

This game requires your puppy to think. Keep the game simple, use lots of praise and train in very short increments—two or three minutes at a time.

When the puppy has figured out how to play the game with these two toys, add another toy. Teach the puppy this toy's name just as you did with the first two toys. When your puppy understands that one, add another toy. After three toys, you will find your puppy catching on very quickly. He will have learned that certain sounds pertain to specific toys, and your command to get that specific toy means he should bring that one back.

Later, when your puppy is grown up—long past puppyhood—and is reliable around the house, teach him other words. Teach your adult dog to find your car keys, the television remote, your cellular phone and anything else that you lose (and use!) regularly.

What Games Are Not Good to Play?

Some games teach your puppy things it's better that he doesn't know. For example, to your puppy, the leader is the one who is the biggest, strongest, fastest and smartest, or the one who thinks he is! If you play games that teach the puppy that you are not as strong as he is or not very fast, he could seriously doubt your leadership abilities.

G-r-r-r!

Don't teach a puppy to find things like a cell phone, or they will end up being chewed into tiny fragments!

In addition, if the games you play teach your puppy to use his strength against you, he could learn to physically struggle against you—a bad lesson. He could then struggle against you any time you want him to do something he doesn't want to do.

Wrestling

One game that is very popular with most puppies and almost all boys and young men is wrestling. Puppies wrestle with each other in the litter. This wrestling teaches them body coordination, and develops their reflexes and their strength. However, when growing puppies wrestle with their owners, they learn to use their strength and often, their teeth against people. They learn to fight you, to resist you and even to hurt you. Wrestling is *never* a good game to play with a puppy.

Puppy Tails

Phoenix is a small Cattle Dog mix. His owners complained that Phoenix liked to use his teeth against them whenever they wanted him to do something. I had already told them in class to correct any mouthing and biting, so I asked Phoenix's owners if they played rough with him. It turned out Dad liked to wrestle with him every night. They were correcting biting, but encouraging wrestling. No wonder the puppy was so confused!

Tug-of-War

Most dogs really enjoy tug-of-war games. They play them with each other, and usually the games are relatively peaceful—although there can be some growling as the dogs use their strength against each other.

Dax and Kes, my two Australian Shepherds, like to play tug-of-war together and will pull each other back and forth. This is fine. They are evenly matched and are playing much more naturally than they could ever play with me.

However, when a puppy plays tug-of-war against his owner, he's learning to use the strength of his jaws and body against his owner. Obviously, this is rarely, if ever, a good idea.

In addition, when an owner plays tug-of-war with the puppy, the owner usually gets tired of the game first and drops the toy, allowing the dog to get it. What did that teach the puppy? That if he fights enough and tries hard enough, he will win! Again, a bad lesson for the puppy to learn.

Think About the Games You Play

When you're playing with your puppy, try to think about what the game is teaching your puppy. It's hard to do, but try to think about the game from your puppy's perspective.

Also, don't play any game with your puppy that encourages any aspect of behavior that you will be uncomfortable with when your dog is full-grown. If you are allowing him to jump in the middle of your chest now when he's 10 pounds, are you still going to like it in eight months when he's 60 pounds of hard muscle?

What Toys Are Good for Your Puppy?

Just as there are good and bad games to play with your puppy, there are good and bad toys. Unlike games, toys by themselves don't usually give a puppy a wrong message. Instead, bad toys are usually considered bad because they're dangerous to the puppy. Balls that are small enough to be inhaled or swallowed are obviously dangerous, as are toys that come apart easily with small pieces that can be swallowed, or toys made from substances that are dangerous or poisonous.

The Best Toys

I often joke with the owners of Labrador Retrievers and Golden Retrievers that these two breeds seem to come out of the womb with a tennis ball in their mouth! Tennis balls weren't invented for the game of tennis—that's a sidelight for these balls. They were, in fact, invented for dogs. Tennis balls bounce well, are easy to throw and, most important, are soft on the teeth and big enough that they are not a choking danger for most dogs.

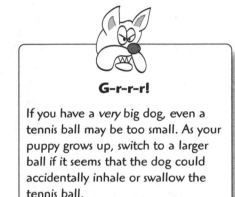

G-r-r-r!

If you have a *very* big dog, even a tennis ball may be too small. As your puppy grows up, switch to a larger ball if it seems that the dog could accidentally inhale or swallow the tennis ball.

For smaller breeds, such as those in the Toy group, smaller balls that are just as soft and bouncy are manufactured for cats to play with. You'll find plenty of them at pet supply stores. Just make sure whatever ball you buy is big enough that your small dog can't swallow it.

The Buster Cube is also a wonderful toy. This big plastic cube is about five inches square on each side and looks like a blue box. On one side there is a hole with an adjustable opening. You can open the hole and fill the cube with dry dog food, then adjust it to spill out a lot or just a few pieces of food each time the dog knocks the cube over. When you first introduce the dog to the cube, you can have it wide open so the dog gets a lot of reinforcement for knocking this around. Later, when he knows that goodies come out of it, you can adjust it so fewer treats come out. This will keep dogs occupied for hours on end, especially those that are very fond of food.

There are a variety of toys made for dogs to retrieve. Some, such as soft fabric flying disks, are great toys. Canvas dummies—like the ones used to train retrieving bird dogs—also make good toys. If your dog likes to retrieve, browse through the shelves at your local pet supply store and see what's available.

Kong toys are also a lot of fun for dogs, and are safe. A Kong looks like a hard rubber snowman or three balls (small, medium and large) squashed together. Kongs come in different sizes, and there is an appropriate size for every dog. Make sure the one you

The Buster Cube is a great toy that will keep a puppy amused for hours.

Introduce the Kong toy to your puppy by stuffing it with peanut butter or soft cheese.

get for your dog is big enough so that he can't swallow it or choke on it. Kongs are hollow inside, and if you fill that hollow space with peanut butter or soft cheese, you can keep a puppy occupied and out of trouble for a long time. Kongs are also great for retrieving games, because they bounce every which way.

Some Toys to Use with Caution

The clerk at my local pet supply store says some of the most popular toys are the ones made from thick knotted rope. These cotton ropes really seem to appeal to dogs, and when I brought one home, my dogs liked it, too. These toys seem to be made for tug-of-war games—which, as you know, are not good games for your puppy. However, if two dogs want to play tug-of-war with the rope, that's fine. The smaller ropes can also be thrown, and that makes for a different kind of retrieving game.

Rubber or plastic squeaky toys are also popular. Some dogs can play with these with no problems, but many dogs seem to be focused on chewing the toy up to get at the squeaky part inside. If your dog chews up these toys, make sure he doesn't swallow any of the small pieces. If he does swallow some, call your veterinarian right away. The vet will probably want to you watch your puppy's stools to make sure he passes all of the pieces. If you find your dog regularly destroys his squeaky toys, you might want to stop buying them.

Another popular group of toys is the plastic flying disks and Frisbees. Although most dogs love to chase and catch these disks, the plastic ones can cut the dog's tongue, gums and lips. I prefer to use the fabric disks made specifically for dogs. These are more durable, last longer and don't hurt the dog's mouth.

Chew Toys

Chew toys are very necessary for puppies, especially when they are teething. Chews are also needed to help teach the puppy what is right for him to chew on and what is wrong. You need to be able take away your things and hand him something he can chew and that he wants to chew on. The key to keeping chew toys safe is to find something your puppy will chew on without detaching small pieces. Many of the hard rubber toys, such as Kongs and Nylabones, are great for this.

G-r-r-r!

Don't give your puppy anything to chew on that you won't want him chewing on later. Old shoes should never be given as a toy—you'll regret it when he chews on your new shoes!

Rawhide chews are popular chew toys, both at the pet supply store and with my dogs. However, I have to be very careful with rawhides, because several of my dogs like to chew off big pieces and try to swallow those pieces whole. Many times during Ursa's lifetime, I had to reach down her throat to pull out a piece of rawhide. When she passed away (due to old age) I thought I could relax, but Dax is now doing the same thing. I suggest you do as I do, and only allow the puppy to chew on rawhides while you can supervise.

Use the same caution with other edible chews. The pig ears, snouts, hooves and other edible chew treats are extremely popular, and dogs seem to gobble them up—literally! However, some are very brittle, especially the ears, and I would be concerned about those brittle pieces in the mouth, throat and digestive tract. After giving your puppy any chew toy, watch his stools carefully for pieces of the chew toy coming through. In addition, if the puppy is passing blood or stops passing stools, get him in to the vet right away.

The Least You Need to Know

➤ There are good games that teach your puppy lessons you want him to learn, and bad games that teach him things he should not learn.

➤ Retrieving games, hide-and-seek games and the name game are all good games, while wrestling and tug-of-war are not so good.

➤ The Buster Cube, Kong toys and retrieving toys are good, safe toys for your puppy.

➤ Give your puppy edible chew toys only while he's supervised, and use them with caution.

Dog Activities and Sports

If you and your puppy enjoy training and cherish your time spent together, you might want to check out some of these canine activities and sports. Getting involved in a dog sport gives you a chance to set specific training goals and work on new skills together. It also enables you to meet other people and dogs, and develop a wide circle of friends you can learn from and laugh with.

There is something for everyone, from the dedicated couch potato to the athlete. See what strikes your fancy and what you think is appropriate for your dog. Some activities can be a training challenge or just plain fun. Others are very competitive sports. A few of the activities, such as search and rescue and therapy work, are not sports at all, but are serious activities you can train for that make worthwhile, rewarding careers or volunteer opportunities.

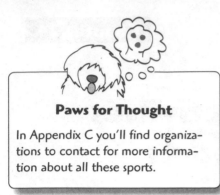

Paws for Thought

In Appendix C you'll find organizations to contact for more information about all these sports.

Agility for the Active Dog

Agility is an active sport that is a combination of a child's playground, a grand prix jumping course (modeled after those for horses) and a law enforcement K-9 obstacle course. The dog must run through tunnels, leap over jumps of different heights and shapes and climb obstacles.

Agility training helps develop a puppy's body awareness. The dog learns where her feet are and how to step, jump or climb, and becomes more aware of her balance. A puppy involved in agility training also gains confidence, both in herself and in you as her trainer—because you will make sure the dog doesn't hurt herself, that she can succeed and that you both will have fun.

Agility training is also good for you, as your dog's trainer. You learn how to communicate with your dog, showing her what you want her to do. After all, your dog has no idea why you want her to jump through a tire when it's so much easier to go around!

Some Agility Caveats

Agility competition does require a physically fit dog and owner. To compete, your dog will also need obedience training so you have good, reliable off-leash control.

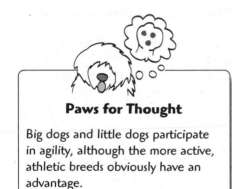

Paws for Thought

Big dogs and little dogs participate in agility, although the more active, athletic breeds obviously have an advantage.

Agility can also be tough on a puppy's growing bones, and practice equipment must be scaled down to puppy size. Most agility organizations will not allow a dog to compete before it is 12 months old, because high jumping can damage growing joints and bones.

Does this mean agility is not right for your puppy? No. It does mean you should keep the jumps very low at first (low enough so she can step over them), so your pup learns the idea of going over an obstacle but is not stressing her joints. When can she start jumping for real? The larger the breed, the later she should start jumping, but eight months is a good rule of thumb. It's always a good idea to check with your veterinarian or your dog's breeder to be sure.

Another drawback to agility is that it requires equipment, such as hurdles and tunnels. If you have the space and the skills, you can build your own. And if you have the imagination, you can improvise. A sheet thrown over a coffee table can make a good tunnel, for example. Many dog training clubs or training schools also have agility equipment.

Canine Good Citizen

The American Kennel Club began the Canine Good Citizen program in hopes of combating some of the negative publicity dogs have had recently. The AKC wanted to show the general public (and the media) that there are a lot of good dogs and responsible owners in local communities that are not normally in the media spotlight, simply because they aren't in trouble. Bad news is news! However, the AKC wants to promote good dogs and good owners, and is doing so by promoting this program and by helping community clubs and dog trainers publicize the Canine Good Citizen tests.

The Canine Good Citizen (CGC) program is open to all dogs, registered or not, purebred or mixed breed, large or small. The dog and owner take a short, noncompetitive test, and they either pass or fail. The test is one of basic manners, and does require some training. The dog must allow a stranger to approach the dog and the owner. The stranger will shake hands with you and greet your dog. The dog should not move from the sit by your side, should not jump on the stranger, growl, bark or misbehave in any other way. The dog must also allow someone to touch, pet and groom her. Again, she must remain sitting by your side and should not show any shyness or resentment.

Paws for Thought

If a local dog trainer does not offer the tests, write to the AKC for information about someone in your area who does.

You and your dog must also demonstrate that the dog will walk on a leash without pulling, even in a crowd situation, do a sit on command, a down and stay, and come when called. Your dog will then be subject to several distractions, including another dog, a loud sound such as a book being dropped and a jogger dashing past. The last part of the test is supervised isolation. You will tie your dog and leave her under the judge's supervision, going out of sight for five minutes. Your dog should not bark, whine, pace or howl.

At the successful completion of the test, the dog is awarded a certificate that says she is a Canine Good Citizen and is entitled to use the initials "CGC" after her name. The test is given by dog training clubs and dog trainers, and is sometimes given at dog show matches.

Carting and Draft Dogs

Carting and draft dogs, such as the Newfoundland and Bernese Mountain Dog, have been used by dog owners for thousands of years. Dogs like the Alaskan Malamute have pulled sleds, wagons

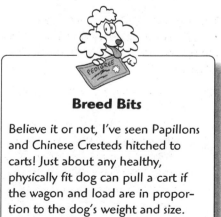

Breed Bits

Believe it or not, I've seen Papillons and Chinese Cresteds hitched to carts! Just about any healthy, physically fit dog can pull a cart if the wagon and load are in proportion to the dog's weight and size.

Lucy herds sheep, but that isn't her only job. She also pulls her wagon through a carting obstacle course.

and travois, carrying or pulling home the fruits of a hunt, household furnishings, people and supplies. In many parts of the world horses, oxen or other large beasts of burden were not available or practical, but dogs of suitable strength and size usually were.

Today carting can be a fun sport with competitions much like harness racing for horses, or it can be a practical skill, helping you around the house or yard. When you go shopping and bring home a 40-pound bag of dog food, hook your dog up to her wagon and let her bring in her food. When the trash cans have to go out to the end of the driveway, load them into your dog's wagon.

Showing Off at Dog Shows

At a conformation dog show, each dog competes against the other dogs and against a written description of the breed (called the standard) to see which dog most closely measures up to the standard of perfection for the breed. This competition serves two purposes: First, the best dog of the day wins, and winning your breed or a Best in Show is a wonderful accomplishment. In addition, show competition gives breeders a chance to evaluate many dogs for present and possibly future breeding.

G-r-r-r!

Dogs competing in AKC shows must be registered with the AKC. Dogs competing in UKC shows must be registered with the UKC.

The American Kennel Club and United Kennel Club license conformation competitions. Each has slightly different rules and emphasizes different things, but their shows are not all that different.

Earthdog Trials

Most terrier breeds were developed to hunt rodents and other vermin, and these dogs have retained those instincts today. Earthdog trials give these dogs a chance to use their working instincts in a way that may not be otherwise possible.

Breed Bits

Earthdog trials are limited to those breeds originally bred to hunt vermin, primarily the terriers and Dachshunds.

At a trial, the dog is released at one end of a tunnel. She must work her way to the other end, where there is a caged (for safety) rat. The dog notifies her owner (usually by barking) that she's found the rat. Tests are run at four levels, with each level requiring a greater degree of skill in detecting and following a scent.

Field Trials and Hunt Tests

Many of today's breeds were originally bred to flush, point and/or retrieve birds for hunters. For many years, the talents of these dogs provided food for hungry families. Today, although many dogs still pursue this time-honored occupation, many of the sporting breeds are now simply pets. These trials give these dogs a chance to use their instincts and to compete to titles and prizes.

Most of the dogs competing in field trials and hunt tests are sporting dogs. There are different tests for retrievers, pointers, setters and spaniels, measuring the different hunting skills these breeds were developed to have.

Breed Bits

While the sporting dogs come to mind when you think about hunt tests, there are also tests for Beagles and Basset Hounds. These dogs work in packs or pairs. And there are Coonhound trials, where dogs follow and tree a raccoon.

G-r-r-r!

Flyball involves jumping over hurdles, so the same warning about young puppies and growing bones that I gave you for agility also applies here.

Both field trials and hunt tests measure a dog's skill at finding, indicating and retrieving game. What's the difference between them? The most obvious difference is that all hunt tests programs are noncompetitive. Dogs either pass and receive a qualifying score and credit toward a hunt test title, or fail and come back to try again. Hunt tests also more closely simulate a real hunting situation, while field trials require skills that have been honed to a razor-sharp edge.

Flyball

Flyball is a team sport. Each team consists of four dogs and four owners. The dogs are sent one at a time, in a relay format, to run and jump over a series of hurdles, and then step on the lever of a box that throws a tennis ball. When the dog catches the ball, she turns around and runs and jumps over the hurdles again, bringing the ball back to her owner. Then the next dog starts. The team that finishes first, wins.

Flyball is a lot of fun, especially for dogs that are tennis ball crazy. Dogs of all sizes play flyball, although the athletic breeds do have an advantage. However, it does require some equipment. You will need four hurdles per team, plus one flyball box. And, of course, you need lots of dogs and owners so you can practice and compete together.

Frisbee Dogs

Frisbees are almost as popular with dogs as they are with people. Chasing a flying disc that swerves, climbs, banks and otherwise tantalizes the dog is even more fun than a tennis ball. (Frisbee is a trademarked name for a flying disc manufactured by Wham-O toys. The word Frisbee has, however, become synonymous with flying disc toys.)

If your dog is enthused about chasing a Frisbee, she can play to use up some of that excess energy, or she can chase a Frisbee in competition. Each year communities throughout the country sponsor local competitions for Frisbee-catching canines. The dogs chase the flying disc, leap incredible heights to catch it and then chase it again. Regional competitions follow the community competitions, and the winners go on to the World Finals. The athletic breeds have an advantage in Frisbee competitions, but any dog can play Frisbee for fun and exercise.

Puppy Tails

Eldon McIntire and his Australian Shepherd, Hyper Hank, were pioneers in the sport. McIntire and Hyper Hank performed their Frisbee magic at National Football League game halftimes, and were featured at an exhibition at Super Bowl XII. But the very first Frisbee dog to perform for a large audience was Ashley, a Whippet that belonged to Alex Stein. Stein broke onto the field during a Dodger baseball game in 1974 and dazzled the fans with Ashley's brilliant technique. Despite the enthusiastic response of the crowd, Alex was arrested.

Herding

Herding dogs were bred to help the shepherd, farmer or rancher control his livestock. Taking the place of two, three or more farmhands, a good herding dog is priceless. Today many dogs still work on farms, ranches and pastures all over the world. Many herding dogs are also pets, though, and herding competitions allow these dogs an opportunity to use their natural instincts. Herding tests and trials are limited to those breeds traditionally used for herding and livestock work.

Hiking and Packing

Do you like to go for walks in the country? Do you love the smell of a meadow in bloom in the spring? Or the smell of a pine forest after a rain? Is a weekend walk a

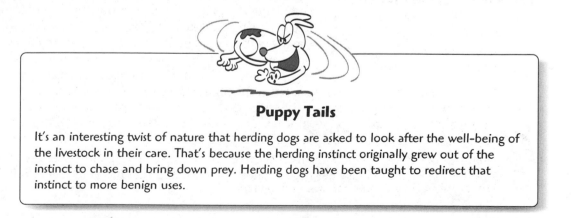

Puppy Tails

It's an interesting twist of nature that herding dogs are asked to look after the well-being of the livestock in their care. That's because the herding instinct originally grew out of the instinct to chase and bring down prey. Herding dogs have been taught to redirect that instinct to more benign uses.

good stress reliever for you after a hard week at work? If so, then take your dog with you when you walk. Many hiking and walking clubs are devoted specifically to activities with dogs, and many more welcome dogs on leash to their hikes. Some take day hikes, others go camping, backpacking and hiking.

Hiking is not competitive, but it is great exercise and, when shared with friends, a great social activity. Short hikes, gradually increasing in length or difficulty, can help you and your dog get back into shape if you have both been couch potatoes. As your dog gets more fit, she can start wearing a dog pack, carrying water, first aid supplies and treats.

Lure Coursing

The sighthound breeds are so named because they use their excellent vision to follow and hunt down their prey. Lure coursing gives these breeds a chance to chase an artificial lure. The lure is pulled mechanically around a 1,000- to 1,500-yard course that zigs and zags to test the dog's speed, agility and endurance.

The sighthounds are the only breeds allowed to run in official competitions, but many, many dogs love to chase a lure. Lure coursing clubs often hold fun matches where any breed can compete. Call the AKC or the American Sighthound Association (you'll find them listed in Appendix C) for a list of clubs in your area.

Paws for Thought

Obedience competitions are often included at conformation dog shows, and local clubs are easy to find through the AKC.

Obedience for the Competitive

Obedience trials test a dog's ability to perform a set of exercises that are scored by a judge. Competition in the obedience ring is divided into three levels, each more difficult than the previous one.

Obedience work emphasizes precision in executing commands. Dogs need to demonstrate heeling both on- and off-leash at different speeds, coming when called, staying with a group of other dogs when instructed to do so and standing for a physical examination. Retrieving, jumping and scent discrimination tests are also required at the higher levels.

Scent Hurdle Racing

Scent hurdle racing is much like flyball, except that after your dog races over the hurdles, she must then use her nose to choose a dumbbell that has your scent on it.

Once your dog finds the correct dumbbell, she has to pick it up and return over the hurdles to you. Again, like flyball, scent hurdle racing is a team sport, with four dogs and owners. The first team to finish, wins.

Contact your local dog trainer or dog training club to see if they have a team, or if they would be interested in starting one. And remember what I told you about young puppies, big jumps and growing bones.

Schutzhund

The sport of schutzhund originated in Germany, where it was first developed to test military and law enforcement dogs, as well as working dogs, to see if they were suitable for breeding. In the United States, schutzhund is a competitive sport combining obedience, tracking and protection work. Dogs compete at three levels, with each demanding more exacting work and a greater show of precision, control and courage from the dog. In addition, there are tests for endurance, traffic safety, drafting, companion dogs and watchdogs. Again, your dog can earn titles in each area of competition.

Some schutzhund clubs allow only the traditional German working breeds: German Shepherds, Rottweilers and Doberman Pinschers. Other clubs allow any dog capable of doing the work. Any dog that participates in schutzhund training must be of sound, stable temperament and physically fit.

G-r-r-r!

You, as the trainer, must take this training seriously. A protection or attack-trained dog is not a play-thing. She is a potentially dangerous weapon.

Search and Rescue

Search and rescue work is extremely rewarding. There is nothing like the feeling you get when you and your dog find a small child lost in the woods or an elderly man who wandered away from a nursing home. Search and rescue dogs have worked at the sites of the San Francisco, Mexico City, Armenia and Los Angeles earthquakes, as well as flood emergencies, collapsed buildings and mudslides. Search and rescue dogs helped during the aftermath of the Oklahoma City bombing.

Search and rescue work requires a serious commitment and a lot of training—sometimes as much as a year or two, depending upon the level of training you and your dog have before you begin. You will need to know map reading, how to orient yourself using a compass and natural signs such as stars, wilderness survival, emergency first aid and much more. Your dog will need to learn how to use her nose, both for air scenting and tracking, and must be able to alert you when she has found a scent.

You and your dog both will have to be in good physical condition to do this rigorous work. Your dog will also need obedience training, to a level where you have very good off-leash control. And you must be ready to be called upon whenever you're needed, no matter what the time or day.

Puppy Tails

Traditionally, search and rescue dogs have been the larger, more athletic breeds that are best able to withstand the rigors of the work. However, some smaller dogs are now starting to be used as part of a team. The larger dog does the major search work, climbing through rubble and racing across fields. When the big dog finds a promising scent but can go no farther, the little dog is dispatched to scoot into the smaller openings to continue the search.

Sled Dog Racing and Skijouring

Skijouring has been around for centuries in Northern Europe, and probably originated when a cross-country skier got a little tired, hooked up a reindeer and allowed the animal to pull him. Horses have been used for skijouring for a number of years in both Europe and North America. But not everyone has a horse or a reindeer, so it's inevitable that eventually a dog would be used to pull the skier.

When people think of sled dog racing, they traditionally think of the Alaskan tundra and a half-frozen musher on a sled pulled by half-wild Huskies traversing mile upon mile of frozen wasteland. Sled dog racing, however, can be for anyone with a sled and a team of dogs that like to run. Some of the more unusual teams have included Standard Poodles and Irish Setters.

Sledding can also be a fun way to exercise your dog. When my husband and I lived in Virginia, the neighborhood kids would come knocking on the door every morning after a snowfall, asking if the dogs could come out and play. They would hook up each dog to a sled or saucer and then have races. The dogs and kids both loved it!

Therapy Dogs

Dax has an instinct for knowing who needs her, and during visits to nursing homes or Alzheimer's care facilities, she will go directly to that person, sitting quietly by their side, nudging their hand until they pet her. She will allow kids to pull her ears, sit on her, climb all over her or cry into her coat. Her love and affection, given without reservation, have helped numerous people.

We know that our dogs are good for us—physically, mentally and emotionally. And recently, researchers have come to the same conclusion. Out of this knowledge has emerged therapy dogs. Therapy dogs can help many people: the emotionally distraught, the mentally ill, abused children, orphaned or runaway kids, the sick, ill or elderly, the disabled and the lonely.

Researchers have not been able to pinpoint exactly why or how therapy dogs help people, but they do have some guesses. First of all, therapy dogs provide love and affection without making demands—the dogs simply give love. Dogs are non-judgmental; they don't care what people look like, how much money they have or what ethnic background they come from. And finally, dogs make people smile. Laughter is good for our souls, and dogs love to make us laugh.

A therapy dog must be well trained, with a good foundation in the basic obedience commands, especially sit, lie down and stay. The dog cannot jump on people, or paw or scratch at them. During the specialized training for therapy dog work, the dog must be exposed to a variety of sights, sounds and smells that she will face in a nursing home, hospital or day care center. That might include strollers, wheelchairs or gurneys, respirators, urine bags and diapers. The dog must be able to climb stairs, and use an elevator and an escalator.

Many therapy dogs are taught specialized behaviors that can make their work easier, including putting their front feet up on the arm of a wheelchair or on the side of the bed and turning around, so people in a chair or in bed can reach to pet them. Many therapy dog owners also teach their dog tricks to amuse the people they are visiting.

Therapy work with your dog requires a commitment from you. The people at a local institution will soon come to expect and look forward to your visits, and you can't disappoint them. However, everyone involved in therapy work agrees that you get back a hundredfold what you put into it. You'll see people speak to your dog who haven't spoken to anyone in years, and a hundred other little miracles that only dogs can make happen.

Tracking

Tracking is a natural outgrowth of the hide-and-seek games you and your puppy learned in Chapter 23. You can use tracking as a fun activity, teaching your dog to "Go find Dad" or the kids, or you can use it as a competitive sport, earning tracking titles through several organizations.

Dingo is a therapy dog. He and his owner are at a fair where people can meet them and learn about what therapy dogs do.

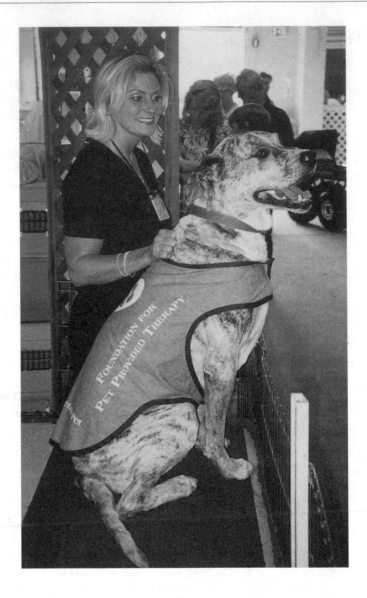

Tracking allows a dog to use her natural ability to smell. It's an ability that seems amazing to us. Dogs can smell the subtle differences in our body chemistry that signal changing emotions. They can also smell where a person has walked hours ago. In fact, a dog can smell a teaspoonful of salt dissolved in 13 gallons of water!

Tracking is taught through specialty tracking clubs, search and rescue groups and schutzhund clubs. The AKC can help you find competitive clubs in your area.

The Least You Need to Know

➤ There are many different dog sports and activities—enough to suit any dog and any owner.

➤ Some activities have certain requirements, either physical or training, and some activities are limited to certain breeds.

➤ If you're interested in an activity, find out more about it. Appendix C is a good place to start. You and your dog will have a blast learning and participating.

Chapter 25

Why Does My Puppy Do That?

In This Chapter

➤ Translating canine body language

➤ Understanding how a dog's physical make-up affects his behavior

➤ Common questions about doggy behaviors—and the answers

Many dog owners are disgusted to see their dog drink water out of the toilet or eat feces from the cat's litterbox. "How can he *do* that?" they ask in absolute horror! Other dog behavior can be confusing as well, such as a female dog mounting another dog. Why does she do that? After all, she's a female, not a male.

Dogs are not people, and their behavior can be very different from ours. Because dog owners don't know why these behaviors happen, the behaviors cause misunderstandings between dog and owner. Sometimes nobody knows why dogs do what they do, but we can make educated guesses.

Understanding Canine Body Language

Dogs do use their voices to communicate, and most dog owners recognize several different types of barks and whines their dogs use in different situations. But when it comes to language, dogs use their bodies best. Your dog conveys a wealth of information with his body, and it's a language you can definitely learn.

Why Does He Wag His Tail When He's Not Happy?

Although most people interpret a wagging tail as a sign of a happy dog, a wag usually has a more subtle meaning. With most dogs, a wagging tail is a sign of emotion, usually strong emotion.

With all strong emotions (including happiness), the tail wag is part of a complex set of physical signs that can also involve the body, ears, nose, eyes and mouth. When the dog is feeling submissive or worried, he will crouch down with his tail between his back legs; only the tip will be wagging. When he is feeling strong and dominant, his body will lift and he'll lean forward. The tail will be held above his hips and will be wagging slowly from side to side. When he's happily greeting you, the tail will be lower than the hips and will be wagging wildly.

Paws for Thought

Tailless dogs often twitch their stub just as if they had a tail, or they wag their entire back end.

Why Does He Lower His Front End When He Wants Me to Play With Him?

When a puppy (or an adult dog) lowers his front end, including the head and shoulders, leaving his hips high, it's called a *play bow*. This body language is an invitation to play, and is used by dogs, wolves, coyotes and many of the other canine species.

Puppies will use the play bow when they want their littermates to play with them. They'll also use it to invite adult dogs and their human playmates, including you.

Paws for Thought

If you wish to invite your puppy to play, you can use the same body language. Lift your hands high, then bring them down in front of you, making a bowing motion.

Why Does He Pant When He Isn't Hot?

Dogs pant to lose heat. With his big, wet tongue hanging out, a dog can lose a lot of heat through evaporation. Since dogs do not sweat anywhere except on the pads of their feet, this cooling process is very important.

Panting is also a sign of stress. When he's in a situation that bothers him for any reason, your dog may begin to pant. If he anticipates something bad happening at the veterinarian's office, your dog may begin to pant even though the air conditioning is on in the office.

Remember, too, that just because you aren't hot doesn't mean your dog isn't. Your dog may begin panting to lose heat even while you're still comfortable. Keep in mind, he's wearing a fur coat and can't sweat.

Why Does He Yawn When He's Not Tired?

Yawning when a dog is not sleepy is what is called a *calming signal*. If, during your training sessions for example, your puppy looks away from you and yawns, he is trying to tell you to calm down. Apparently he is feeling stress, either from himself or from you, and he's trying to relieve it.

Other calming signals include eye blinking, sneezing, looking away and scratching. So if your puppy begins scratching at his collar during training sessions, he is also telling you to calm down.

Understanding the Canine Physique

The way dogs behave has a lot to do with how they are built and how they perceive the world. For example, while we probably rely most on our sense of sight for information about the world around us, dogs more likely depend on their senses of smell and hearing—which are much, much keener than ours. There's no doubt dogs smell and hear things we will never be aware of. It's one reason why they sometimes seem to be reacting to nothing—it's only nothing to us.

There are also other physical characteristics that make dogs behave the way they do. Their digestive systems often compel them to make choices that seem strange to us. And their reproductive systems exert powerful forces on their behavior.

How Well Do Dogs Smell?

We can't even imagine how well dogs smell the world around them. For example, we think salt is odorless, but a trained scenting dog can discriminate between a bucket of plain water and one that has one teaspoon of salt dissolved in it. That *is* amazing!

This ability is why dogs are used so frequently by law enforcement agencies to detect drugs and other illegal substances, bombs and even animals and animal products that are being transported illegally.

Paws for Thought

A trained scenting dog's nose is more accurate than any machine yet built by humans.

If My Dog's Nose Is so Sensitive, Why Does He Roll in Stinky Stuff?

This is another habit that puzzles many dog owners. Why would an animal with such a sensitive nose roll himself in cow manure, rotting carcasses or other stinky stuff? Although the dogs can't tell us why, some experts say that many predators, including dogs, roll in filth to help disguise their scent. Other experts say the dog may simply like a particular scent, for whatever reason. Some dogs will roll in cat urine, some will roll on tobacco products and other appear attracted to petroleum products. Some dogs don't roll in anything! It seems to be a personal fragrance statement some dogs make.

Should I Let My Vet Spay My Female Puppy?

Your veterinarian wants to spay your puppy for several reasons. Having a dog in season is not fun. Male dogs will come calling, and your little girl will become an escape artist. The vet is concerned about her health, as well. The chances of your dog getting mammary cancer are greatly reduced, and the chance of cancer of the reproductive system is eliminated if your female puppy is spayed before her first season.

Paws for Thought

Myths and old wives' tales aside, a female dog need not have a litter of puppies or go through a season before she's spayed. It is much healthier for her if she is spayed before her first heat.

Last but certainly not least, there are too many puppies out there in need of homes. Thousands are euthanized (killed) at shelters all over the country every month. Only the very best dogs need to be bred, and that means the best dogs as compared to their respective breed standards.

Why Should I Neuter My Male Puppy?

A male should be neutered for many of the same reasons a female should be spayed. A neutered male will not normally have any of the bad behaviors associated with intact male dogs, including mounting or humping behaviors, marking territory, escaping from the yard to find a bitch in season and fighting. Chances of cancers of the reproductive system are eliminated in a dog that's been neutered, and the risk of prostate disease is greatly reduced. In addition, there are too many puppies being produced and then killed because there aren't enough homes for them all. There is really no reason *not to* neuter a male pet.

Why Does He Eat Grass?

For many years, experts believed dogs ate grass to induce themselves to vomit, since some dogs do vomit after eating grass. However, most dogs don't seem to have any trouble vomiting and will do so whenever something doesn't settle well in their stomach, so that explanation doesn't seem to make much sense.

Instead, it seems many dogs just like some plant material and fresh, growing grass is attractive to them. When given a chance, many dogs will eagerly consume tomatoes, green beans, strawberries, apples, carrots, grapes and many other fruits and vegetables, especially sweet ones.

Although dogs are scientifically classified as carnivores, behaviorally they appear to be omnivores—animals that consume both animal and plant matter. In the wild, dogs and wolves mostly hunt animals that graze, and eat the contents of the digestive system of the animals they hunt.

Why Does He Lick His Genitals?

Although licking the genitals is not all that attractive from a human perspective, it is a natural action for your puppy. Cleanliness is important to continued good health, and your puppy licks himself to keep himself clean.

Occasionally in a male dog, this behavior will progress from simple cleaning to self-pleasure. If this happens, you can stop the behavior with a verbal correction, especially if it occurs in public.

Why Do Dogs Smell Each Others' Rear Ends?

This is another behavior that people don't appreciate, but is very natural and necessary to dogs. Dogs have scent glands on either side of the anus that produce a smell that is unique to each dog. These glands, called anal glands, contain a material that is expressed in small amounts each time the dog has a bowel movement. When greeting each other, dogs will take a sniff at these glands to get to know each other better. Think of this as a personal perfume!

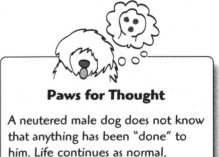

Paws for Thought

A neutered male dog does not know that anything has been "done" to him. Life continues as normal, except that hormone levels will decrease.

Why Does He Scoot His Rear End on the Ground?

This behavior is also related to the anal glands. When these glands get full, they become sore and uncomfortable. A dog will sit down and then drag himself using his front legs so that these glands are scratched on the ground. Sometimes this is enough to express or empty the glands.

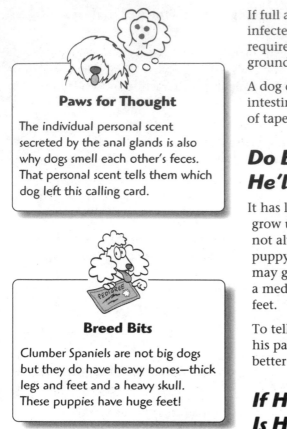

Paws for Thought

The individual personal scent secreted by the anal glands is also why dogs smell each other's feces. That personal scent tells them which dog left this calling card.

Breed Bits

Clumber Spaniels are not big dogs but they do have heavy bones—thick legs and feet and a heavy skull. These puppies have huge feet!

If full anal glands are not relieved, they can become infected and impacted, sometimes badly enough to require surgery. If your dog is scooting his rear on the ground, take him to see your veterinarian.

A dog dragging his rear on the ground could also have intestinal worms. Watch his stool for rice-like segments of tapeworms, or take a stool sample in for analysis.

Do Big Feet on a Puppy Mean He'll Be Very Big as an Adult?

It has long been said that a puppy with big feet will grow up to be a big dog. This is usually correct, but not always. In reality, big feet seem to signify that the puppy has lots of what is commonly called *bone*. He may grow up to be a big dog, or he may grow up to be a medium-size dog with heavy bone, or thick legs and feet.

To tell how big your puppy will grow up to be, look at his parents and grandparents. That will give you a better idea of his adult size.

If His Nose Is Not Cold and Wet, Is He Sick?

Your puppy's nose should not be dry and chapped. If it is, call your veterinarian. However, a dog's nose feels cold because of the moisture that evaporates off it. His body temperature is actually higher than ours, so if there is no evaporation, his nose will feel warm.

Strange Quirks of Canine Behavior and Training

All dogs do things that just don't seem to make sense—to us. However, dogs are sensible animals, and everything they do has a very good reason to them. We can never know what a dog is thinking, but we can try to understand things from his perspective.

When My Husband Gives Me a Hug and a Kiss, Why Does My Puppy Try to Get Between Us?

Ah, jealousy! Your puppy sees that someone is getting attention and affection other than him, and he just wants his share. It doesn't matter how much you give him, he'll probably still try to get in between the two of you. That's just how jealousy works.

You can, however, correct the behavior. Don't let the puppy run your life, or worse yet, ruin your love life! There's another reason, too. As your puppy becomes an adult, this behavior can change into a protective one. And a dog that tries to protect you from your husband can be a real problem.

Why Does He Try to Smell My Crotch?

Your puppy smells your crotch because it is part of you and smells like you. Just as with another dog, it's where your calling card is for a scent-driven animal. Your puppy has no social taboos about the crotch area—in fact, to your puppy that's a very natural place to sniff. For many puppies, the crotch is nose height, so it's just convenient.

You can, of course, correct him every time he tries to sniff you or other people there. Use your voice, "Acckk! No sniff!" and move his nose away.

Why Does my Female Puppy Mount My Friend's Male Puppy?

Your puppy is just expressing dominance over the male puppy. There are many ways of showing dominance, and mounting is one of them. Very dominant females will often continue this behavior into adulthood, mounting subordinate males during play time. You can correct the behavior when it happens if it bothers you, but it is normal and is not related to the sexual act.

Why Does He Bury the Bone I Give Him?

Most dogs bury bones when they are finished chewing them. Burying the bone hides it from other predators and preserves it for future use. This behavior probably has its roots in hunting behavior. When survival depended upon what was caught during the hunt, every scrap of meat or bone was important to a dog pack, and they buried the leftovers.

Will a Choke-Type Training Collar Hurt Him?

Most puppies start training with a buckle collar. This kind of collar is flat, doesn't slip or tighten and is right for most puppies. However, at some point many puppies do need more correction, and for these puppies a training collar can be the right choice.

Paws for Thought

Remember, there are a variety of training tools you can use. You are not limited to just a choke chain.

A training collar (also called a choke chain) will not hurt your puppy if it is used properly. Always take it off your puppy when you're not closely supervising him. Never allow him to pull the collar tight, and don't try to hold him in place with the collar, which also pulls it tight. If he's gasping or choking, the collar is too tight and is not being used correctly.

This collar works with a snap and release correction—just enough snap to tighten on the neck, with an immediate release. The snap of the leash must be appropriate to the size and age of your puppy. It should tighten and release just enough so that your puppy looks at you in response.

Most of the effect comes from the sound of the chain rubbing against the metal ring. A collar correction is never to be used alone, either. Use the snap as you tell the dog what he did wrong.

Why Does He Still Pull on the Leash, Even When He's Choking Himself?

Puppies aren't people, even though we've made them a part of our family, and they don't think like people. Your puppy is often so focused on going somewhere to see something, that he isn't thinking about the discomfort on his neck. That's why you need to teach the puppy to walk properly so he can go places without choking himself.

My Puppy Is Fine at Home; Why Do We Need a Puppy Class?

Puppy class is not just for "bad" puppies, it's for all puppies. I'm sure there is still more you can learn, even though your puppy is good, and the instructor can teach you as well as your puppy.

The socialization at puppy class is also very important. Your puppy will learn to get along with lots of different dogs and people, and to feel comfortable and follow your commands in a variety of situations.

Why Can't He Sleep with Me?

There is no reason why your puppy can't sleep in the bedroom with you, but he needs his own bed. After all, it's your house, you are taking the place of his mother and you must be his leader as well as his friend. Puppies sleep with their littermates, who are their equals. They do not sleep with their mother, who is their leader. Therefore, you need your bed and your puppy needs his.

If you really like to have your puppy on your bed, make him wait for an invitation. Then, when you're lazing in bed on a Sunday morning, invite him up and it will seem like a special occasion.

I'm Trying to Train My Puppy, But He Doesn't Pay Attention!

There are several things that could be happening. First of all, does your puppy get enough exercise? If not, paying attention to you could be hard. Does he get enough time with you when you aren't trying to train him? Play time, time for grooming and cuddling are all important.

Breed Bits

Labrador Retriever puppies are wiggle worms with short attention spans. Keep training sessions short, use food treats and lots of praise and make sure these guys get enough exercise.

When you are training, use some really good food treats to teach the puppy to pay attention. And keep the training sessions short and sweet so you aren't asking more than he can give you. Five minutes at a time is more than enough for most young puppies.

He Has Lots of Toys, So Why Does He Still Chew on My Stuff?

You may have given your puppy too many toys. If a puppy is surrounded by toys, he thinks everything is his and he can play with and chew on everything. However, if you limit his toys and only give him two or three at a time, he learns that only some things are his.

Take away a few of his toys. When he touches something of yours, let him know that's wrong, "Acckk! No!" Take it away and hand him one of his toys, "Here, this is yours!"

Keep in mind, too, that your puppy may be chewing on your stuff because it's yours and he likes your smell (which is on your stuff). With these puppies, prevention is the key. Put your stuff away and don't let your puppy have too much freedom around the house.

Why Does My Puppy Keep Stealing the Toilet Paper?

Some dogs just love to grab the end of the toilet paper roll and run with it all over the house. Others love the pop of a tissue as it is pulled out of the box. This behavior is more common in females, and may be related to their instinct to build a nice, comfy nest for their own puppies. Many unspayed females steal paper and shred it. Some do this only right before coming into heat.

Sometimes puppies do things just to get your attention. If you see your pup reaching for a tissue and shout and start grabbing for him, that's a really fun game, and you've just joined in!

The best way to deal with this problem is simply to prevent it. Keep the bathroom door closed, and move the tissue box to a higher shelf. If you do catch your puppy in the act, give a matter-of-fact correction, "Acckk!, No!" and redirect his attention to an appropriate toy.

All That Other Confusing Canine Stuff

Myths abound about dogs, how they behave and what's good for them. Your neighbors tell you one thing, your mother tells you another and your friend tells you a third. Who should you listen to? Your dogs' breeder, your veterinarian and your trainer.

Does One Year of a Dog's Life Really Equal Seven Human Years?

No, dogs mature much faster in their first year. A one-year-old dog is as mature mentally, physically and sexually as a 16-year-old human. After that, each year of your dog's life is roughly equal to about five to seven years of a human life.

These are *very* rough figures, however, because every breed is different. The giant breeds, such as Newfoundlands, St. Bernards and Mastiffs, age much more quickly and are old dogs by the time they are eight. Toy breeds live much longer, and may be active at 12 and not considered old until 14 or 15. Medium and large breed dogs may live to 12 or 14.

My Puppy Likes My Cat!

I hope that isn't a problem! Many dogs and cats live happily together, especially when raised together. When the dog is taught as a puppy to respect cats and not to chase them, the two species can live together quite nicely.

Why Does He Drink Out of the Toilet?

Your dog drinks out of the toilet to get a drink. It's that simple. The water in the toilet is sometimes colder, cleaner and fresher than the water in his dish. He doesn't think about what happens in the toilet before he went there for some water, and he has no social taboos about it. He just wants a drink!

Why Does He Eat the Cat's Feces?

Ah, the cat litter candy problem! Cats are true carnivores, and evolved to eat prey—the whole prey, including skin, small bones, meat and guts. Commercial cat food includes meat but also contains grain and grain products that cats usually do not digest well. Therefore, cats are often passing through only partially digested food. Your puppy, smelling this, thinks this is a wonderful treat!

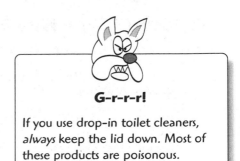

G-r-r-r!

If you use drop-in toilet cleaners, *always* keep the lid down. Most of these products are poisonous.

When he helps himself and you get all excited, it becomes a *really* special treat because, after all, you are excited!

Put the litterbox somewhere where the cats can get into it but the puppy can't. Or get a covered box, and make sure the puppy can't get in. Simple prevention is the cure here, because you aren't going to change your cats' digestive system and the puppy is going to continue to search for kitty treats.

Why Does He Eat His Own Feces?

This problem is most often seen in puppies under six months old. Nobody is sure why they do this, but there are several theories. Some of the more common ones are that the puppy has a vitamin or mineral deficiency or internal parasites, or is simply bored or hungry.

Paws for Thought

This habit is common enough that it actually has a name: *coprophagy.*

Whatever the reason, this is not a healthy habit for your dog. It can lead to vomiting, diarrhea and internal parasites. Your veterinarian may be able to give you something you can feed your puppy that will make his stool distasteful to him (you already thought it was, right?). Increasing the fiber in his diet also seems to help. And be sure to pick up after your pup as quickly as possible after he eliminates.

Why Does He Walk in Circles Before He Lies Down?

He's tamping down the grass! Not really, of course, but some instinct remains of dogs' wild days on the plains. Your puppy is rearranging his bed to make sure it's comfortable, as dogs have done for thousands of years.

I Want to Chain Him in the Backyard, But My Neighbor Says That's Cruel. Why?

If you need to restrict or contain your puppy, build a dog run—an enclosed fenced area—for your puppy rather than chaining him. A chained dog is restricted yet vulnerable. He can't get away should a stray dog decide to torment or tease him. Even in a small dog run, he is protected by the fence.

A chained dog also gets very frustrated at his limited movement, and this can cause aggression or other problem behaviors. If a small child walks within his reach, the child could bear the brunt of his frustration and could be seriously hurt or even killed.

A chained dog may constantly whine, bark or howl to express his displeasure. He may also pace, dig or lick and chew at himself. In addition, a dog's neck can be physically damaged by constantly pulling on the end of the chain. All of these behaviors are related to frustration and boredom.

Even if you keep your dog in a well-designed run, with proper shelter, shade, water and lots of toys, no dog can live happily out in the yard all day. A dog is a pack animal, and needs to be with his pack. That's you. Without you, your puppy will become lonely, bored, frustrated and depressed. And that is cruel.

The Least You Need to Know

➤ Puppies do things for a reason. We may not understand why, but they do.

➤ Dogs aren't people, and their body language, instincts and behavior are different.

➤ A dog's senses and physical make-up greatly affect how he perceives the world.

➤ It's important to know as much about our dogs as we can, so that we can make both our lives and theirs more enjoyable.

➤ If any of these behaviors escalate into aggression against a person or another dog, it's time to call in a professional trainer.

Dogs in the Community

As I write these words, a dog is lying on my feet under my desk. Even though my leg is falling asleep, I hesitate to move because if I disturb her, she may decide to nap somewhere else. That's silly, isn't it? It is, but I enjoy her company.

Unfortunately there are places in the United States (and other countries as well) where it is illegal to own a dog or illegal to own certain breeds of dogs. I can't imagine a dogless home; it is unthinkable. But it has happened, and it's up to us to keep it from happening again.

Dog Ownership Is Sometimes a Problem

Anti-dog legislation is not something new. It has been enacted at various times throughout our history. However, the extent of anti-dog legislation that we are seeing now is new. In towns, cities and counties throughout the United States, legislation has been proposed and enacted that places all kinds of limits on dog ownership.

Home ownership associations have placed a one- or two-dog limit, or said only dogs under 30 pounds are allowed. Cities have said that it is illegal to own a Rottweiler, Doberman Pinscher or Pit Bull. Vicious dog legislation has been passed, and is strictly and sometimes too emphatically enforced.

Insurance companies have refused to insure people with certain breeds of dogs, or they require expensive policy riders for certain breeds.

It's a very tough time to be a dog owner. Why did this happen, and how can we change it?

Paws for Thought

When staying in a hotel, I always inform the clerk that my dogs have kennel crates and that they will never be left in the room alone.

It Only Takes One!

Many pieces of legislation are enacted in response to one incident. Perhaps a person was bitten or a child was mauled by a dog of a certain breed. Emotions run high after something bad has happened—understandably so—and legislation affecting all dogs of that breed is rushed through.

Other legislation may be enacted after a history of complaints. Perhaps several dog owners have not cleaned up after their dogs relieved themselves in a local park. People are disgusted by the messes and complain. A law is then enacted to ban all dogs from the park, not just the ones owned by irresponsible owners.

Many hotels and motels now forbid pets, even though they had allowed them for many years. This is because a few thoughtless people let their dog eliminate inside the hotel, or in its gardens, or washed their dog in the bathtub in their room. It has gotten so bad in some areas that dog shows have to be cancelled because there are no hotels in the area that will allow dogs. How sad!

Arguing Against Breed-Specific Laws

A few years ago the American Kennel Club started getting involved in several legislative debates. The AKC asked that legislators enact laws penalizing irresponsible owners and individual dogs that misbehave, instead of specific breeds or all dogs. They argued that no one breed is "bad" and that penalizing an entire breed is unfair. Their efforts were successful in many cases, although breed-specific laws have still been enacted in some places.

It's important that dog owners become involved in their community and remain aware of official attitudes regarding dogs. When dog owners know about pending legislation, they can get involved. If many responsible dog owners and professionals show up at a city council meeting and state their opinion about proposed legislation, that legislation can be prevented or amended.

Changing the Way People Look at Dogs

Dog owners sometimes forget that when they are out in public with their dog, all dog owners will be judged by their actions. It's not fair, but that's the way people tend to be. When one dog owner is irresponsible, all dog owners suffer.

When people see a well-mannered dog walking nicely on the leash, sitting to greet people, her owner cleaning up after her, they see no need to ban or limit dogs. However, when a dog is leaping at the end of her leash, barking and growling, and her owner walks away from a pile of feces, the attitude is totally different.

Public Manners

Public manners are necessary for all dogs, no matter whether the dog lives in New York City or a small town. Public manners prevent problems.

When you are teaching your puppy, make sure she can:

G-r-r-r!

Male dogs do *not* have to lift their leg on every vertical surface. The world is not their territory—although some seem to think it is. Males can learn to urinate once or twice as needed and then ignore the scent markings of other dogs. Just tell them to heel.

➤ Sit to greet people. If she will sit when people greet her and pet her, she won't be jumping on people, nosing them in the crotch or getting into other trouble.

➤ Walk nicely on the leash.

➤ Pay attention to you and ignore distractions. That means she'll pay attention to you and not other dogs barking behind a gate or kids playing on their skateboards.

➤ Lie down and stay when you are busy. She can stay while you talk to a neighbor or get the mail out of the box.

➤ Relieve herself on command. When you can give her a command to relieve herself (or at least try), you can ask her to try before going out in public where it might be distasteful to other people.

When I am out in public, I want my dogs to behave so that when people watch us, they smile. I want people to say to themselves, "I wish *my* dog was that good!" or "I wish *all* dogs behaved like that!" If I see people smile as we go by, I know I'm accomplishing that goal.

Meeting the Unexpected

One of my favorite mottoes is "Life is never boring," and that certainly includes life with dogs. There is always something happening. And that something can affect how the world perceives you and your dog.

Recently, while walking my two Australian Shepherds, Dax and Kes, at the local harbor, Kes reacted violently and fearfully to something. She pulled away from me, almost strangling herself on the leash. I stopped her by putting my hands on her and helping her sit. I talked to her in a soft but firm voice, "Kes, stop! That's enough!" I understood something was frightening her, but I also wanted her to know that wasn't the way to react.

As soon as she was sitting and controlling herself, I stepped away to see if I could see what was so scary. Just over the edge of the rocks by the sidewalk was a dead pelican. I couldn't see it when I was walking on the sidewalk, but Kes could smell it and it scared her. Dax, who is three years old, was not frightened at all, but Kes, at nine months old, was very frightened.

I didn't want to reinforce her fear, so we just walked by. When she walked nicely, I praised her. On the way back to the car we had to pass that place again, and as we approached, I simply told Kes to walk nicely. When she started to react to the dead pelican, I told her to be calm and to walk nicely. As we walked by, I praised her. And then I praised Dax, too, because I'm sure her calm attitude helped show Kes that it was nothing to be afraid of.

When out in public with your puppy, you will constantly be teaching her. Everything you do teaches her something. You must reinforce the behaviors you want—with praise, your tone of voice, your hands and with food treats—and discourage the behaviors you don't want.

Anything out of the ordinary can be scary to a puppy. Some of these things include:

➤ Manhole covers

➤ Stairs

➤ Wind chimes

➤ Flags

➤ Balloons

➤ Signs

➤ Newspaper racks

➤ Motorcycles

➤ Big trucks

In addition, some puppies are more visual, and for these puppies many of the things they see can be scary. Some puppies are more stimulated by sounds. Their hearing is acute, so imagine how frightening some noises can be! They need not be loud sounds, either. I know one Border Collie that reacts to the quiet whine of the autofocus on an automatic camera.

Be prepared for anything when you take your puppy out in public, and don't be afraid to do whatever you need to do to teach her. Don't be embarrassed just because you *are* out in public. Your puppy deserves your best efforts.

Paws for Thought

Don't coddle your puppy when she's afraid. Be matter-of-fact or even funny, and work her through it instead of reinforcing the fear.

When Dogs Aren't Welcome

If dogs are not welcome somewhere in your neighborhood and you disagree with this rule or law, what can you do? You can fight it or try to change it, but you have to work with the system, not against it.

If dogs are not welcome in the local park, don't take your dog there and let her play. That violation will not show the powers that be that dogs should be welcome. Instead, it reinforces the idea that dog owners are not responsible. Work *with* the system. Find out who instituted the rule and what the procedure is to get it changed. Invite other dog owners to work with you, as well as some pet professionals in the community. Show up at the hearing, prepared with facts or statements that demonstrate how you've researched the subject and talked to people in the community. State your case calmly and clearly. Don't lose your temper!

Paws for Thought

Your local librarian can be a great help in your research. Tell her what you want to do and let her guide you. The local animal control office can also help you with pertinent local laws.

You can also talk to local legislators. Explain your goals to them and ask for help. If they cannot help you, they can steer you towards someone else who can. If the legislator refuses to help, don't get irritated and storm out of his office. Instead, ask why and listen to the answer. Perhaps there is a very real reason.

It's an old cliché, but it works: Make sure you're part of the solution and not part of the problem. Working with the system is the best way to get things changed, so play the game, even if it seems convoluted and confusing. And remember that change sometimes comes slowly. Keep at it.

Being a Good Neighbor

Many people come to my classes with the same comment: "My neighbor said my dog barks too much when I'm gone." Barking dogs can be very irritating. As I write these words, I can hear two of my neighbors' dogs barking, and one of them has been barking on and off all day. It is *very* irritating!

What is even more irritating is that I have talked to both dog owners and given them information about how to control this problem, and neither one is the least bit interested. Their whole attitude says they really don't care!

My husband spent 20 years in the military, and we were transferred regularly. We always had dogs and found places to live where dogs were allowed. Every time we moved into a neighborhood, we would go to our neighbors and introduce ourselves and our dogs. I would always tell our neighbors to *please, please* speak up if there was a problem with the dogs *before* it became a big problem. If the dogs started barking when we left for work, they should let me know. If one of the dogs was lifting a leg on the fence, burning the flowers on the other side, let me know. By being active and showing our neighbors we were concerned about being good neighbors, we have never had a problem with anyone.

G-r-r-r!

When your neighbor comes to you with a problem, don't bite his head off! Receive the complaint gracefully and thank him for telling you.

Paws for Thought

A good fence is the best neighbor. If you can afford it, a five- to six-foot high, solid fence is the best investment you can make for your puppy, your neighbors and you.

Unfortunately, many people do have neighbor problems, and sometimes it takes a great deal of effort to overcome them. You can avoid becoming a problem neighbor if you take some action now, while your dog is still a puppy.

➤ Talk to your neighbors. Tell them you want to be a good neighbor. Ask them what their concerns are about having a dog next door.

➤ Tell your neighbors you would like to know about any potential problems (or misbehavior) before they turn into big problems.

➤ Make sure your dog's feces are picked up daily from your yard and instantly from the street. Cleanliness is next to good neighborliness!

➤ Teach your puppy not to bark every time your neighbor goes out into his backyard.

Consideration works both ways, though. If the neighbor's kids are teasing your puppy through the fence, please let your neighbor know. Say it nicely and explain that you're concerned because it could cause your puppy to want to chase the kids, should she meet them outside. Also, if they tease her through the fence and stick a finger through, the puppy might bite the finger.

The Canine Good Citizen

As I mentioned in Chapter 24, the American Kennel Club instituted the Canine Good Citizen (CGC) program to try to counteract some of the negative publicity surrounding dogs recently. When people hear of dog bites and terrible maulings, they are horrified—and have every right to be. Unfortunately, the good dogs that behave themselves never make front-page news!

Paws for Thought

Dogs that pass get an official certificate and may add the initials "CGC" after their name. For example, my three-year-old Aussie is Dax, CGC.

The CGC program gives those good dogs a chance to make the news. Dog trainers and obedience clubs can hold a Canine Good Citizen test, invite the public and the local media, and people can see that there are many responsible owners and good dogs in their own community.

The CGC test consists of 10 exercises. The dog and owner must successfully do all 10 to pass the test.

1. **Accepting a friendly stranger.** Your dog must allow a friendly stranger to approach and speak to you in a friendly manner.

2. **Sitting politely for petting.** Your dog must sit nicely while someone comes up and pets her.

3. **Appearance and grooming.** Your dog should appear healthy and well-groomed, and will allow someone to gently run a comb or brush over her. She will allow her ears to be touched, and a front paw.

4. **Out for a walk.** Your dog should walk nicely while you make a left turn, right turn and about turn, without pulling or other undesirable behavior.

5. **Walking through a crowd.** Your dog should walk nicely with you as you weave through a crowd of people. Your dog should pay attention to you, although she can acknowledge the people.

6. **Sit, down and stay.** Your dog should demonstrate the proper response to the sit, down and stay commands. The dog should stay while you walk 20 feet away and then return.

7. **Come when called.** Your dog should come to you when you call her from 10 feet away.

Paws for Thought

Enrolling in a basic obedience training class before taking the CGC test is usually a good idea. The class will help you (and your dog) with the basic commands, plus your dog will have more practice dealing with distractions.

8. **Reaction to another dog.** Your dog should demonstrate good behavior when another dog and handler walk up to you and stop in front of you.

9. **Reaction to distractions.** This shows your dog is confident and well-behaved around common distractions, including a jogger, a sharp sound or something flapping in the breeze.

10. **Supervised separation.** Your dog should behave herself when left with a friend as you go out of sight for three minutes.

To find a CGC test locally, call dog clubs, dog trainers or obedience training clubs. Many will sponsor tests several times a year.

The Least You Need to Know

➤ Anti-dog legislation and restrictions are a threat to all dog owners.

➤ It's the responsibility of all dog owners to make sure they are not part of the problem.

➤ Make sure your dog (and you) set a good example, out in public and with your neighbors.

➤ The Canine Good Citizen program was instituted to show the world there are good dogs and responsible dog owners. Train your dog, and take the test.

A Doggy Dictionary

aggression A hostile reaction; self-defense in the face of a real or perceived threat. Aggression is the fight part of the "fight or flight" instinct.

agility An obstacle course for dogs that can be used for fun training and confidence or as a competitive sport.

allergies Dogs can have allergies, just as people can, and often to the same things.

alpha The dominant member of a dog or wolf pack.

American Kennel Club (AKC) An organization that registers purebred dogs and licenses dog shows and other dog sporting events.

anticipation When the dog reacts before you give a command, because he knows what's going to happen next.

body language Positions of the body, of body parts and facial expressions; dogs use canine body language to communicate.

bonding The deep commitment dog and owner feel for each other; a responsibility towards each other.

boundary training Teaching the puppy to remain behind you and to respect boundaries.

buckle collar A wide nylon, cotton or leather collar that fastens with a buckle.

Canine Good Citizen A program administered by the AKC to promote basic good behavior and responsible dog ownership.

choke collar A training collar that works with a snap and release motion.

come A command that requires the dog to stop everything and come directly to you.

compulsion training A training method or technique where the dog must do as it is told with no leeway; forceful training.

conformation competition Dog shows for evaluating a dog as compared to others of his breed and as compared to the breed standard.

correction Verbal or physical way of telling the dog he's made a mistake.

CPR An emergency first aid procedure to keep your dog's heart beating and to keep him breathing.

cue Command, signal.

distractions Things that can break the dog's concentration.

dominance Levels of hierarchy within the pack or family group.

fearful aggression A timid or shy dog reacting in an aggressive manner; aggression caused by fear.

field trial A trial or evaluation for sporting dogs.

force Making the dog do what you want; also, physical strength.

group classes Training classes where dogs and owners are taught in a small group by an obedience instructor.

halter A training tool that fits over the dog's head, much like a horse's halter; used instead of a training collar.

heartworm A parasitic worm that lives in the heart; untreated, it causes death.

heel The dog walks by your left side, with his neck and shoulders even with your left leg.

herding trial Working trials for herding dogs.

hip dysplasia A deformity of the hips.

hookworm An intestinal parasite.

housetraining Teaching the puppy to relieve himself outside, not in the house.

instinct Inborn urges to respond to things in a specific manner.

leash awareness Teaching the puppy to be aware of the leash and owner; to respect the leash.

let's go A command used to teach the puppy to walk nicely on the leash without pulling.

long line A longer length of leash or clothesline rope, used as a training tool for the "come" command and for boundary training.

lure Something the dog will follow to be shaped into a position or learn a command.

lure coursing Working evaluation for sighthounds.

Lyme disease A disease transmitted by ticks.

mimic When the dog learns by watching, and then copies another's actions.

motivation Helping the dog want to do something; providing a reward.

motivator The reward for doing something right; the lure to do something right.

negative attention Attention with unpleasant consequences; some dogs will get into trouble simply for the attention, even negative attention.

parasite An organism that lives off another.

pinch or prong collar A multi-link training collar that pinches when it is pulled.

positive reinforcement Anything positive: verbal praise, petting, food treats, toys.

praise Verbal affirmation, approval.

Rocky Mountain spotted fever A disease transmitted by ticks.

shaping Using a training tool to help the dog do what you want; shaping into position.

shock A life-threatening condition caused by a trauma.

sit A training position with the hips down and the front end up.

socialization Introducing the puppy to different people, sights, sounds and smells.

stay A training command that means "hold that position without moving."

submissive Showing respect for dominance.

temperament Personality and character.

therapy dogs Trained and certified dogs that visit people in nursing homes, schools and hospitals.

time-out A time away from training that gives the dog a chance to rest and think, and breaks the thought process, especially if the dog has been misbehaving.

tourniquet A device used to stop major blood flow after an injury.

vaccination Injections of a small amount of a specified disease that enables the body to develop antibodies to protect itself from the disease.

wait A training command that means "hold still and wait for another command."

Dogs on the Internet

There's a lot of information available on the Internet for dog owners. Typing "dogs" into a search engine will lead to thousands and thousands of entries. However, if you type in specific terms, such as a breed, or "dog training, competition" or "dog training, pets," you'll get more specific items of interest.

The pet food company sites often have lots of general information on care and nutrition. There are also many pages that have lists and lists of links to other sites. You'll find them here under "General Information and Links to Other Sites."

A word of warning, however. Do *not* accept everything that is written on the Internet as expert opinion. Anyone can write their opinion on a Web page or a bulletin board, and they are not always right. And pages sponsored by companies that sell dog supplies obviously have business to do. Consider the source, take everything with a grain of salt and don't hesitate to ask more questions.

Health Care

Alternative Veterinary Medicine
www.altvetmed.com
A list of alternative veterinary associations and natural food companies.

American Animal Hospital Association
www.healthypet.com
The site includes pet care tips and a library.

American Veterinary Medical Association
www.avma.org/care4pets
Pet care, including health and safety, buying a pet and breed statistics.

NetVet and the Electronic Zoo
www.avma.org/netvet.default.htm
A link to veterinary medical and animal-related online resources.

Nutritional Navigator
www.navigator.tufts.edu
Nutrition news from Tufts University School of Veterinary Medicine.

Pfizer Animal Health
www.petnet.com
This site includes information about dog and cat health care, as well as emergency first aid.

Quack Watch
www.quackwatch.com
This site is about human medicine, and is designed to help people avoid quackery or false information. It is very informative for dog owners, too.

Veterinary Pet Insurance
www.petinsurance.com
Information about their veterinary health insurance plan.

Dog Food Companies

Canidae Pet Foods
www.canidae.com

Hill's Pet Nutrition, Inc.
www.hillspet.com
The makers of Science Diet pet foods.

Iams Co.
www.iamsco.com

Nature's Choice
www.naturzchoice.com

Nature's Recipe
E-mail: t.coon@heinzpet.com

Nutro Products
www.petconnect.com/nutro

Purina
www.purina.com

Waltham dog foods
www.waltham.com
The makers of Pedigree dog foods.

Wysong Corp.
E-mail: sfree4@aol.com

Organizations

American Dog Owners Association
www.global2000.net/adoa/

American Kennel Club
www.akc.org

Delta Society Pet Partners
www2.deltasociety.org/deltasociety/

North American Dog Agility Council
www.teleport.com/~jhglund.nadachom.htm

North American Flyball Association
muskie.fishnet.com/~flyball/flyball.htm

United Kennel Club
www.ukcdogs.com

United States Dog Agility Association
www.usdaa.com

Training and Behavior

Association of Pet Behaviour Counsellors
www.apbc.org.uk/

Association of Pet Dog Trainers
www.familyinternet.com/pet/apdt

National Association of Dog Obedience Instructors
www.kimberly.uidaho.edu/nadoi

General Information and Links to Other Sites

Acme Pet
www.acmepet.com
Articles and information, plus links to many other sites.

Cyber-Pet
www.cyberpet.com
Incorporates breeders, products, rescue clubs, links to other Web sites and chat.

Dog Owner's Guide
www.canismajor.com/dog/guide
A wide variety of articles and links.

Dog Patch
www.dogpatch.org
News, photos and links to many other canine pages.

Dog-Play
www.dog-play.com
Descriptions of a wide variety of dog sports, and links to other pages with more information.

Fancy Publications
www.animalnetwork.com
Information from their magazines, including Dog Fancy *and* Dogs USA.

Pet Finder
www.petfinder.org
Pet adoption center.

The Tame Beast
www.tamebeast.com/index.html
A huge clearing house for links to other sites.

Books

Dog and Cat Book Catalog
www2.dogandcatbooks.com/directbook/

Dog Lovers Bookshop
www.dogbooks.com

Hoflin Publishing
www.hoflin.com
This publishing company includes general pet information and links to other pages.

The Working Dogs Bookstore
www.workingdogs.com/books.htm

Supplies

Blue Ribbon Pet Supplies
www.blueribbonpet.com

Canine Equipment
www.caninequp.com
This is, as they put it, "gear fer dogs." Ask for their catalog.

Cardinal Laboratories
www.cardinalpet.com
Pet supplies, including shampoos.

Coastal Pet Products
www.coastalpet.com
Supplies, including collars and leashes.

Dr. Goodpet Laboratories
www.goodpet.com
A major supplier of natural pet products.

Flexi USA Inc.
www.flexiusa.com
Retractable leashes.

4Dogs
www.4dogs.com
Supplies, foods, supplements and treats.

Four Paws Products
www.fourpaws.com

Fox and Hound Ltd.
www.foxandhounds.com
A pet supplier and a manufacturer of pet collars.

Happy Dog Toys
www.happydogtoys.com

Hydrosurge Inc.
www.hydrosurge.com
Grooming supplies and shampoos.

J-B Pet Supplies
www.jbpet.com
Ask for their catalog.

JB Wholesale
www.pet-expo.com
A catalog company that stocks just about everything.

J & J Supplies
www.jandjdog.com
Competitive obedience and agility supplies.

Kong Co.
www.kongcompany.com
The original hard rubber toys.

Lambert Kay
www.lambertkay.com
Shampoos and more.

Midwest Homes for Pets
www.midwesthomes4pets.com
Kennel crates and more.

Pup Tents
www.puptents.com
A wide variety of supplies.

SitStay
www.sitstay.com/store/toys
Dog toys.

Just for Fun

Animal Planet
www.animal.discovery.com/
News and schedules from the cable television channel that's all about animals.

Blue Dog
kao.ini.cmu.edu:5500/bdf
This is a site for kids that teaches elementary math skills.

The Late Show
www.cbs.com/lateshow/ttlist
Search for "dogs" and you'll get David Letterman's top ten lists concerning dogs.

Dog Organizations and Publications

Multi-Sport Organizations

American Kennel Club
5580 Centerview Dr.
Raleigh, NC 27606
(919) 233-9767
www.akc.org
Agility, conformation, field trials, earthdog tests, lure coursing, herding, obedience, tracking.

United Kennel Club
100 E. Kilgore Road
Kalamazoo, MI 49001
www.ukcdogs.com
(616) 343-9020
Agility, conformation, Coonhound hunts, obedience, field trials.

Australian Shepherd Club of America
6091 E. SH 21
Bryan, TX 77808
(409) 778-1082
www.asca.org
Australian Shepherd conformation; all-breed obedience, agility, herding and tracking.

All-Breed Canine Publications

AKC Gazette
American Kennel Club
260 Madison Ave.
New York, NY 10016
(212) 696-8314

Dog Fancy
Fancy Publications
PO Box 6500
Mission Viejo, CA 92690
(714) 855-8822

Dog & Kennel
7-L Dundas Circle
Greensboro, NC 27407
(336) 292-4047

Dog World
PO Box 6500,
Chicago, IL 60680
(312) 609-4340

Agility

North American Dog Agility Council
HCR 2, Box 277
St. Maries, ID 83861
www.teleport.com/~jhaglund/nadachom.htm

United States Dog Agility Association
PO Box 850955
Richardson, TX 75085-0955
www.usdaa.com

The Contact Line
Cascade Publications
401 Bluemont Circle
Manhattan, KS 66502-4531

The Clean Run
35 Walnut Street
Turner Falls, MA 01376

Carting and Draft Dogs

Bernese Mountain Dog Club of America
5266 East Ford Road
Greenwood, FL 32443
www.csn.net/~pshaffer/bmdca.html

Newfoundland Club of America
NCA Working Dog
5208 Olive Road
Raleigh, NC 27606
www.geocities.com/~newfdogclub/

North American Working Bouvier Association
19007 Millstream Road
Marengo, IL 60152

Working Dogs
www.workingdogs.com

An Internet magazine and list of links to working dog organizations.

Earthdog Trials

The American Working Terrier Associaltion
Patricia Adams Lent
503 NC 55 West
Mt. Olive, NC 28465
(919) 658-0929
The AKC also sponsors earthdog trials.

Field Trials and Tests

North American Hunting Retreiver Association
PO Box 6
Garrisonville, VA 2463
starsouth.com/nahra/
For all types of hunt tests and field trials, contact the AKC and UKC, listed above.

Flyball

North American Flyball Association
1002 E. Samuel Ave.
Peoria Heights, IL 61614
muskie.fishnet.com/~flyball/flyball.htm

The Finish Line
4365 Glancaster Rd.
Mt. Hope, Ontario
Canada L0R 1W0

Freestyle Obedience

Footloose Canine Freestyle Association
Carolyn Scott
7830 Whispering Wood
Houston, TX 77086
(281) 444-0560
E-mail: ranlyn@swbell.net

Uptempo Canine Freestyle
Association
Deb & Julie Norman
1221 Twining Road
Dresher, PA 19025
E-mail: furfun@aol.com

Musical Canine Sports International
Val Culpin
3466 Creston Drive
Abbotsford, British Columbia
Canada V2T 5B9
E-mail: val_culpin@bc.sympatico.ca

Canine Freestyle Federation
Alison Jaskiewicz
576 Jackson Rd.
Mason, NH 03048
E-mail: alison@jaskiewicz.mv.com

Heinz Professional Services
Pup-Peroni Canine Freestyle
PO Box 3750
Lawrence, KS, 66046-0750
www.woofs.org/freestyle/frstyl.html

Frisbee

Alpo Frisbee Contest
(888) 444-ALPO

Friskies Canine Frisbee Championships
(800) 423-3268

National Capitol Air Canines
2830 Meadow Lane,
Falls Church, VA 22042.
(703) 532-0709
www.discdog.com/index.html

Woof! Sports USA
www.mindspring.com/~woofsportsusa/

Herding, Herding Trials and Livestock

United States Border Collie Handler's Association
Francis Raley
2915 Anderson Lane
Crawford, TX 76638
(254) 486-2500
E-mail: fraley@iamerica.net

National Stock Dog Magazine
Route 1
Butler, IN 46721
Also check out the the multi-sport organizations above, especially the AKC and the Australian Shepherd Club of America.

Lure Coursing

American Sighthound Field Association
PO Box 1293M
Woodstock, GA 30188
www.asfa.org
Also see the AKC, listed above.

Schutzhund

DVG America
5718 Watson Circle
Dallas, TX
(303) 674-4655
webusers.anet-stl.com/~dugamer

United Schutzhund Clubs of America
3810 Paule Ave.
St Louis, MO 63125
(314) 638-9686
www.germanshepherddog.com/

Search and Rescue

The American Rescue Dog Association
PO Box 151
Chester, NY 10918
www.ardainc.org

National Association for Search and Rescue
4500 Southgate Place, Suite 100
Chantilly, VA 22021
www.nasar.org

Sled Dog Racing and Skijouring

International Sled Dog Racing Association
(218) 765-4297
E-mail: isdra@uslink.net
uslink.net/~isdra/

Northern Dog News Magazine
6436 Mullen Road
Olympia, WA 98503

Team and Trail Magazine
Center Harbor, NH 03226

Therapy Dogs

Delta Society
289 Perimeter Rd E.
Renton, VA 98055-1329
(800) 869-6898
www2.deltasociety.org/deltasociety/

Foundation for Pet Provided Therapy
3809 Plaza Dr., No. 107-309
Oceanside, CA 92056
(760) 630-4824

Therapy Dogs Inc.
PO Box 2786
Cheyenne, WY 82003
(307) 638-3223
homt.ptd.net/
~compudog.tdi.html

Therapy Dogs International
88 Bartley Rd.
Flandres, NJ 07836

Weight Pulling Competitions

International Weight Pull Association
PO Box 994
Greeley, CO 80632
www.eskimo.com/~samoyed/iwpa/index.html

Index